AUGUSTINE TO GALILEO

By the same author

ROBERT GROSSETESTE AND THE
ORIGINS OF EXPERIMENTAL SCIENCE, 1100–1700
(*Clarendon Press, Oxford*, 1953)

A. C. CROMBIE

AUGUSTINE TO GALILEO

The History of Science
A.D. 400–1650

WILLIAM HEINEMANN LTD

MELBOURNE LONDON TORONTO

FIRST PUBLISHED 1952
RE-ISSUED IN THIS EDITION 1957

PUBLISHED BY
WILLIAM HEINEMANN LTD.
99 GREAT RUSSELL STREET, W.C.1.

PRINTED BY
WATERLOW & SONS LIMITED,
LONDON AND DUNSTABLE.

1411434

CONTENTS

PLATES

To
NANCY

ACKNOWLEDGEMENTS

Acknowledgements are made to the following for supplying photographs for illustrations: the Chief Librarian of the Oeffentliche Bibliothek der Universität Basel (Figs. 7 and 8); Bodley's Librarian, Oxford (Fig. 17 and Plate 4); the Director of the British Museum (Figs. 6, 16, 22, 24, 27, 29, 36 and Plates 3, 5, 8, and 9); the Librarian of Cambridge University (Figs. 1, 4, 14, 15, 28, 30, 31, 35, 37, 38, 41, 42, 43, 45, 46, 48, 49 and Plates 6, 10 and 11); the Librarian of Christ Church, Oxford (Fig. 32); the Director of the Biblioteca Nazionale di S. Marco, Venice (Fig. 8); the Rev. M. A. Laurent, O.P., Scriptor of the Vatican Library (Plate 2); the Director of the Wellcome Museum of Medical History (Fig. 21). The following lent blocks for illustrations: Messrs. Macmillan & Co. Ltd. (Plate 12); Oxford University Press (Plate 1 and Figs. 23, 25 and 26); Penguin Books, Ltd. (Plate 7).

PREFACE

ONE OF THE MOST REMARKABLE DEVELOPMENTS IN the world of scholarly letters in the last generation, and especially since the end of the late War, has been the growth of the study of the history of science both as a professional historical discipline and among the interests of the general reader. Considering how science has quietly come to take a central position in our culture this is perhaps not surprising; some knowledge of the history of science has become unavoidably part of the acquisition of historical awareness. It is precisely the period covered by this book that has attracted perhaps the most attention, and it is because of the interest shown in the original edition that it is now being re-issued.

Certainly the interest shown in this period is not difficult to explain. It has long been a matter of curiosity to know something of the scientific thought of those medieval centuries in which so many other essential aspects of our civilisation, ranging from the theory and practice of law and government to the character of feeling and execution in poetry and the plastic arts, had their genesis and formation. I hope that in these pages the reader curious to know something of the history of medieval science, not simply as the background to modern science but as interesting in itself, may find at least a general guide to his inquiries. Deceptive both in its similarities to and in its differences from 17th-century science, the scientific thought of the period from Augustine to Galileo was a series of actions in the great adventure of philosophical reformation that separates the classical world from our own.

Although the stories of Greek science and of modern science have been told more than once in recent works, both separately and as parts of general histories of science, there exists no adequate short history of the science of the period connecting the classical with the modern world. My purpose in writing this book has been to fill this gap.

The scholarship of the last half-century has long since banished the time when the rumours about medieval science, put about after the revival of interest in classical literature in the 15th century, could be regarded as an adequate substitute for the study of contemporary sources. In the pages that follow I have tried to use the results of recent research to tell, within the covers of a single general history, the story of Western science from its decay after the collapse of the Roman Empire in the West to its full reflowering in the 17th century. Especially I have tried to bring out, what I believe to be the most striking result of recent scholarship, the essential continuity of the Western scientific tradition from Greek times to the 17th century and, therefore, to our own day.

I am indebted to many friends for their help with different aspects of this book, especially to Mr. J. Crompton and Mr. A. D. M. Cox for reading the proofs and making many valuable suggestions; to Dr. J. Lindsay for some discussions during the early stages of writing; to Professor H. Butterfield and Drs. N. H. de V. Heathcote and D. McKie for advice on special points; and to Messrs. R. R. Raymo and T. J. Smiley for checking final proofs and index.

A.C.C.

Oxford, 1956.

INTRODUCTION

THE HISTORY OF SCIENCE is the history of systems of thought about the natural world. Though the most obvious characteristic of science in modern civilisation is the control it has given over the physical world, even while such practical control was being acquired, and certainly for long periods before it became possible, men were trying to bring nature within the grasp of their understanding. The inventions and practical achievements of applied science are of great interest to the historian and so are the effects of natural science on the layman's view of the world as seen in literature, art, philosophy and theology; of even greater interest is the internal development of scientific thought itself. The chief problems before the historian of science are, therefore: what questions about the natural world were men asking at any particular time? What answers were they able to give? And why did these answers cease to satisfy human curiosity? An obsolete system of scientific thought, which may appear very strange to us looking back from the 20th century, becomes intelligible when we understand the questions it was designed to answer. The questions make sense of the answers, and one system has given place to another not simply because new facts were discovered that falsified the old system, but more significantly because for some reason, sometimes the result of fresh observations, scientists began to rethink their whole position, to make new assumptions, to ask new questions, to look at long familiar evidence in a new way.

In ancient Greece men were concerned with trying to discover the intelligible essence underlying the world of change, and they pursued natural science more for understanding than for use. In their search for what was permanent in the changing world of observation, the Greeks hit upon the brilliant idea of a generalised use of scientific theory, of assuming a permanent, uniform, abstract order from which the changing order of observations could be deduced. With this idea, of which geometry became the paradigm giving it the most precise expression, Greek science must be seen as the origin of all that has followed; it was the triumph of order brought by abstract thought into the chaos of immediate experience. With the rise of Christianity, to this Greek rationalism was added the idea of nature as sacramental, symbolic of spiritual truths, and both attitudes are found in St. Augustine. In Western Christendom in the Dark Ages men were concerned more to preserve the facts which had been collected in classical times than to attempt original interpretations themselves. Yet, during this period, a new element was added from the social situation, an activist attitude which initiated a period of technical invention and was to have an important effect on the development of scientific apparatus. Early in the 12th century men asked how the facts recorded in the book of *Genesis* could best be explained in terms of rational causes. With the recovery of the full tradition of Greek and Arabic science in the 12th and early 13th centuries, and particularly of the works of Aristotle and Euclid, there was born, from the marriage of the empiricism of technics with the rationalism of philosophy and mathematics, a new conscious empirical science seeking to discover the rational structure of nature. At the same time a more or less complete system of scientific thought was provided by Aristotle's works. The rest of the history of medieval science consists of the working out of the consequences of this new approach to nature.

Gradually it was realised that the new science did not conflict with the idea of Divine Providence, though it led to a variety of attitudes towards the relation between reason and faith. Internal contradictions, contradictions with other authorities, and contradictions with observed facts eventually led to radical criticisms of the Aristotelian system. At the same time, extension of the use of experiment and mathematics produced an increase in positive knowledge. By the beginning of the 17th century the systematic use of the new methods of experiment and mathematical abstraction had produced results so striking that this movement has been given the name 'Scientific Revolution'. These new methods were first expounded in the 13th century, but were first used with complete maturity and effectiveness by Galileo.

The origins of modern science are to be found at least as far back as the 13th century, but from the end of the 16th century the Scientific Revolution began to gather a breathtaking speed. The changes in scientific thought occurring then so altered the type of question asked by scientists that Kant said of them: 'a new light flashed on all students of nature'. The new science also profoundly affected man's idea of the world and of himself, and it was to have a position in relation to society unknown in earlier times. The effects of the new science on thought and life have, in fact, been so great and special that the Scientific Revolution has been compared in the history of civilisation to the rise of ancient Greek philosophy in the 6th and 5th centuries B.C. and to the spread of Christianity throughout the Roman Empire in the 3rd and 4th centuries A.D. For this reason the study of the changes leading up to that revolution, the study of the history of science from the Middle Ages to the 17th century, is of unique interest for the historian of science. The position of science in the modern world cannot be fully understood without a knowledge of the changes that occurred during that time.

The plan of this book is to start, in Chapter I, with a brief account of ideas about the natural world in Western Christendom from the Dark Ages to the 12th century and then, in Chapter II, to show how the system of scientific thought accepted in the 13th century was introduced from Greek and Arabic sources. The purpose of Chapter III is to give a description of that system and to indicate the additions of fact and modifications in detail made to it during the century or more following its introduction. Chapter IV is concerned with the relation of technical activity to science during the whole medieval period. In Chapter V an account is given of the development of ideas on scientific method and criticism of the fundamental principles of the 13th-century system made from the end of the 13th to the end of the 15th century, which prepared the way for the more radical changes of the 16th and 17th centuries. The last chapter is devoted to the Scientific Revolution itself.

I

SCIENCE IN WESTERN
CHRISTENDOM UNTIL THE
12TH CENTURY RENAISSANCE

*' Our play leaps o'er the vaunt and firstlings
of these broils
Beginning in the middle'*

(Troilus and Cressida)

THE CONTRAST BETWEEN THE scientific ideas of the Dark
Ages and the early Middle Ages, that is from about the 5th
to the early 12th century, and those of the later Middle Ages,
can best be seen in a conversation which is supposed to have
taken place between the widely travelled 12th-century
scholar and cleric Adelard of Bath and his stay-at-home
nephew. Adelard's contribution to the discussion introduces
the newly-recovered ideas of the ancient Greeks and the
Arabs; that of his nephew represents the traditional view of
Greek ideas as they had been preserved in Western Christendom since the fall of the Roman Empire.

The conversation is recorded in Adelard's *Quæstiones
Naturales*, written, probably, after he had studied some
Arabic science but before he had achieved the familiarity
with it which is shown in his later translations, such as
those of the Arabic text of Euclid's *Elements* and the astronomical tables of al-Khwarizmi. The topics covered range
from meteorology to the transmission of light and sound,
from the growth of plants to the cause of the tears which the
nephew shed for joy at the safe return of his uncle.

When not long ago, while Henry, son of William [Henry I, 1100-
35], was on the throne, I returned to England after my long period
of study abroad, it was very agreeable to meet my friends again.
After we had met and made the usual enquiries about one

B   I

another's health and that of friends, I wanted to know something about the morals of our nation . . . After this exchange, as we had most of the day before us and so lacked no time for conversation, a nephew of mine who was with the others—he was interested rather than expert in natural science—urged me to disclose something new from my Arab studies. To this, when the rest had agreed, I delivered myself as in the tract that follows.

The nephew declared himself delighted at such an opportunity of showing that he had kept his youthful promise to work hard at philosophy, by disputing the new ideas with his uncle, and declared that

if I were only to listen to you expounding a lot of Saracen theories, and many of them seemed to me to be foolish enough, I would get a little restless, and while you are explaining them I will oppose you wherever it seems fit. I am sure you praise them shamelessly and are too keen to point out our ignorance. So for you it will be the fruit of your labour if you acquit yourself well, while for me, if I oppose you plausibly, it will mean that I have kept my promise.

The scientific inheritance of the Latin West, represented by the nephew's contribution to the dialogue, was limited almost exclusively to what fragments of Greco-Roman learning had been preserved in the compilations of the Latin encyclopæ-dists. The Romans themselves had made hardly any original contributions to science. The emphasis of their education was upon oratory. But some of them were sufficiently interested in trying to understand the world of nature to make careful compilations of the learning and observations of Greek scholars. One of the most influential of these compilations which survived throughout the Dark, and early Middle Ages as a text-book was the *Natural History* of Pliny (23-79 A.D.), which Gibbon described as an immense register in which the author has 'deposited the discoveries, the arts, and the errors of mankind'. It cited nearly 500 authorities. Beginning with the general system of astronomy it passed to geography, anthropology, physiology and zoology, botany, agriculture and horticulture, medicine, mineralogy and the fine arts.

Until the 12th century, when translations of Greek and Arab works began to come into Western Europe, Pliny's was the largest known collection of natural facts, and it was drawn on by a succession of later writers.

The mathematics and logic of the Latin West rested on the work of the 6th-century Boethius who did for those studies what Pliny had done for natural history. Not only did he compile elementary treatises on geometry, arithmetic and astronomy, based respectively on the work of Euclid, Nicomachus and Ptolemy, but he also translated the logical works of Aristotle into Latin. Of these translations only the *Categories* and the *De Interpretatione* were widely known before the 12th century, but until that time these translations and commentaries of Boethius were the main source for the study of logic as of mathematics. Knowledge of mathematics was, however, largely confined to arithmetic, the so-called 'Geometry of Boethius' containing only fragments of Euclid and being concerned mostly with such practical operations as surveying. Cassiodorus (*c*.490-580) in his popular writings on the liberal arts, gave only a very elementary treatment of mathematics.

Another of the compilers of the Dark Ages who helped to keep alive the scientific learning of the Greeks in the Latin West was Isidore of Seville (560-636). His *Etymologies*, based on often fantastic derivations of various technical terms, remained popular for many centuries as a source of knowledge of all kinds from astronomy to medicine. For Isidore the universe was limited in size[1], only a few thousand years

---

[1] The littleness of man in the universe was, however, a familiar theme for reflection and this passage from Boethius' *De Consolatione Philosophiæ* (II, vii) was well known throughout the Middle Ages: 'Thou hast learnt from astronomical proofs that the whole earth compared with the universe is not greater than a point, that is, compared with the sphere of the heavens, it may be thought of as having no size at all. Then, of this tiny corner, it is only one-quarter that, according to Ptolemy, is habitable, to living things. Take away from this quarter the seas, marshes, and other desert places, and the space left for man hardly even deserves the name of infinitesimal.'

old and soon to perish. The earth, he thought, was shaped like a wheel with its boundaries encircled by the ocean. Round the earth were the concentric spheres bearing the planets and stars, and beyond the last sphere was highest heaven, the abode of the blessed.

Bede (673-735), though he knew Greek, derived most of his scientific material from Isidore and more especially from Pliny, whose works he knew better than Isidore had done. Bede's followers, such as Alcuin of York (735-804) and the German Hrabanus Maurus (776-856), borrowed freely from all the previous encyclopædists.

From the 7th century onwards the Latin West had to rely almost exclusively on these compilations for scientific knowledge. The gradual penetration of the barbarians into the Western Roman Empire from the 4th century caused some material destruction and eventually serious political instability, but it was the eruption of the Mohammedan invaders into the Eastern Empire in the 7th century that gave the most serious blow to learning in Western Christendom. The conquest of much of the territory of the Eastern Empire by the Arabs meant that the main reservoir of Greek learning was cut off from Western scholars for centuries by the intolerance and mutual suspicion of opposing creeds, and by the dragon wing of the Mediterranean. In this intellectual isolation Western Christendom could hardly have been expected to make many original contributions to man's knowledge of the material universe. All the West was able to do was to preserve the collection of facts and interpretations already made by the encyclopædists. That so much was preserved in spite of the gradual collapse of Roman political organisation and social structure under the impact, first, of Goths, Vandals and Franks, and then, in the 9th century, of Norsemen, was due to the appearance of monasteries with their attendant schools which began in Western Europe after the foundation of Monte Cassino by St. Benedict in 529. The existence of such centres made possible a temporary revival of learning under Charlemagne in the

9th century. And it was in a monastic school at Laon that the nephew of Adelard received his education in the 12th century when the curriculum was still based on the work of the encyclopædists. Studies were limited to the seven liberal arts as defined by Varro in the first century B.C. and by Martianus Capella six hundred years later. Grammar, logic and rhetoric made up the first stage or *trivium*, and geometry, arithmetic, astronomy and music made up the more advanced *quadrivium*. The texts used were the works of Pliny, Boethius, Cassiodorus and Isidore.

One development of importance which had taken place in the studies of the Latin West between the days of Pliny and the time when Adelard's nephew pursued his studies at Laon was the assimilation of Neoplatonism. And this was of cardinal importance for it determined men's views of cosmology until the second half of the 12th century. St. Augustine (354–430) was the principal channel through which the traditions of Greek thought passed into the reflections of Latin Christianity and St. Augustine came profoundly under the influence of Plato and of Neoplatonists such as Plotinus (*c.* 203–270 A.D.). The chief aim of Augustine was to find a certain basis for knowledge and this he found in the conception of eternal ideas as expounded by the Neoplatonists and in the Pythagorean allegory, the *Timæus*, by Plato himself. According to this school of thought eternal forms or ideas existed quite apart from any material object. The human mind was one of these eternal essences and had been formed to know the others if it would. In the process of knowing, the sense organs merely provided a stimulus spurring on the mind to grasp the universal forms which constituted the essence of the universe. An important class of such universal forms was mathematics. 'If I have perceived numbers by the sense of the body', Augustine said in *De Libero Arbitrio* (book 2, chapter 8, section 21),

I have not thereby been able by the sense of the body to perceive also the nature of the separation and combination of numbers . . . And I do not know how long anything I touch by a bodily sense

5

will persist, as, for instance, this sky and this land, and whatever
other bodies I perceive in them. But seven and three are ten
and not only now but always; nor have seven and three in any
way at any time not been ten, nor will seven and three at any
time not be ten. I have said, therefore, that this incorruptible
truth of number is common to me and anyone at all who
reasons.

In the 9th century such scholars as John Scot Erigena
(d. 877) re-emphasised the importance of Plato. In addition
to the work of the Latin encyclopædists and others, he
began to use some original Greek works, some of the most
important being the 4th-century translation by Chalcidius
of Plato's *Timæus* and commentary by Macrobius, and the
5th-century commentary by Martianus Capella. Erigena
himself showed little interest in the natural world and seems
to have relied for his facts almost entirely on literary sources,
but the fact that among his sources he included Plato, for
whom St. Augustine had also had so marked a preference,
gave to men's interpretations of the universe a Platonic or
Neoplatonic character for about 400 years, though it was not
till the development of the school of Chartres in the 12th
century that the more scientific parts of the *Timæus* were
particularly emphasised.

In general the learning of Western Christendom as
represented by the views of Adelard's nephew, the Latin
encyclopædists and the cathedral and the monastic schools
was predominantly theological and moral. Even in classical
times there had been very little attempt to pursue scientific
enquiry for 'fruit' as Francis Bacon called the improvement
of the material conditions of life. The object of Greek science
had been understanding and under the influence of later
classical philosophers such as the Stoics, Epicureans and
Neoplatonists natural curiosity had given way almost entirely
to the desire for the untroubled peace which could only be
won by a mind lifted above dependence on matter and the
flesh. These pagan philosophers had asked the question:
What is worth knowing and doing? To this Christian teachers

also had an answer: that is worth knowing and doing which conduces to the love of God. The early Christians continued their neglect of natural curiosity and at first also tended to disparage the study of philosophy itself as likely to distract men from a life pleasing to God. St. Clement of Alexandria in the 3rd century poked fun at this fear of pagan philosophy which he compared to a child's fear of goblins, and both he and his pupil Origen showed that all knowledge was good since it was a perfection of mind and that the study of philosophy and of natural science was in no way incompatible with a Christian life. St. Augustine himself in his searching and comprehensive philosophical inquiries had invited men to examine the rational basis of their faith. But in spite of these writers natural knowledge continued to be considered of very secondary importance during the Dark Ages. The primary interest in natural facts was to find illustrations for the truths of morality and religion. The study of nature was not expected to lead to hypotheses and generalisations of science but to provide vivid symbols of moral realities. The moon was the image of the Church reflecting the divine light, the wind an image of the spirit, the sapphire bore a resemblance to divine contemplation, and the number eleven which 'transgressed' ten, representing the commandments, stood itself for sin.

This preoccupation with symbols is shown clearly in the bestiaries. Since the time of Aesop stories about animals had been used to illustrate various human virtues and vices, and this tradition was continued in the 1st century A.D. by Seneca in his *Quæstiones Naturales,* and by later Greek works, culminating in the 2nd century with a work of Alexandrian origin known as the *Physiologus,* which was the model for all the medieval moralising bestiaries. In these works facts of natural history collected from Pliny were mixed with entirely mythical legends to illustrate some point of Christian teaching. The phœnix was the symbol of the risen Christ. The ant-lion, born of the lion and the ant, had two natures and so was unable to eat either meat or seeds and perished miserably like the man who tried to follow God and the Devil. The *Physiologus* had enormous popularity. It was translated into Latin in the 5th century and into many other languages, from Anglo-Saxon to Ethiopian. In the 4th century when St. Ambrose wrote a commentary on the Bible he made liberal use of animals as moral symbols. As late as the early years of the 13th century when Alexander Nequam wrote his *De Naturis Rerum,* in which he showed very considerable interest in scientific fact, he claimed that he had written the book for purposes of moral instruction. In the 12th century there were many signs, as, for instance, in the illustrations to certain manuscripts and the descriptions of wild life by Giraldus Cambrensis (*c.* 1147–1223) and other travellers, that men were capable of observing nature very clearly, but their observations were usually simply interpolations in the course of a symbolic allegory which to their minds was all important. In the 13th century this passion for pointing out moral symbolism invaded even the lapidaries, which in the Ancient World as represented in the works of Theophrastus (*c.* 372–288 B.C.), Dioscorides (1st century A.D.) and Pliny and even in the Christian works of 7th–century Isidore or 12th–century Marbode, Bishop of Rennes, had been concerned with the medical value of stones or with their magical properties.

This preoccupation with the magical and astrological properties of natural objects was, with the search for moral symbols, the chief characteristic of the scientific outlook of Western Christendom before the 13th century. There was a wealth of magic in the works of Pliny and one of its characteristic ideas, the doctrine of signatures according to which each animal, plant or mineral had some mark indicating its hidden virtues or uses, had a profound effect on popular natural history. St. Augustine had to bring all the skill of his dialectic against the denial of free will which astrology implied, but had not been able to defeat this superstition. Isidore of Seville admitted that there were magical forces in nature, and though he distinguished between the part of astrology which was natural, since it led man to study the courses of the heavenly bodies, and the superstitious part which was concerned with horoscopes, he yet admitted that these heavenly bodies had an astrological influence on the human body and advised doctors to study the influence of the moon on plant and animal life. It was a very general belief during the whole of the Middle Ages and even into the 17th century that there was a close correspondence between the course of a disease and the phases of the moon and movements of other heavenly bodies, although throughout that time certain writers, as, for instance, the 14th-century Nicole Oresme and the 15th-century Pierre d'Ailly, had made fun of astrology and had limited celestial influence to heat, light and mechanical action. Indeed, medical and astronomical studies came to be closely associated.[1] Salerno and later Montpellier were famous for both and in a later age Padua welcomed both Galileo and Harvey.

An example of this astrological interpretation of the world of nature as a whole is the conception of the correspondence between the universe, or Macrocosm, and the individual man, or Microcosm. This theory had been expressed in the *Timæus* and had been elaborated in relation to astrology by the Stoics. The classical medieval expression of the belief was given in the 12th century by Hildegard of Bingen who thought that various parts of the human body were linked with special parts of the Macrocosm so that the

(1) Cf. the Prologue to Chaucer's *Canterbury Tales* (ll. 411 *et seq.*)
> 'With us ther was a Doctour of Physik;
> In all this world ne was ther noon hym lik,
> To speke of physik and of surgerye;
> For he was grounded in astronomye.
> He kepte his pacïent a ful greet deel
> In hourès, by his magyk natureel.
> Wel koude he fortunen the ascendent
> Of his ymáges for his pacïent.
> He knew the cause of everich maladye,
> Were it of hoot, or cold, or moyste, or drye,
> And where they engendred and of what humour;
> He was a verray parfit praktisour.'

'humours' were determined by the movements of the heavenly bodies.

Gilson has said of the world of the Dark Ages and of the early Middle Ages, typified by the nephew of Adelard: 'to understand and explain anything consisted for a thinker of this time in showing that it was not what it appeared to be, but that it was the symbol or sign of a more profound reality, that it proclaimed or signified something else'. But this exclusively theological interest in the natural world had already begun to be modified even before the writings of the Greek and Arab natural philosophers became more fully and widely known in Western Christendom as a result of increasing intellectual contact with the Arab and Byzantine worlds. One aspect of this change in outlook is to be seen in the increasing activity of the computists, doctors and writers of purely technical treatises of which there had been a continuous tradition throughout the Dark Ages. In the 6th century Cassiodorus, when making arrangements for an infirmary in his monastery[1], had in his *Institutio Divinarum Litterarum*, book 1, chapter 31, given some very precise and practical advice on the medical use of herbs:

Learn, therefore, the nature of herbs, and study diligently the way to combine various species . . . and if you are not able to read Greek, read above all translations of the *Herbarium* of Dioscorides, who described and drew the herbs of the field with wonderful exactness. After this, read translations of Hippocrates and Galen, especially the *Therapeutics* . . . and Aurelius Celsus' *De Medicina* and Hippocrates' *De Herbis et Curis*, and divers other books written on the art of medicine, which by God's help I have been able to provide for you in our library.

At the beginning of the 8th century Bede had shown that the habit of observation was not entirely lost when he produced a careful study of tides, part of which was derived from Pliny and part seems to have been based on the results of careful personal observation. He recorded from his

[1] At Monte Cassino St. Benedict had also established an infirmary. The care of the sick was regarded as a Christian duty for all such foundations.

own experience that tides are higher at the equinox than at the solstice, and that at any given port high tide lagged behind the meridian passage of the moon by a definite time characteristic of that port. In the 8th century appeared the earliest known Latin manuscript on the preparation of pigments, gold making and other practical problems which might confront the artist or illuminator. In the monastic schools established by Charlemagne there was some criticism of traditional literary advice on the treatment of disease, and similar criticism in the light of practical experience is found in the 11th–century *Practica* of Petrocellus of the famous medical school of Salerno. There was also the body of experience collected by the computists or practical mathematicians who were concerned with the calculation of the dates of movable feasts. This was one of the chief uses of arithmetic, and various improvements in technique were attempted from the beginning of the 8th century, when Bede produced his chronology and 'finger reckoning', to the end of the 10th century when the monk Helperic produced his text-book on arithmetic, and down to the 11th and 12th centuries when there appeared numerous manuscripts on this subject. The calculation of dates led also to an interest in astronomical observations, and more accurate observations became possible when knowledge of the astrolabe was obtained from the Arabs by Gerbert and other scholars of the 10th century. The chief scientific centre at that time was Lotharingia, and Canute and later Earl Harold and William the Conqueror all encouraged Lotharingian astronomers and mathematicians to come to England, where they were given ecclesiastical positions.

The other tendency which did even more to substitute another approach to the world of nature for that of moralising symbolism was the change in the philosophical outlook associated especially with the 11th-century nominalist, Roscelinus, and his pupil Peter Abelard (1079-1142). At the end of the 11th century the teaching of Roscelinus opened the great dispute over 'universals' which led men to take a greater interest in the individual, material object as such and not, as St. Augustine had done, to regard it as simply the shadow of an eternal idea. The debate began over some remarks of Boethius concerning the relation of universal ideas such as 'man', 'rose' or 'seven' both to individual things and numbers and to the human minds that knew them. Did the universal 'rose' subsist with individual roses or as an eternal idea apart from physical things? Or had the universal no counterpart in the real world, was it a mere abstraction? One of the most vigorous attacks on St. Augustine's point of view was made by Roscelinus' pupil Abelard, almost an exact contemporary of Adelard of Bath; his dialectical skill and violence won him the nickname of *Rhinocerus indomitus*. Abelard did not accept Roscelinus' view that universals were simply abstractions, mere names, but he pointed out that if the only reality were the eternal ideas then there could be no real difference between individual roses or men, so that in the end everything would be everything else. The outcome of this criticism of the extreme Augustinian view of the universal was to emphasise the importance of the individual, material thing and to encourage observation of the particular.

The effect of this changed philosophical outlook, of the increasing number of practical treatises and of the rediscovery of Greek works through contact with the Arabs, is shown in the answers given by Adelard of Bath to the scientific questions put to him by his nephew. The first of the *Quæstiones Naturales* was:

Why do plants spring from the earth? What is the cause and how can it be explained? When at first the surface of the earth is smooth and still, what is it that is then moved, pushes up, grows and puts out branches? If you collect dry dust and put it finely sieved in an earthenware or bronze pot, after a while when you see plants springing up, to what else do you attribute this but to the marvellous effect of the wonderful divine will?

Adelard admitted that it was certainly the will of the Creator that plants should spring from earth, but he asserted his opinion that this process was 'not without a natural reason too'. He repeated this opinion in answer to a later question when his nephew asked him if it were not 'better to attribute all the operations of the universe to God', since his uncle could not produce natural explanations for them all. To this Adelard replied :

I do not detract from God. Everything that is, is from him and because of him. But [nature] is not confused and without system and so far as human knowledge has progressed it should be given a hearing. Only when it fails utterly should there be recourse to God.

With this remark the medieval conception of nature began to cross the great watershed that divides the period when men looked to nature to provide illustrations for moralising from that in which men began to study nature for its own sake. The realisation of such a conception became possible when Adelard demanded 'natural causes' and declared that he could not discuss anything with someone who was 'led in a halter' by past writers.

Those who are now called authorities reached that position first by the exercise of their reason . . . Wherefore, if you want to hear anything more from me, give and take reason.

The first explanation of the universe in terms of natural causes, after the dissatisfaction with the attempt to interpret it merely in terms of moral symbols, was associated with the school of Chartres and was deeply influenced by the teaching of Plato. Early in the 12th century Chartres had shown a renewed interest in the scientific ideas contained in the *Timæus*. Such scholars as Gilbert de la Porrée (*c.* 1076–1154), Thierry of Chartres (d. *c.* 1155) and Bernard Silvester (*fl.c.* 1150) studied Biblical questions with greater attention than before to the scientific matters involved, and all were deeply influenced by St. Augustine. Thierry of Chartres in his *De Septem Diebus et Sex Operum Distinctionibus*, in which he attempted to give a rational explanation of the creation, declared that it was impossible to understand the story in *Genesis* without the intellectual training provided by the *quadrivium*, that is without the mastery of mathematics, for on mathematics all rational explanation of the universe depended. Thierry interpreted the story of the creation as meaning that in the beginning God created space or chaos, which for Plato had been pre-existing and had been shaped into the material world by a demiurge. In St. Augustine's writings, the demiurge had been replaced by the Christian God, and the forms given to the material world were reflections of the eternal ideas existing in the mind of God.

According to Plato's *Timæus* the four elements out of which all things in the universe were made, earth, water, air and fire, were composed of small invisible particles, those of each element having a characteristic geometrical shape by which the demiurge had reduced to order the originally disorderly motions of chaos.[1] The elements were mutually transformable by breaking down each geometrical shape into others,

(1) The conception of matter as being made up of small particles had been put forward by various Greek philosophers in an attempt to explain how change was possible in a world in which things still retained their identity. In the 5th century B.C. Parmenides had brought philosophers to an impasse by pointing out that the earlier Ionian school's conception of one, homogeneous substance such as water, air or fire as the identity persisting through change would in fact make change impossible, for one homogeneous substance could do nothing but remain one and homogeneous. Change would then involve the coming into being of something out of nothing, which was impossible. Change was therefore unintelligible. In order to overcome this difficulty other philosophers later in the 5th century assumed that there were several ultimate substances and that the rearrangement of these produced the changes observed in the world. Anaxagoras said that each kind of body was divisible into homogeneous parts or 'seeds' each of which retained the properties of the whole and was again divisible and so on to infinity. Empedocles, on the other hand, said that after a certain number of divisions of bodies there would be reached the four elements, earth, water, air and fire; all bodies were formed from combinations of these elements, each of which was itself permanent and unchanging. The Pythagorean school supposed that all objects were made up of points or units of existence, and that natural objects were made up of these points in combinations corresponding to the various geometrical figures. It

but their main masses were arranged in concentric spheres with earth in the centre, water next it, then air and finally fire, so as to form a finite spherical universe in a limitless space. The sphere of fire extended from the moon to the fixed stars, and contained within it the spheres of those heavenly

should then have been possible for a line to be made up of a finite number of such points, and the Pythagorean theory broke down when faced with such facts as that the ratio of the diagonal to the side of a square could not be expressed in terms of an exact number but was $\sqrt{2}$, which to the Pythagoreans was 'irrational'. The Pythagoreans had in fact confused geometrical points with ultimate physical particles and this seems to have been the point of Zeno's paradoxes. The atomists Leucippus and Democritus avoided this difficulty by admitting that geometrical points had no magnitude and that geometrical magnitudes were divisible to infinity, but held that the ultimate particles which made up the world were not geometrical points or figures but physical units which were indivisible, that is, atoms. According to the atomists the universe was made up of atoms moving continually at random in an infinite void. Atoms differed in size, shape, order and position, the number of different shapes being infinite. In their continual movements they formed vortices in which were produced first the four elements and then other bodies by mechanical attachments of like atoms, for instance, by a hook-and-eye mechanism. Since the number of atoms was limitless so was the number of worlds they might form in the infinite void. For the atomists the only 'truth' consisted in the properties of the atoms themselves, hardness, shape and size. All other properties such as taste, colour, heat or cold were simply sense impressions which did not correspond to anything in 'reality'. Both Pythagoreans and atomists agreed in thinking that the intelligible, persisting and real amid the changing variety of the physical world was something that could be expressed in terms of mathematics. This was also the view which Plato put forward in the *Timæus*, in which he was strongly influenced by the Pythagoreans. Down to the time of Plato the result of Greek efforts to explain change was thus to refine and make intelligible the idea of the identity persisting through change. This identity, which formed the 'being' or 'substance' of physical things, had been converted from something material into an intangible essence. For Plato this essence was the universal idea or 'form' which he held existed apart from physical things as the object of their aspiration. Change or 'becoming' was a process by which sensible likenesses of such eternal forms were produced in space and time.

15

bodies and of the other intermediate planets. Fire was the chief constituent of heavenly bodies.

In Thierry's view fire vaporised some of the waters on the earth and raised them to form the firmament dividing the waters which were under the firmament from the waters which were above the firmament. This reduction in the waters covering the central sphere of earth led to the appearance of dry land. The warmth of the air and the moisture of the earth engendered plants and trees. Next the stars were formed as conglomerations in the supercelestial waters, and the heat developed by their subsequent motions hatched birds and fishes out of the terrestrial waters, and animals out of the earth itself. The animals included man—made in the image of God. After the sixth day nothing more was created, but Thierry adopted from St. Augustine a theory which accounted for the appearance of new creatures. Augustine had brought into agreement two apparently contradictory accounts in *Genesis*, in one of which, all things were created at once while in the other, creatures, including man, appeared in succession. He had accepted the idea, put forward in the 5th century B.C. by Anaxagoras and subsequently developed by the Stoics, of originative seeds or germs, and he had suggested that in the first stage of creation plants, animals and men had all been made simultaneously in germ or in their 'seminal causes' and that in the second stage they had actually and successively appeared.

The falling and rising of bodies was explained by the Platonists of Chartres, following the *Timæus*, by supposing that bodies of like nature tended to come together. A detached part of any element would thus tend to rejoin its main mass: a stone fell to the earthy sphere at the centre of the universe, whereas fire shot upward to reach the fiery sphere at the outermost limit of the universe. This Platonic theory of gravity had been known also to Erigena, who had held that heaviness and lightness varied with distance from the earth, the centre of gravity. Adelard of Bath had also accepted this theory of gravity and was able to satisfy his nephew's curiosity by saying that if a stone were dropped into a hole passing through the centre of the earth it would fall only as far as the centre.

The movement of the heavenly bodies was explained by supposing that the universe, being spherical, had a proper motion of uniform eternal rotation in a circle about a fixed centre, as could be seen in the daily rotation of the fixed stars. The different spheres in which the seven 'planets', moon, sun, Venus, Mercury, Mars, Jupiter and Saturn were set, revolved with different uniform velocities such as would represent the observed movements of those bodies. Each of the spheres had its own Intelligence or 'soul' which was the source of its motion.

It was not only the cosmogony and cosmology of Thierry and his contemporaries that was influenced by the *Timæus;* it also coloured their physical and physiological conceptions. They followed Plato in holding that within the universe there was no void. Space was a *plenum*, that is, it was full. Movement could therefore take place only by each body pushing that next to it away and taking its place in a kind of vortex. Such functions as respiration and digestion Plato had explained as purely mechanical processes based on the movement of fiery and other particles. Sensations he supposed were produced by the motions of particles in the organs of the body. The particular quality of a member of any given class of sensations, for instance a particular colour or sound, he explained by the inherent qualities of the external object depending on its structure, which in turn brought about particular physical processes in the special sense organ concerned. Vision he supposed to take place by means of a visual ray emitted from the eye to the object, colours being attributed to different sized fire particles which streamed off objects and interacted with this ray. Sounds he connected with the motion of air particles, though he ignored the role of the ear drum. Different tastes and odours he related to the character of the particles composing or coming off the objects. Many of these views were taken over by the natural philosophers of the 12th century. The direct influence of the *Timæus* is seen in their belief in the indestructibility of matter and their explanation of the properties of the elements in terms of the motion of particles in which velocity and solidity were complementary, for no body could be set in motion without the corresponding reaction against a motionless body. One 12th-century philosopher, William of Conches, adopted a form of atomism based on a combination of Plato's ideas with those of Lucretius.

This Platonist conception of the universe continued to exert an important influence until the days of Roger Bacon, who, as a young man, sometime about 1245, lectured on physics from the point of view of the Chartres school. But Chartres itself was already in touch with the schools of translators who were working on Arabic and Greek texts at Toledo and in southern Italy, and it was in Chartres that the Ptolemaic astronomy and Aristotelian physics were first welcomed. Thus, because of developments within the thought of Western Christendom itself, the system of ideas represented by Adelard's nephew was beginning to appear a little antiquated by the middle of the 12th century. It was soon to be replaced by ideas developed by those who followed his uncle in the study of the Arabs and the Greeks and the pursuit of natural causes.

II

THE RECEPTION OF GRECO-ARABIC
SCIENCE IN WESTERN CHRISTENDOM

The new science which began to percolate into Western Christendom in the 12th century was largely Arabic in form, but it was founded on the works of the ancient Greeks. The Arabs preserved and transmitted a large body of Greek learning, and what they added to its content themselves was perhaps less important than the change they made in the conception of the purpose for which science ought to be studied.

The Arabs themselves acquired their knowledge of Greek science from two sources. Most of it they eventually learned directly from the Greeks of the Byzantine Empire, but their first knowledge of it came at second hand from the Syriac-speaking Nestorian Christians of Eastern Persia. During the 6th and 7th centuries Nestorian Christians at their centre of Jundishapur translated most of the important works of Greek science into Syriac, which had replaced Greek as the literary language of Western Asia since the 3rd century. For a time after the Arab conquests Jundishapur continued to be the first scientific and medical centre of Islam, and there Christian, Jewish and other subjects of the Caliphs worked on the translation of texts from Syriac into Arabic. The centre of this work later moved to Damascus and then in the early 9th century to Baghdad, where translations were also made direct from Greek. By the 10th century nearly all the texts of Greek science that were to become known to the Western world were available in Arabic.

Gradually the learning which had been amassed by the Arabs began to penetrate into Western Christendom as trading relations slowly revived between Christendom and

Islam. By the 9th century, towns such as Venice, Naples, Bari and Amalfi, later joined by Pisa and Genoa, were carrying on trade with the Arabs of Sicily and the eastern Mediterranean. In the 11th century a Benedictine monk of Monte Cassino, Constantine the African, was sufficiently familiar with Arab scientific work to be able to produce a paraphrase of Galen and Hippocrates from the medical encyclopædia of the Persian doctor Haly Abbas (d. 994). In the 12th century Adelard of Bath is known to have travelled in south Italy and even in Syria and, at the beginning of the 13th century, Leonardo Fibonacci of Pisa was in North Africa on business where he acquired his knowledge of Arabic mathematics.

The chief centres from which the knowledge of Arabic and ultimately of Greek science spread were Sicily and Spain. Toledo fell to Alfonso VI in 1085 and towards the middle of the 12th century became, under the patronage of its archbishop, the Spanish centre of translation from Arabic into Latin. The very great number of versions attributed to such men as Gerard of Cremona suggest the existence of some sort of school. The names of known translators, Adelard of Bath, Robert of Chester, Alfred of Sareshel (the Englishman), Gerard of Cremona, Plato of Tivoli, Burgundio of Pisa, James of Venice, Eugenio of Palermo, Michael Scot, Hermann of Carinthia, William of Moerbeke, bear witness to the wide European character of the movement, as do their own words, of which Adelard's are typical, to the feeling of excitement with which the earlier scholars set out to gain Arab learning for the Latin West. Many of the translations were works of collaboration, for example, the work of the Hispano-Jew John of Seville, who translated the Arabic into vernacular Castilian which was then rendered into Latin by Dominicus Gundissalinus. The earliest known Latin-Arabic glossary is contained in a Spanish manuscript dating, perhaps, from the 12th century, but the work of translating Greek and Arabic texts was severely hampered by the difficulty of mastering the languages involved, the intricacy of the subject matter and the complicated technical terminology. The translations were often literal and often words whose meanings were imperfectly understood were simply transliterated from their Arabic or Hebrew form. Many of these words have survived down to the present day as, for example, alkali, zircon, alembic (the upper part of a distilling vessel), sherbet, camphor, borax, elixir, talc, the stars Aldebaran, Altair and Betelgeuse, nadir, zenith, azure, zero, cipher, algebra, algorism, lute, rebeck, artichoke, coffee, jasmine, saffron and taraxacum. Such new words went to enrich the vocabulary of medieval Latin, but it is not surprising that these literal translations sprinkled with strange words provoked complaints from other scholars. Many of the translations were revised in the 13th century either with a better knowledge of Arabic or directly from the Greek.

In Sicily, in addition to translations from the Arabic, there appeared some of the earliest translations to be made directly from Greek. Conditions in the island specially favoured the exchange of ideas between Arabic, Greek and Latin scholars. Until the fall of Syracuse in 878 it had been dominated by Byzantium. Then it passed under the control of Islam for nearly two hundred years until 1060 when a Norman adventurer with a small following captured Messina and was so successful in establishing his power that by 1090 the island had become a Norman kingdom in which Latin, Greek and Moslem subjects lived together in conditions even more favourable than those in Spain for the work of translation.

From the end of the 12th century to the end of the 13th the proportion of translations made direct from Greek to those made at second hand through Arabic gradually increased, and in the 14th century translation from Arabic practically ceased when Mesopotamia and Persia were overrun by the Mongols. It is said that from the end of the 12th century shiploads of Greek manuscripts came from Byzantium to Italy, though few can be definitely traced as having done so. When the Fourth Crusade was diverted against Byzantium, which was captured by the Westerners in 1204, one result was that many manuscripts passed to the Latin West. In 1205 Innocent III exhorted masters and scholars of Paris to go to Greece and revive the study of literature in the land of its birth, and Philip Augustus founded a college on the Seine for Greeks of Constantinople to learn Latin. Later in the 13th century Roger Bacon wrote a Greek grammar and, at the suggestion of St. Thomas Aquinas, William of Moerbeke revised and completed the translation of almost all Aristotle's works in a literal version made direct from the Greek.

By the middle of the 12th century the number of new works added to the store of European learning included Aristotle's *logica nova*, that is, the *Analytics* and the other logical works not in the long familiar translations by Boethius which were included in the *logica vetus*, Euclid's *Elements*, *Optics* and *Catoptrics* and Hero's *Pneumatica*. From the 12th century dates also the Latin version of the pseudo-Euclidean *De Ponderoso et Levi*, a work of Greek origin which provided both Islam and Western Christendom with their knowledge of specific gravity, the lever and the balance. In the third quarter of the century translations were made of the principal works of Ptolemy, Galen and Hippocrates, of which the popular versions came chiefly from Spain, and of Aristotle's *Physics* and *De Cælo* and other *libri naturales* and the first four books of the *Metaphysics*. Early in the 13th century the complete *Metaphysics* was translated, and about 1217 appeared his *De Animalibus* comprising the *History*, *Parts* and *Generation of Animals*. At the same time was translated the pseudo-Aristotelian *Liber de Plantis* or *de Vegetabilibus*, which modern scholarship has attributed to the 1st-century B.C. Nicholas of Damascus and which, apart from the herbals deriving from Dioscorides and Apuleius, was the most important single source of later medieval botany. By the middle of the 13th century nearly all the important works of Greek science were available in Latin translations (Table 1). Some works were also translated into vernacular languages,

TABLE 1

THE PRINCIPAL SOURCES OF ANCIENT SCIENCE IN WESTERN CHRISTENDOM BETWEEN 500 AND 1300 A.D.

Author	Work	Latin translator and language of original of translation	Place and date of Latin translation
(1) *Early Greek and Latin Sources*			
Plato (428–347 B.C.)	*Timaeus* (first 53 chapters)	Chalcidius from Greek	4th century Italy
Aristotle (384–322 B.C.)	Some logical works (*logica vetus*)	Boethius from Greek	6th century
Dioscorides (1st century A.D.)	*Materia Medica*	from Greek	by 6th century
Anon.	*Physiologus* (2nd century A.D. Alexandria)	from Greek	5th century
Anon.	Various technical *Compositiones*	from Greek sources	earliest MSS. 8th century
Lucretius (c. 95–55 B.C.)	*De Rerum Natura* (known in 12th century)		
Vitruvius (1st century B.C.)	*De Architectura* (known in 12th century)		
Seneca (4 B.C.–65 A.D.)	*Quaestiones Naturales*		
Pliny (23–79 A.D.)	*Historia Naturalis*		
Macrobius (*fl.* 395–423)	*In Somnium Scipionis*		

23

Author	Work	Latin translator and language of original of translation	Place and date of Latin translation
Martianus Capella (5th century)	Satyricon, sive De Nuptiis Philologiae et Mercurii et de Septem Artibus Liberalibus		
Boethius (480–524)	Works on the liberal arts, particularly mathematics and astronomy, and commentaries on the logic of Aristotle and Porphyry		
Cassiodorus (c. 490–580)	Works on the liberal arts		
Isidore of Seville (560–636)	Etymologiarum sive Originum De Natura Rerum		
Bede (673–735)	De Natura Rerum De Temporum Ratione		
(2) Arabic Sources from c. 1000			
Jabir ibn Hayyan (fl. c. 776)	Various chemical works	from Arabic	12th and 13th centuries
Al-Khwarizmi (9th century)	Liber ... Alchorismi (arithmetic)	Adelard of Bath from Arabic	c. 1126
	Astronomical tables (trigonometry)	Adelard of Bath from Arabic	c. 1126

24

Author	Work	Latin translator and language of original of translation	Place and date of Latin translation
Al-Khwarizmi (9th century)	Algebra	Robert of Chester from Arabic	Segovia 1145
Alkindi (d. c. 873)	De Aspectibus; De Umbris et de Diversitate Aspectuum	Gerard of Cremona from Arabic	Toledo 12th century
Thabit ibn Qurra (d. 901)	Liber Charastonis (on the Roman balance)	Gerard of Cremona from Arabic	Toledo 12th century
Rhazes (d. c. 924)	De Aluminibus et Salibus (chemical work)	Gerard of Cremona from Arabic	Toledo 12th century
	Liber Continens (medical encyclopædia)	Moses Farachi from Arabic	Sicily 1279
	Liber Almansoris (medical compilation based on Greek sources)	Gerard of Cremona from Arabic	Toledo 12th century
Alfarabi (d. 950)	Distinctio super Librum Aristotelis de Naturali Auditu	Gerard of Cremona from Arabic	Toledo 12th century
Haly Abbas (d. 994)	Part of Liber Regalis (medical encyclopædia)	Constantine the African (d. 1087) and John the Saracen from Arabic	South Italy 11th century
	Liber Regalis	Stephen of Antioch from Arabic	c. 1127

Author	Work	Latin translator and language of original of translation	Place and date of Latin translation
pseudo-Aristotle	*De Proprietatibus Elementorum* (Arabic work on geology)	Gerard of Cremona from Arabic	Toledo 12th century
Alhazen (*c.* 965–1039)	*Optice Thesaurus*	From Arabic	End of 12th century
Avicenna (980–1037)	Physical and philosophical part of *Kitab al-Shifa* (commentary on Aristotle)	Dominicus Gundissalinus and John Seville from Arabic	Toledo 12th century
	De Mineralibus (geological and alchemical part of *Kitab al-Shifa*)	Alfred of Sareshel from Arabic	Spain *c.* 1200
	Canon (medical encyclopaedia)	Gerard of Cremona from Arabic	Toledo 12th century
Alpetragius (12th century)	*Liber Astronomie* (Aristotelian concentric system)	Michael Scot from Arabic	Toledo 1217
Averroës (1126–1198)	Commentaries on *Physica, De Celo et Mundo, De Anima* and other works of Aristotle	Michael Scot from Arabic	early 13th century

Author	Work	Latin translator and language of original of translation	Place and date of Latin translation
Leonardo Fibonacci of Pisa	*Liber Abaci* (first complete account of Hindu numerals)	using Arabic knowledge	1202

(3) *Greek sources from c. 1100*

Author	Work	Latin translator and language of original of translation	Place and date of Latin translation
Hippocrates and school (5th, 4th centuries B.C.)	*Aphorisms*	Burgundio of Pisa from Greek	12th century
	Various treatises	Gerard of Cremona and others from Arabic / William of Moerbeke from Greek	Toledo / 12th century / after 1260
Aristotle (384–322 B.C.)	*Posterior Analytics* (part of *logica nova*)	Two versions from Greek	12th century
		from Arabic	Toledo / 12th century
	Meteorologica (Book 4)	Henricus Aristippus from Greek	Sicily *c.* 1156
	Physica, De Generatione et Corruptione, Parva Naturalia, Metaphysica (1st 4 books), *De Anima*	from Greek	12th century

Author	Work	Latin translator and language of original of translation	Place and date of Latin translation
Aristotle (384–322 B.C.)	*Meteorologica* (Books 1–3), *Physica, De Caelo et Mundo, De Generatione et Corruptione*	Gerard of Cremona from Arabic	Toledo 12th century
	De Animalibus (*Historia animalium, De partibus animalium, De generatione animalium* trans. into Arabic in 19 books by el-Batric, 9th century)	Michael Scot from Arabic	Spain *c.* 1217–20
	Almost complete works	William of Moerbeke, new or revised translations from Greek	*c.* 1260–71
Euclid (*c.* 330–260 B.C.)	*Elements* (15 books, 13 genuine)	Adelard of Bath from Arabic revised by Campanus of Novara	*c.* 1126 *c.* 1254
	Optica and *Catoptrica*	from Greek	
Apollonius (3rd century B.C.)	*Conica*	perhaps Gerard of Cremona from Arabic	probably Sicily 12th century

Author	Work	Latin translator and language of original of translation	Place and date of Latin translation
Archimedes (287–212 B.C.)	*De Mensura Circuli*	Gerard of Cremona from Arabic	Toledo 12th century
	De Iis quæ in Humido Vehuntur (on floating bodies)	William of Moerbeke from Greek	1269
Diocles (2nd century B.C.)	*De Speculis Comburentibus*	Gerard of Cremona from Arabic	Toledo 12th century
Hero of Alexandria (1st century B.C.?)	*Pneumatica*	from Greek	Sicily 12th century
	Catoptrica (attributed to Ptolemy in Middle Ages)	William of Moerbeke from Greek	after 1260
pseudo-Aristotle	*Mechanica*	from Greek	early 13th century
	De Plantis or *De Vegetabilibus* (now attributed to Nicholas of Damascus, 1st century B.C.)	Bartholomew of Messina from Greek	Sicily, *c*.1260
		Alfred of Sareshel from Arabic	Spain, probably before 1200
pseudo-Euclid	*Liber Euclidis de Ponderoso et Levi* (statics)	from Arabic	12th century

29

Author	Work	Latin translator and language of original of translation	Place and date of Latin translation
Galen (129–200 A.D.)	Various treatises	Burgundio of Pisa from Greek	c. 1185
	Various treatises	Gerard of Cremona and others from Arabic	Toledo 12th century
	Various treatises	William of Moerbeke from Greek	1277
Ptolemy (2nd century A.D.)	Almagest	from Greek	Sicily c. 1160
		Gerard of Cremona from Arabic	Toledo 1175
	Optica	Eugenius of Palermo from Arabic	c. 1154
Alexander of Aphrodisias (fl. 193–217 A.D.)	Commentary on the Meteorologica	William of Moerbeke from Greek	13th century
	De Motu et Tempore	Gerard of Cremona from Arabic	Toledo 12th century
Simplicius (6th century A.D.)	Part of commentary on De Cælo et Mundo	Robert Grosseteste from Greek	13th century
	Commentary on Physica	from Greek	13th century
	Commentary on De Cælo et Mundo	William of Moerbeke from Greek	1271
Proclus (410–85 A.D.)	Physica Elementa (De motu)	from Greek	Sicily 12th century

in particular into Italian, Castilian, French and later into English. Of all these works the most influential were those of Aristotle, who had provided the basis for the natural philosophy of the Greeks and of the Arabs and was now to perform the same function for Western Christendom. The translations of his writings were chiefly responsible for the shift in educational interest that took place round about 1200 towards philosophy and science which John of Salisbury (*c.* 1115–80) had complained were even in his time being preferred to the poetry and history of his youth.

Of the actual knowledge from the stores of Greek learning which was transmitted to Western Christendom by the Arabs together with some additional observations and comments of their own, some of the most important was the new Ptolemaic astronomy (below, pp. 56–62) and its associated trigonometry. This reached Europe through the translations of works by such writers as al-Khwarizmi, al-Battani (d. 929) and al-Fargani (9th century), but these authors had, in fact, added nothing new to the principles on which the astronomical system of Ptolemy had been founded. In the 12th century al-Bitruji, known in Latin as Alpetragius, revived the astronomical work of Aristotle, though here again the Arab did not advance much on the Greek. What the Arabs did do was to improve observing instruments and construct increasingly accurate tables for both astrological and nautical purposes. The most famous of these were prepared in Spain, which, from the time of the editing of the *Toledan Tables* by al-Zarquali (d. *c.* 1087) to their replacement under the direction of King Alfonso the Wise (d. 1284) by others compiled in the same town, had been a centre of astronomical observation. The meridian of Toledo was for a long time the standard of computation for the West and the *Alfonsine Tables* remained in use till the 16th century.

The second body of fact transmitted from Greek works to Western Christendom by way of Arabic translations and commentaries was the work on medicine and to this Arab scholars, though they did not modify the underlying principles much, added some valuable observations. Most of the information was derived from Hippocrates and Galen and became enshrined in the encyclopædias of Haly Abbas (d. 994), Avicenna (980–1037) and Rhazes (d. *c.* 924)[1], but the Arabs were able to add some new minerals such as mercury and a number of other drugs to the predominantly herbal *materia medica* of the Greeks, and Rhazes was able to contribute original observations such as in his diagnosis of smallpox and measles.

The original Arabic contribution was more important in the study of optics and perspective for here, though the works of Euclid, Hero and Ptolemy had dealt with the subject, Alkindi (d. *c.* 873) and Alhazen (*c.* 965–1039) made a big advance on what had been known by the Greeks. Alhazen discussed, among other things, spherical and parabolic mirrors, the *camera obscura*, lenses and vision.

In the field of mathematics the Arabs transmitted to Western Christendom a body of most valuable knowledge which had never been available to the Greeks, though here the Arabs were not making an original contribution but simply making more widely known the developments in mathematical thought which had taken place among the Hindus. Unlike the Greeks, the Hindus had developed not so much geometry as arithmetic and algebra. The Hindu mathematicians, of whom Aryabhata (b. 476 A.D.), Brahmagupta (b. 598 A.D.) and later Bhaskara (b. 1114) were the most important, had developed a system of numerals in which the value of a digit was shown by its position; they knew the use of zero, they could extract square and cube roots, they understood fractions, problems of interest, the

(1) Cf. the Prologue to Chaucer's *Canterbury Tales* (ll.429 *et seq.*)
    'Wel knew he the olde Esculapius
    And Deÿscorides, and eek Rufus,
    Olde Ypocras, Haly and Galyen,
    Serapion, Razis and Avycen,
    Averrois, Damascien and Constantyn,
    Bernard and Gatesden and Gilbertyn'.

summation or arithmetical and geometrical series, the solution of determinate and indeterminate equations of the first and second degrees, permutations and combinations and other operations of simple arithmetic and algebra. They also developed the trigonometrical technique for expressing the motions of the heavenly bodies and introduced trigonometrical tables of sines.

The most important mathematical idea which the Arabs learnt from the Hindus was their system of numerals and the adoption of this system in Christendom was one of the great advances in European science. The great merit of this system, which is the basis of the modern system, was that it contained the symbol for zero and that any number could be represented simply by arranging digits in order, the value of a digit being shown by its distance from zero or from the first digit on the left. It had very great advantages over the cumbrous Roman system. In the system which the Arabs learnt from the Hindus the first three numbers were represented by one, two and three strokes respectively, and after that 4, 5, 6, 7, 9 and possibly 8 were probably derived from the initial letters for the words representing those numbers in Hindu. The Arabs had learnt something of this system from the Indians, with whom they had considerable trading relations, as early as the 8th century, and a complete account of it was given by al-Khwarizmi in the 9th century. It was from a corruption of his name that the system became known in Latin as 'algorism'.

The Hindu numerals were introduced into Western Europe gradually from the 12th century onwards. It was symptomatic of the practical trend among mathematicians that al-Khwarizmi himself, whose work on algebra was translated by Adelard of Bath, said (as he is rendered by F. Rosen in his edition, *The Algebra of Mohammed ben Musa*, London, 1831, p. 3) that he had limited his activities

to what is easiest and most useful in arithmetic, such as men constantly require in cases of inheritance, legacies, partition, law-suits, and trade, and in all their dealings with one another, or where the measuring of lands, the digging of canals, geometrical computation, and other objects of various sorts and kinds are concerned.

Later in the same century Rabbi ben Ezra, by origin a Spanish Jew, fully explained the Arabic system of numeration and specially the use of the symbol O. Gerard of Cremona reinforced this exposition. But it was not till the 13th century that the Arabic system became widely known. This was due very largely to the work of Leonardo Fibonacci, or Leonardo of Pisa (d. after 1240). Leonardo's father was a Pisan merchant who was sent out to Bugia in Barbary to take charge of a factory and there Leonardo seems to have learnt a great deal about the practical value of Arabic numerals and about the writings of al-Khwarizmi. In 1202 he published his *Liber Abaci* in which in spite of the name he fully explained the use of the Arabic numerals. He was not personally interested in commercial arithmetic and his work was highly theoretical, but after his time Italian merchants generally came gradually to adopt the Arabic, or Hindu, system of numeration.

During the 13th and 14th centuries the knowledge of Arabic numerals was spread through Western Christendom by the popular almanacks and calendars. As the dates of Easter and of the other festivals of the Church were of great importance in all religious houses, one almanack or calendar was usually found in these establishments. A calendar in the vernacular had been produced in France as early as 1116, and Icelandic calendars go back to about the same date. This knowledge was reinforced in the West by popular expositions of the new system by mathematical writers such as Alexander of Villedieu and John Holywood or, as he was called, Sacrobosco, and even in a surgical treatise by Henry of Mondeville. About the middle of the 13th century two Greek mathematicians explained the system to Byzantium. The Hindu numerals did not immediately drive out the Roman ones and in fact until the middle of the 16th century Roman numerals were widely used outside Italy, but by 1400

Arabic numerals were widely known and generally under-stood at least among men of learning.

*   *   *   *

The spheres in which the Arabs made their most important and original contribution to the development of European science were alchemy, magic and astrology, and this was partly because of the different approach of the Arabs to the problems of the world of nature. They asked not what aspects of nature most vividly illustrated the moral purposes of God nor what were the natural causes which would provide a rational explanation of the facts described in the Bible or observed in the world of everyday experience, but what knowledge would give power over nature. They wanted to find 'the Elixir of Life, the Philosopher's Stone, the Talisman, the Word of Power and the magic properties of plants and minerals', and the answer to their questions was alchemy. It was partly a desire to share this rumoured magical power that sent the first translators on their journeys from Western Christendom to such centres of Arabic learning as Toledo or Sicily. Some scholars believed that the ancient Greeks had had such knowledge and had hidden it in cryptic writings and alchemical symbols.

Latin works written before the 12th century had been by no means free from magic and astrology (see above, pp. 8–10), but among the Arabs and those Latins who, after the 12th century, were influenced by their works magic and astrology fruited tropically. No sharp distinction was drawn between natural science and the magical or occult, for physical and occult causes were recognised as equally able to be respons-ible for physical phenomena. This point of view was expressed clearly by Alkindi, the 9th-century Arab Neo-platonist, in his work *On Stellar Rays* or *The Theory of the Magic Art.* The stars and terrestrial objects, and also the human mind through the potency of words suitably uttered, exerted 'influence' by means of rays whose ultimate cause was celestial harmony. The effects of the rays were supposed to vary with the configurations of the heavenly bodies. 'Celestial virtue' was admitted as a cause by nearly all the Latin writers of the 13th century, and Roger Bacon's famous discussion of the old theory of the 'multiplication of species' has been variously interpreted as a contribution to physics and as an account of astral influences going in straight lines. 'Marvels', when not the work of demons and therefore evil, might be produced by occult virtues resident in certain objects in nature, that is by 'natural magic'. The distinction between evil and natural magic was maintained by a number of scholastic natural philosophers, William of Auvergne, Albertus Magnus and Roger Bacon. The discovery of occult virtues was one of the principal objects of many medieval experimenters. The alchemists hoped to transmute metals, prolong human life, perhaps gain sufficient power over nature to discover the names of those who had committed theft or adultery.

Well down into the 16th century the connection between magic and one side of experimentation was close. In the 17th century Bishop Wilkins, one of the founders of the Royal Society, was to include in a book on mechanics called *Mathematicall Magick*, being borne through the air by birds and by witches among recognised methods of human transport. But even in the 13th century many of the natural philosophers of Western Christendom were able to keep magic out of their work. Albertus Magnus, Petrus Peregrinus and Rufinus are examples of observers and experimenters who did so. Roger Bacon (*c*. 1214–92), though he certainly derived the desire for power over nature as the object of his science, as well as his belief in the occult virtues of stones and herbs, from the ambitions and assumptions of magic, yet developed a view of scientific experiment which was perhaps the earliest explicit statement of the practical conception of the aims of science. With him the practical European genius was beginning to transform the magic of the Arabian Nights into the achievements of applied science.

In his *Opus Tertium*, chapter 12, Roger Bacon, having discussed speculative alchemy, goes on to say:

But there is another alchemy, operative and practical, which teaches how to make the noble metals and colours and many other things better and more abundantly by art than they are made in nature. And science of this kind is greater than all those preceding because it produces greater utilities. For not only can it yield wealth and very many other things for the public welfare but it also teaches how to discover such things as are capable of prolonging human life for much longer periods than can be accomplished by nature . . . Therefore this science has special utilities of that nature; while nevertheless it confirms theoretical alchemy through its works.

In his view of what could usefully be achieved by science Roger Bacon had the outlook common to his age: the future would be read more accurately than in the stars; the Church would overcome Antichrist and the Tartars. The ultimate value of science was to be in the service of the Church of God, the community of the faithful: to protect Christendom through power over nature and to assist the Church in her work of evangelising mankind by leading the mind through scientific truth to the contemplation of the Creator already revealed in theology, a contemplation in which all truth was one. But in his conception of the immediate use of science he had the outlook of the 19th century.

'Next', he says of agriculture in his *Communia Naturalium*,

comes the special science of the nature of plants and all animals, with the exception of man who by reason of his nobleness falls under a special science called medicine. But first in the order of teaching is the science of animals which precede man and are necessary for his use. This science descends first to the consideration of every kind of soil and the productions of the earth, distinguishing four kinds of soil, according to their crops; one soil is that wherein corn and legumina are sown; another is covered with woods, another with pastures and heaths; another is garden ground wherein are cultivated trees and vegetables, herbs and roots, as well for nutriment as for medicine. Now this science extends to the perfect study of all vegetables, the knowledge of which is very imperfectly delivered in Aristotle's treatise *De Vegetabilibus*; and therefore a special and sufficient science of plants is required, which should be taught in books on agriculture. But as agriculture cannot go on without an abundance of tame animals; nor the utility of different soils, as woods, pastures and heaths, be understood, except wild animals be nurtured; nor the pleasure of man be sufficiently enhanced, without such animals; therefore this science extends itself to the study of all animals.

Bacon did not develop this discussion of the sciences, but his appreciation of the potential usefulness of such studies is clear. His prophecies about the submarine and the motor car in the *Epistola de Secretis Operibus*, chapter 4, are well known and are another example of the extremely practical turn which he gave to scientific studies.

Machines for navigation can be made without rowers so that the largest ships on rivers or seas will be moved by a single man in charge with greater velocity than if they were full of men. Also cars can be made so that without animals they will move with unbelievable rapidity; such we opine were the scythe-bearing chariots with which the men of old fought. Also flying machines can be constructed so that a man sits in the midst of the machine revolving some engine by which artificial wings are made to beat the air like a flying bird. Also a machine small in size for raising or lowering enormous weights, than which nothing is more useful in emergencies. For by a machine three fingers high and wide and of less size a man could free himself and his friends from all danger of prison and rise and descend. Also a machine can easily be made by which one man can draw a thousand to himself by violence against their wills, and attract other things in like manner. Also machines can be made for walking in the sea and rivers, even to the bottom without danger. For Alexander the Great employed such, that he might see the secrets of the deep, as Ethicus the astronomer tells. These machines were made in antiquity and they have certainly been made in our times, except possibly the flying machine which I have not seen nor do I know anyone who has, but I know an expert who has thought out the way to make one. And such things can be made almost without limit, for instance, bridges across rivers without piers or supports, and mechanisms, and unheard of engines.

Bacon also urged the reform of the calendar, as had his master Robert Grosseteste, and described how this might be done, though, in fact, his suggestions had to wait until 1582 to be put into practice. In the later Middle Ages, however, scientific knowledge as distinguished from merely technical rule of thumb led to improvements in building and surgery and to the invention of spectacles, though in general the practical mastery over nature which the Arabs had sought through magic was not achieved for many centuries.

Most influential of all the contributions of Greco-Arabic learning to Western Christendom was the fact that the works of Aristotle, Ptolemy and Galen constituted a complete rational system explaining the universe as a whole in terms of natural causes. Aristotle's system included more than natural science as it is understood in the 20th century. It was a complete philosophy embracing all existence from 'first matter'. to God. But just because of its completeness the Aristotelian system aroused much opposition in Western Christendom where scholars already had an equally comprehensive system based on the facts revealed in the Christian religion.

Moreover, some of Aristotle's theories were themselves directly contrary to Christian teaching. For instance, he held that the world was eternal and this obviously conflicted with the Christian conception of God as a creator. His opinions were doubly suspect because they reached the West accompanied by Arab commentaries which stressed their absolutely determinist character. The Arab interpretation of Aristotle was strongly coloured by the Neoplatonic conception of the chain of being stretching from first matter through inanimate and animate nature, man, the angels and Intelligences to God as the origin of all. When such commentators as Alkindi, Alfarabi, Avicenna and particularly Averroës (1126–98) introduced from the Mohammedan religion into the Aristotelian system the idea of creation, they interpreted this in such a way as to deny free will to man and even to God himself. According to them the world had been created not directly by God but by a hierarchy of necessary causes starting with God and descending through the various

Intelligences which moved the celestial spheres, until the Intelligence moving the moon's sphere caused the existence of a separate Active Intellect which was common to all men and the sole cause of their knowledge. The form of the human soul already existed in this Active Intellect before the creation of man and after death each human soul merged again into it. At the centre of the universe within the sphere of the moon, that is, in the sublunary region, were generated a common fundamental matter, *materia prima*, and then the four elements. From the four elements were produced, under the influence of the celestial spheres, plants, animals and man himself.

Several points in this system were entirely unacceptable to the philosophers of Western Christendom in the 13th century. It denied the immortality of the individual human soul. It denied human free will and gave scope for the interpretation of all human behaviour in terms of astrology. It was rigidly determinist, denying that God could have acted in any way except that indicated by Aristotle. This determinism was made even more repulsive to Christian thinkers by the attitude of the Arab commentators and especially of Averroës who declared that

Aristotle's doctrine is the sum of truth because his was the summit of all human intelligence. It is therefore well said that he was created and given us by Divine Providence, so that we should know what it is possible to know.

Some allowance may be made here for oriental exaggeration, but this point of view came to be characteristic of the Latin Averroïsts. For them the world emanated from God as Aristotle had described it, and no other system of explanation was possible.

The 13th century saw first the categorical condemnation of Aristotle, but before the end of the century he had been accepted as the most important of the philosophers. In 1210 at Paris, which by the end of the 12th century had already replaced Chartres as the greatest centre of learning in France, the provincial ecclesiastical council prohibited the teaching of Aristotle's views on natural philosophy or of commentaries on them. In 1215 a similar decree was issued against reading his metaphysical and natural works. Other prohibitions were issued subsequently, but it was not possible to enforce them. In 1231 Pope Gregory IX appointed a commission to revise some of the natural works and in 1260 William of Moerbeke began his translation from the Greek. Eminent teachers like Albertus Magnus and his pupil Thomas Aquinas expounded the works of Aristotle, and by 1255 his most important metaphysical and natural works were set by the faculty of arts in Paris as a subject for examination.

Throughout the Middle Ages there were various schools of thought about the Aristotelian system of the universe. In the 13th century in Oxford the Franciscan friars, who tended to remain loyal to the main features of Augustinianism, such as the theory of knowledge and of universals, accepted some important Aristotelian additions in the explanation of such natural phenomena as the movements of the heavenly bodies, but were often hostile to Aristotle's influence as a whole. At the same time in Oxford there was an interest characteristic of another aspect of Franciscan thought, exemplified by Roger Bacon, who was keenly alive to the mathematical, physical, astronomical and medical learning of Aristotle and the Arabs and less concerned with their metaphysical views. In the University of Paris black-habited Dominicans, such as Albertus Magnus and Thomas Aquinas, accepted the main principles of Aristotle's physics and philosophy of nature (see below, pp. 44 *et seq.*) but rejected his absolute determinism. A fourth school of thought, represented by Siger of Brabant, who was thorough-going Averroïst, accepted an entirely determinist interpretation of the universe. Yet a fifth group was in the Italian universities of Salerno, Padua and Bologna where theological matters counted for less than in England or France and where Aristotle and the Arabs were studied principally for their medical learning.

Those mainly responsible for making Aristotle acceptable to the Christian West were Albertus Magnus (1193/1206–1280) and his pupil Thomas Aquinas (1225–74). The main problem confronting them was the relation between faith and reason. In his attempt to resolve this difficulty Albertus based himself on two certainties: the realities of revealed religion and the facts which had come within his own personal experience. Albertus and St. Thomas did not regard Aristotle as an absolute authority as Averroës had done, but simply as a guide to reason. Where Aristotle, either explicitly or as interpreted by Arab commentators, conflicted with the facts either of revelation or of observation he must be wrong: that is, the world could not be eternal, the individual human soul must be immortal, both God and man must enjoy the exercise of free will. Albertus also corrected him on a number of points of zoology (see below, pp. 120–6). But Albertus and more definitely St. Thomas realised, as Adelard of Bath had done a century earlier, that theology and natural science often spoke of the same thing from a different point of view, that something could be both the work of Divine Providence and the result of a natural cause. In this way they established a distinction between theology and philosophy which assigned to each its appropriate methods and guaranteed to each its own sphere of action. There could be no real contradiction between truth as revealed by religion and truth as revealed by reason. Albertus said that it was better to follow the apostles and fathers rather than the philosophers in what concerned faith and morals. But in medical questions he would rather believe Hippocrates or Galen, and in physics Aristotle, for they knew more about nature.

The determinist interpretation of Aristotle's teaching associated with the commentaries of Averroës was condemned by the Archbishop of Paris in 1277, and his example was followed in the same year by the Archbishop of Canterbury. In so far as this affected science it meant that in northern Christendom the Averroïst interpretation of

Aristotle was banished. The Averroïsts retired to Padua where their views gave rise to the doctrine of the double truth, one for faith and another, perhaps contradictory, for reason. This condemnation of determinism has been taken by some modern scholars, notably by Duhem, as marking the beginning of modern science. The teaching of Aristotle was to dominate the thought of the later Middle Ages, but with the condemnation of the Averroïst view that Aristotle had said the last word on metaphysics and natural science, the Archbishops in 1277 left the way open for criticism which would, in turn, undermine his system. Not only had natural philosophers now through Aristotle a rational philosophy of nature, but because of the attitude of Christian theologians they were made free to form hypotheses regardless of Aristotle's authority, to develop the empirical habit of mind working within a rational framework and to extend scientific discovery.

III

THE SYSTEM OF SCIENTIFIC
THOUGHT IN THE 13TH CENTURY

(I) EXPLANATION OF CHANGE AND CONCEPTION
OF SUBSTANCE

THE SYSTEM OF SCIENTIFIC thought that was made
known to Western Christians in the 13th century came to
them, in a collection of translations from Greek and Arabic,
as a complete and for the most part coherent whole. This
was a system of rational explanations in power and range
quite beyond anything known earlier in the Latin West, and
one the general principles of which in fact dominated
European science until the 17th century. This Greco-Arabic
scientific system was not, however, received merely passively
in the 13th century. The activity of mind that had shown
itself in the 12th century in the fields of philosophy and
technology was applied in the 13th century to detect, and to
endeavour to resolve, the contradictions that existed within
the Aristotelian system itself, between Aristotle and other
authorities such as Ptolemy, Galen, Averroës and Avicenna,
and between the various authorities and observed facts. The
Western scholars were trying to make the natural world
intelligible and they seized upon the new knowledge as a
wonderful, but not final, illumination of mind and as a
starting-point for further investigation.

The object of this chapter is to describe this 13th-century
scientific system, indicating the historical sources of each
part of it, and to give a brief account of the additions of fact
and modifications in detail made to it during the century or

more after its introduction. These changes were made for the most part as a result of the gradual extension of observation, experiment and the use of mathematics, and they were made possible to a large extent as a result of habits acquired in technology. It will be necessary to mention some aspects of medieval technics in this chapter, but it is convenient to reserve a fuller discussion of the subject for Chapter IV. The experimental and mathematical methods were themselves the result of a definite theory of science, a theory postulating definite methods of investigation and explanation. Some indication of this theory of science will be necessary to make much of what follows in this chapter intelligible, and many of the additions of fact to be described were the results of its application. A fuller treatment of medieval scientific method will be reserved for Chapter V. Besides additions of fact, other important changes were made in the 13th-century scientific system as a result of criticism from a purely theoretical point of view. Those affecting the details of the system will be described in this chapter, but those involving criticism of its fundamental principles will also be reserved for Chapter V. These more radical criticisms derived for the most part from the change in the theory of science that began during the 13th century, a change which led to the conception that the experimental and mathematical methods should extend over the whole field of natural science. This was the conception that brought about the revolution in science that culminated in the 17th century, and so, while the present chapter is concerned with the 13th century scientific system itself, the two following chapters will give an account of the two traditions of scientific activity, the technical and the theoretical, that made possible the transition to the new scientific system of the 17th century.

For the system of scientific thought accepted in the 13th century to become fully intelligible to the 20th century reader it is necessary to understand the nature of the question it was designed to answer. The natural philosopher of the

13th century regarded the investigation of the physical world as part of a single philosophical activity concerned with the search for reality and truth. The purpose of his inquiry was to discover the enduring and intelligible reality behind the changes undergone by the world perceived through the senses. Exactly the same problem had, in fact, been the main preoccupation of the philosophers of ancient Greece, and their answer had been the conception of 'substance' as the identity persisting through change. This identity Plato had recognised as the universal idea or 'form' of a thing (see note on p. 14) and Aristotle had adopted this idea of form from Plato, though modifying it in various important ways. What makes sense of the general principles of 13th-century science, then, is the realisation that the aim of scientific investigation was to define the substance underlying and causing observed effects.

It was Aristotle's conception of substance that dominated 13th-century science and this is best understood by starting with his conception of the methodological structure of science. According to Aristotle, scientific investigation and explanation was a two-fold process, the first inductive and the second deductive. The investigator must begin with what was prior in the order of knowing, that is, with facts perceived through the senses, and he must proceed by induction to include his observations in a generalisation which would eventually lead him to the universal form. These forms were the intelligible and real identity persisting through and causing the changes observed; therefore, though most remote from sensory experience, they were 'prior in the order of nature'. The object of the first, inductive, process in natural science was to define these forms, for such a definition could then become the starting-point for the second process, that by which the observed effects were shown by deduction to follow from this definition and so were explained by being demonstrated from a prior and more general principle which was their cause. The definition of the form was necessary before demonstration could begin because all effects were considered to be attributes of some substance, and the cause of an effect was shown when the effect could be predicated as an attribute of a defined substance. This definition would include everything about a thing, its colour, size, shape, relations with other things, etc. No attribute, that is, no effect or event, could exist unless it inhered in some substance and, indeed, attributes and substance could be separated only in thought.

Aristotle described the process by which the form was discovered by induction as a process of abstraction from the data provided by the senses, and he held that there were three degrees of abstraction which revealed three different aspects of reality. These corresponded to the sciences of physics (or natural science), mathematics and metaphysics. The subject-matter of physics was change and motion as exemplified in material things; the subjects considered by mathematics were abstracted from change and from matter but could exist only as attributes of material things; metaphysics considered immaterial substances with an independent existence. This classification raised the important question of the role of mathematics in explaining physical events. The subjects considered by mathematics, Aristotle said, were abstract, quantitative aspects of material things. Therefore, different mathematical sciences had subordinate to them certain physical sciences, in the sense that a mathematical science could often provide the reason for facts observed in those material things, facts provided by physical science. Thus geometry could provide the reason for, or explain, facts provided by optics and astronomy, and the study of arithmetical proportions could explain the facts of musical harmony. Mathematics, being an abstraction from change, could provide no knowledge of the *cause* of the observed events. It could merely describe their mathematical aspects. In other words, mathematics alone could never provide an adequate definition of the substance, or, as it was called in the Middle Ages, 'substantial form', causing the change, because it dealt only with mathematical attributes; an adequate definition of the causal substance could be reached only by considering all attributes, non-mathematical as well as mathematical. And, Aristotle held, qualitative differences as between flesh and bone, between one colour and another, and between motion up, down and in a circle could not be reduced simply to differences in geometry. This was a point on which Aristotle differed from Plato and the Greek atomists.

The science that considered the cause of change and motion, then, was physics. In putting forward an explanation that would account intelligibly for change as such, Aristotle attempted to avoid the defects which he considered had vitiated the explanations advanced by some of his predecessors (see note on p. 14). Thus, as he did not accept Plato's theory that the forms of physical things existed apart from them he could not explain change by the aspiration of physical things to be like their eternal archetypes. Nor could he fall back on the atomist's explanation of change by the rearrangement of atoms in the void, for he could see no reason why there should be any limit to the division of physical bodies (or, indeed, of any other *continuum* whether of space, time or motion). For him the conception of void, which the atomists had considered as emptiness, or 'non-being', between the atoms of substance, or 'being', involved a contradiction. 'Non-being' could not exist. His own explanation of change was to introduce between being and non-being a third state of potentiality, and to say that change was the actualisation of attributes potential within any given physical thing because of that thing's nature. Attributes which were at any given time potential were as much part of a substance as those which were at that time actual.

The cause of change Aristotle held to be the substance or 'substantial form' itself which for him, as for Greek philosophers generally, was not only the intelligible aspect of a thing but also the active source of its behaviour. The source of change and movement was the attempt of each thing to fulfil its nature or form whether, as in living things, the adult form into which they grew or, as in the terrestrial elements, their 'natural' place in the universe. Aristotle distinguished four kinds of cause of which two, the material and formal, defined the substance undergoing change, and two, the efficient and final, actually produced the movement. What he meant by each of these causes is most easily seen in his view of the generation of animals. He believed that the female contributed no germ or ovum but simply the passive matter out of which the embryo was made. This passive matter was the material cause. The efficient cause was the male seed which started the process of growth. The male seed also carried to the female matter the specific form that determined what kind of animal the embryo would become. This form was the formal cause, and since it represented the final adult state to which development would proceed it was also the final cause.

All changes of any kind whatever, of colour, growth, spatial relations or any other attribute, Aristotle explained on the same principle that attributes which had been potential became actual. Even the property of suffering eclipses was an attribute of the moon to be included in the definition of the moon's substance. What brought change about was the contact of the substance in which the given attribute was potential with one in which it was actual, as wood burned when brought in contact with the already burning fire.

Within change Aristotle distinguished four different kinds: (1) local motion, (2) growth or decrease, (3) alteration or change of quality and (4) substantial change which took place during the process of generation and corruption. In the first three the perceptible identity of the thing persisted throughout; in the fourth the changing thing lost all its old attributes and in fact became a new substance. This he explained by pushing the idea of substance as the persisting identity to its ideal limit and conceiving it to be pure potentiality, capable of determination by any form and having no independent existence. This pure potentiality was

E   49

called by the medieval scholastics *materia prima*. Any given material thing could then be thought of as *materia prima* determined by a form.

An opinion of Aristotle's based on his idea of substance which was to be the subject of some very important discussions in the 14th century, was his conception of infinity. He held that infinity, whether of the division or addition of time or of material things, was a potentiality implying that there was no assignable limit to the process concerned. Time, whether past or future, could have no limit assigned to it, so that the duration of the universe was infinite. But every material thing had a definite size determined by its form. In discussing the possibility of the existence of an infinitely small body he said that the division of material things could potentially go on to infinity, but this potentiality could never become actual. An infinitely large material body, that is, an infinite universe, was, however, not even a potentiality, for the universe was a sphere of finite size.

The conception of substance as developed by Aristotle was the basis of all natural explanation from the 13th to the 17th century, but even after Aristotle's ideas had became generally accepted they were still subject to criticism from Neoplatonists. The main difference between Aristotle's view of matter and that which had been put forward by such Neoplatonists as St. Augustine and Erigena concerned the nature of the substance that persisted through substantial change. For these Neoplatonists this persisting substance was actual extension, that is pure potentiality or *materia prima* determined by spatial dimensions, and this underlay all other attributes of material things; for Aristotle it was simply pure potentiality. With some Arab philosophers such as Avicenna, al-Ghazzali and Averroës and the Spanish Rabbi Avicebron, the Neoplatonic theory of matter took the form that every material thing possessed a 'common corporeity' making it extended, and, according to Avicebron, this corporeity was continuous through the universe. The importance of this theory was that it introduced the possibility of extending the use of mathematics to the whole of natural science, as is shown, for example, in the speculations of Robert Grosseteste (*c.* 1168–1253). He identified the common corporeity of the Neoplatonists with light, which had the property of dilating itself from a point in all directions and was thus the cause of all extension. He held that the universe arose from a point of light which by auto-diffusion generated the spheres of the four elements and the heavenly bodies and conferred on matter its form and dimensions. From this he concluded that the laws of geometrical optics were the foundation of physical reality and that mathematics was essential to the understanding of nature.

This problem of the use of mathematics in explaining the physical world remained, in fact, one of the central methodological problems, and was in many ways *the* central problem, of natural science down to the 17th century. Even in the 12th century a prominent place had been given to mathematics in the teaching of the seven liberal arts. For example, Hugh of St. Victor, author of one of the most important classifications of science relying on purely Latin sources, insisted that mathematics should be learnt before physics and was essential to it, even though mathematics was concerned with entities abstracted from physical things. Essentially the same view was taken by Dominicus Gundissalinus, author of the most influential 12th–century classification of science based on Arabic sources, most of his ideas being taken from Alfarabi. The mid-13th–century writer Robert Kilwardby (d. 1279), who used both Latin and Arabic sources in his classification of science, also paid special attention to the relation of the mathematical disciplines to physics, but maintained the Aristotelian distinction between them. Geometry, he said, abstracted from all aspects of physical bodies except the formal cause and considered that alone; the consideration of moving causes was the prerogative of physics. With the gradually increasing success of mathematics in solving concrete problems in physical science the reality of the sharp line that Aristotle had drawn between the two disciplines came slowly to be doubted. Indeed, from one point of view, the whole history of European science from the 12th to the 17th century can be regarded as a gradual penetration of mathematics (combined with the experimental method) into fields previously believed to be the exclusive preserve of 'physics'.

(2). COSMOLOGY AND ASTRONOMY

Not only Aristotle's theory of substance and fundamental principles of scientific explanation, but also his ideas on the actual structure of the universe, dominated European thought in the 13th century. Aristotle's cosmology was founded on naïve observation and common sense and it had two fundamental principles: (1) that the behaviour of things was due to qualitatively determined forms or 'natures', and (2) that the totality of these 'natures' was arranged to form a hierarchically ordered whole or cosmos. This cosmos or universe had many features in common with that of Plato and of the astronomers Eudoxus and Callippus (4th century B.C.); all had taught that the cosmos was spherical and consisted of a number of concentric spheres, the outermost being the sphere of the fixed stars, with the earth fixed in the centre; but Aristotle's system showed various refinements.

Aristotle's cosmos was a vast but finite sphere centred upon the centre of the earth and bounded by the sphere of the fixed stars, which was also the *primum mobile* or 'prime mover', the originative source of all movement within the universe (Fig. 1). Fixed in the centre of the universe was the spherical earth, and surrounding it concentrically were a series of spheres like the skins of an onion. First came the spherical envelopes of the other three terrestrial elements, water, air and fire, respectively. Surrounding the sphere of fire were the crystalline spheres in which were embedded and carried round, respectively, the moon, Mercury, Venus, the sun, Mars, Jupiter, and Saturn, which made up the seven

'planets'. Beyond the sphere of the last planet came that of
the fixed stars, and beyond this last sphere—nothing.

FIG. 1. Aristotle's cosmology. From Petri Apiani *Cosmographia*, per
Gemma Phrysius restituta, Antwerp, 1539.

Thus each kind of body or substance in this universe had a
place that was natural to it and a natural motion in relation
to that place. Movement took place with reference to a fixed
point, the centre of the earth at the centre of the universe,
and there was a qualitative difference between the movements of a given body in one direction rather than in
another in relation to that point. The natural behaviour of
bodies depended, therefore, on their actual place within the
universe as well as on the substance of which they were
composed. The sphere of the moon divided the universe into
two sharply distinct regions, the terrestrial and the celestial.

53

Bodies in the former region were subject to all the four kinds of change, and the kind of motion that was natural to them was in a straight line towards their natural place in the sphere of the element of which they were composed. To be in that place was the fulfilment of their 'nature' and there they could be at rest. This was why to someone standing on the earth some substances, for example, fire, whose natural place was upwards, seemed light; while other substances, for example, earth, whose natural place was downwards, seemed heavy. These directions represented an absolute up and down and the tendency to move up or down depended on the nature of the substance of which a particular body was composed. Plato had postulated the same kind of movement, but had explained it rather differently.

From the sphere of the moon outwards bodies were composed of a fifth element or 'quintessence' which was ingenerable and incorruptible and underwent only one kind of change, uniform motion in a circle, being a kind of motion that could persist eternally in a finite universe. This kind of motion Plato had said to be the most perfect of all and his dictum that the motions of the heavenly bodies must be resolved into uniform circular motions was to dominate astronomy until the end of the 16th century. The spheres of the planets and stars composed of this celestial fifth element revolved round the central earth.

Motion as such Aristotle had regarded, as he did all other kinds of change, as a process of becoming from a state of privation (in the case of motion this is rest) to actualisation. Such a process of change required a cause and so every moving body required a mover to keep it going, the velocity of motion being supposed to be proportional to the force or power of the mover. This theory Aristotle justified by the simple observation that bodies do come to rest if nothing continues to push them, just as he justified his theory of light and heavy elements by the simple observation that when released on the earth some bodies do rise while others fall.

54

With the celestial spheres the original source of motion was the *primum mobile* which moved itself, Aristotle said, somewhat obscurely, by 'aspiring' to the eternal unmoved activity of God, eternal uniform circular motion being the nearest approach to that state possible for a physical body. In order that this 'aspiration' might be possible he had to suppose that this sphere had some sort of 'soul'. Indeed, he assigned 'souls' to all the spheres and this was the origin of the hierarchy of Intelligences or Motors that Arab Neoplatonism was to attach to the spheres. Motion was communicated from the *primum mobile* to the inner spheres, Aristotle held, by the mechanical contact of each sphere with that inside it.

With terrestrial bodies moving towards their natural place in the sublunary region the mover was their own 'nature' or 'substantial form', whose fulfilment it was to be at rest in that place. There bodies would remain eternally were it not for two further agencies: the generation of substances outside their natural place by the transformation of one terrestrial element into another, and 'violence' due to an external mover. The ultimate cause of both these agencies was in fact the same, namely, the progress of the sun on its annual course round the ecliptic which, it was thought, produced periodic transformations of the elements into one another (see Fig. 5). The movement of these newly generated elements towards their natural place was the principal source of 'violence' in the regions through which they passed.

This generation of elements outside their natural place was also the reason why the actual bodies found in the terrestrial region were usually not pure but made up of a compound of the four elements: for example, ordinary fire or water were compounds in which the pure elements with those names, respectively, dominated. And further, the annual motion of the sun was held to be the cause of the seasonal generation, growth and decay of plants and animals. Thus all change and motion in the universe was ultimately caused by the *primum mobile*. The remainder of this chapter will be devoted to a description of the explanations given, during the hundred years or more after the introduction of the Aristotelian system in the 13th century, of the different kinds of change observed in the different parts of the universe, beginning with astronomy and passing through the sciences concerned with the intermediate regions to finish with biology.

* * * *

Thirteenth-century astronomy was, on its theoretical side, concerned mainly with a debate as to the relative merits of physical as compared with mathematical theories in accounting for the phenomena. The former were represented by Aristotle's explanations, the latter by Ptolemy's, and in fact the debate itself was an old one: it began in later Greek times and had passed through various vicissitudes among the Arabs. Both the Aristotelian and the Ptolemaic systems were known in the Latin West by the beginning of the 13th century. The controversy was opened by Michael Scot with his translation, in 1217, of the 12th-century Arab astronomer Alpetragius' *Liber Astronomiæ*, in which the Arab had tried to revive the waning fortunes of Aristotelian astronomy in face of the more accurate system of Ptolemy.

All ancient and medieval systems of astronomy were based on Plato's dictum that the observed movements of the heavenly bodies must be resolved into uniform circular motions. Aristotle had attempted to account for the facts by means of his system of concentric spheres. The geometrical refinements of this system he in fact took from Eudoxus and Callippus, but he tried to give physical reality to the geometrical devices with which they had accounted for the irregular movements, the stations and retrogradations, of the seven 'planets' as observed against the background of the fixed stars. Following Eudoxus and Callippus he postulated for each planet not one but a system of spheres (Fig. 2). He supposed then that the axis of the sphere actually bearing the planet was itself attached to the inside of another rotating sphere, whose own axis was attached to a third, and so on. By postulating a sufficient number of spheres, arranging the axes at suitable angles and varying the rates of rotation, he

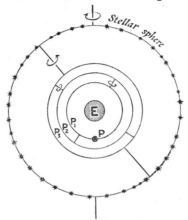

FIG. 2. The system of concentric planetary spheres adopted by Aristotle, showing the system of spheres (p_1, p_2, p_3) for one planet P with the axes all placed in the plane of the paper. If P were Saturn the other planets' spheres would come inside this. The stellar sphere rotates about an axis passing through the centre of the stationary earth E.

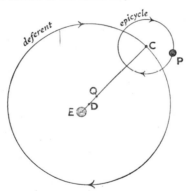

FIG. 3. The device of the epicycle in Ptolemy's system for the motion of a planet P. The centre of the deferent is D which does not coincide with E, the centre of the earth and of the universe. The centre of the epicycle, C, does not rotate uniformly about D but moves so that the line CQ, connecting C with the equant Q, moves through equal angles in equal times. If necessary for the better 'saving of appearances' the system could be complicated by adding further epicycles, as, for example, a second whose centre C_1 revolves round C, a third whose centre C_2 revolves round C_1, and so on, the planet itself always being on the outermost epicycle.

was able to represent the observations to a fair approxima-
tion. The motion of the *primum mobile* was communicated to
the inner spheres mechanically by the contact of each
sphere with that inside it (and this contact also prevented a
void from occurring between the spheres). In order to
prevent any sphere associated with a particular planet from
imposing its motion on all the spheres beneath it, he introduced, between each planet's system and that of the next
planet, compensating spheres which rotated about the same
axis and with the same period as one of the planetary
spheres of the external system, but in the opposite direction.
In all there were 55 planetary and compensating spheres and
one stellar sphere making a total of 56. Further spheres were
added after Aristotle's time: the *primum mobile* was separated
as a further sphere outside that of the fixed stars; and some
medieval writers, such as William of Auvergne (*c.* 1180–1249),
placed beyond the *primum mobile* yet another sphere, an
immobile Empyrean, the abode of the saints.

One weakness of all the systems postulating that the
universe was made up of a series of concentric spheres was
that they had to assume that the distance of each heavenly
body from the earth was invariable. This assumption
made it impossible to account for a number of obvious
phenomena, in particular the variations in the apparent
brightness of the planets and in the apparent diameter of the
moon, and the fact that solar eclipses were sometimes total
and sometimes annular. Later Greek astronomers had tried
to account for these facts by devising different systems, and
the most important of these was that devised by Hipparchus
in the second century B.C. and later adopted by Ptolemy in
the second century A.D. This was the most accurate and the
most widely accepted astronomical system known in
classical Antiquity and in the Arab world. The treatise of
Ptolemy's in which it was described, which in the Middle
Ages went under the Latinised Arabic name of *Almagest*, was
to dominate astronomical thinking on its mathematical side
in the West until the time of Copernicus.

Ptolemy, in the *Almagest*, had adopted the view that his astronomical theory was merely a geometrical device by means of which to account for the observed phenomena, or 'save the appearances'. In his physical ideas he was, in fact, thoroughly Aristotelian and also, like Aristotle, he regarded the centre of the earth as the fixed centre of the universe at the centre of the stellar sphere. But when he came to postulate geometrical devices that would account for the observed movements of the heavenly bodies he allowed himself considerable freedom from the principles of Aristotle's physics. He used two different devices. The first, the device of the movable eccentric, was to suppose that the planets moved in a circle about a point, not necessarily at the centre of the earth, but somewhere on a line joining the centre of the earth with the sun. The second device, that of epicycles, which was in fact geometrically equivalent to that of the eccentric, was to suppose that a planet moved in a circle about a centre, which itself moved in another circle, and so on, until a circle was reached of which the centre was stationary with respect to the earth, though not necessarily on it (Fig. 3). The last, and innermost, circle was known as the deferent and the others as epicycles. There was no limit to the number of epicycles that could be postulated in order to 'save the appearances'. In one point, in allowing that the linear velocity of the centre of the epicycle about the deferent might not be uniform, Ptolemy departed from Plato's dictum that only uniform circular motions could be used, but he made some attempt to preserve orthodoxy by making the angular velocity uniform about a point, the equant, inside the deferent though not necessarily at its centre.

By suitable arrangements of epicycles Ptolemy was able, in most respects, to give a very accurate description of the movements or 'appearances' of the planets. To account for another observed phenomenon, the precession of the equinoxes (that is, the steady increase in longitude of a star while its latitude remains unaltered), he supposed in a further work, his *Hypotheses of the Planets*, that outside the stellar sphere (the 8th in his system) there was a 9th sphere which imparted to the stellar sphere its diurnal motion from East to West, while the stellar sphere itself, together with the spheres of the planets, rotated slowly in the opposite direction with respect to the 9th sphere. When later the *primum mobile* was separated from the stellar sphere, it became a distinct 10th sphere beyond this 9th. An erroneous theory that the equinoxes did not precess but oscillated, or 'trepidated', about an average position was advanced in the 9th century by an Arab astronomer, Thabit ibn Qurra, and gave rise to considerable controversy in Europe from the 13th to the 16th century.

When the natural philosophers and astronomers of Western Christendom were confronted with the choice between the 'physical' system of Aristotle and the 'mathematical' system of Ptolemy, they at first hesitated, as in fact had the Greeks and Arabs before them. Ptolemy himself had at first regarded all astronomical theories merely as convenient geometrical devices or intellectual abstractions, and had said that of two equally complete and accurate theories one should always choose the simpler. Later, in his *Hypotheses of the Planets*, he had attempted to produce a system which would give a physical, mechanical explanation of the heavenly movements. The Ptolemaic system was quickly recognised early in the 13th century as being the best geometrical device for 'saving the appearances', and practical astronomers favoured it as being the only system capable of serving as the basis of numerical tables. The desire was felt for a system that would both 'save the appearances' and also describe the 'real' paths of the heavenly bodies and account for the cause of their movements. Regarded in this light Ptolemy's eccentrics and epicycles were clearly inadequate themselves, and his system conflicted with a number of important principles of the only adequate system of physics known, that of Aristotle. In the first place, the theory of epicycles was not compatible with Aristotle's theory that circular motion required a solid fixed centre round which to revolve; and secondly, Ptolemy's explanation of precession would require that the stellar sphere had two different motions at the same time, and this was in conflict with Aristotle's principle that contradictory attributes cannot inhere in the same substance at the same time. Yet, although Ptolemy's system had these serious physical defects from which Aristotle's astronomical system was free, the latter was clearly inferior as a mathematical description of the observed facts.

The attitude taken to this dilemma in the second half of the 13th century seems to have been determined by that taken by the late Greek philosopher Simplicius in his commentaries on Aristotle's *Physics* and *De Cælo*. It is clearly expressed in a distinction drawn by Thomas Aquinas, who pointed out in the *Summa Theologica*, part 1, question 32, article 1, that there was a difference between a hypothesis which must necessarily be true and one which merely fitted the facts. Physical (or metaphysical) hypotheses were of the first type, mathematical hypotheses of the second. He said:

For anything a system may be induced in a double fashion. One way is for proving some principle as in natural science where sufficient reason can be brought to show that the motions of the heavens are always of uniform velocity. In the other way, reasons may be adduced which do not sufficiently prove the principle, but which may show that the effects which follow agree with that principle, as in astronomy a system of eccentrics and epicycles is posited because this assumption enables the sensible phenomena of the celestial motions to be accounted for. But this is not a sufficient proof, because possibly another hypothesis might also be able to account for them.

A few years later such writers as Bernard of Verdun and Giles of Rome (*c.* 1247–1316) were asserting that astronomical hypotheses must be constructed primarily with a view to explaining the observed facts, and that experimental evidence must settle the controversy between the Aristotelian 'physicists' and Ptolemaic 'mathematicians'. And according to Giles, when there were a number of equally possible hypotheses, the one to be chosen was the simplest. These two principles of 'saving the appearances' and of simplicity were to guide theoretical astronomy down to the time of Kepler and beyond.

By the end of the 13th century the concentric system of Aristotle had been discarded in Paris in the light of practical experience, and the Ptolemaic system became generally accepted. Some attempt was made to bring this astronomical system into line with physics by taking over the product of Ptolemy's later thought, and by considering the eccentric planetary spheres as solid spheres of the fifth element within each of which the epicycles might revolve.

The controversies between the different schools of astronomy by no means at once came to an end. Even in the 13th century at least one astronomer had shown a tendency to branch out with an entirely new hypothesis. Pietro d' Abano, in his *Lucidator Astronomiæ*, suggested that the stars were not borne on a sphere but were moving freely in space. In the 14th century, the even more radical innovation of considering the earth instead of the heavenly spheres to revolve was introduced by Nicole Oresme, though the first reference to this theory occurs at the end of the 13th century in the writings of the Franciscan François de Meyronnes. This and other new hypotheses discussed during the 14th and 15th centuries may have been suggested by ancient Greek speculations, in particular by the semi-heliocentric system postulated in the 4th century B.C. by Heraclides of Pontus, in which Venus and Mercury revolved around the sun while the sun itself revolved around the earth. This system was known in Western Christendom through the writings of Macrobius and Martianus Capella. (The completely heliocentric system of the 3rd-century B.C. Aristarchus of Samos was not known in the Middle Ages.) These innovations were based largely on the fundamental criticisms of Aristotle's physics that occurred in the 14th century and discussion of them will therefore be deferred to a later page (below, pp. 235 *et seq.*)

As regards the practical astronomy of the 13th century, the observations were made largely for the purpose of constructing tables for calculating dates, in particular of Easter, for determining latitude and longitude, and for astrological prediction. The last specially occupied the Italians. At first the practical astronomy of medieval Christendom remained under Arab leadership. Omar Khayyam's calendar of 1079 was at least as accurate as anything produced until the Gregorian reform of the calendar in 1582, and Arab instruments, observations, tables and maps retained their superiority at least until the middle of the 13th century. From that time the astronomy of Western Christendom began to stand on its own feet. One of the earliest independent observations in Western Christendom was, in fact, made as early as 1091 or 1092, when Walcher of Malvern observed an eclipse of the moon in Italy and, by discovering the time it had been observed by a friend in eastern England, determined the difference in longitude between the two points. Another method for determining longitude which was suggested in the 12th century by Gerard of Cremona was to observe the position of the moon at noon and, from the difference between that and what would be expected from tables constructed for a standard place, as for example, Toledo, calculate the difference in longitude between the two places. But the accurate determination of longitude required accurate measurement of time, and this only began to be possible in the 17th century. The determination of latitude, on the other hand, could be made with an astrolabe by observing the elevation of a star, or of the sun at noon. The Arabs had made accurate measurements of latitude, taking as the prime meridian (o) a point to the west of Toledo. Their tables were adapted for various towns in Christendom, for example London, Oxford and Hereford in England, and further observations were also made in the West itself.

The astrolabe was the chief astronomical instrument of both ancient and medieval times and was known as 'the mathematical jewel'. It had been described by Hermann the Lame in the 11th century and considerably improved by al-Zarquali, though this new version did not reach the Christian world until about 1255. An excellent *Treatise on the Astrolabe* was written during the second half of the 14th century by Geoffrey Chaucer. The astrolabe was a device for measuring the angular distance between any two objects and it had been used since the end of the third century B.C. to take the elevation of heavenly bodies. It consisted of a graduated circular metal plate with a datum line and a rotating pointer, called the *alidade*, on which were two sights (Plate 1). The astrolabe was hung from a ring at the top of

Fig. 4. Drawing of an astrolabe. From Chaucer's *Treatise on the Astrolabe*, Cambridge University Library MS. Dd. 3.53 (XIV cent.).

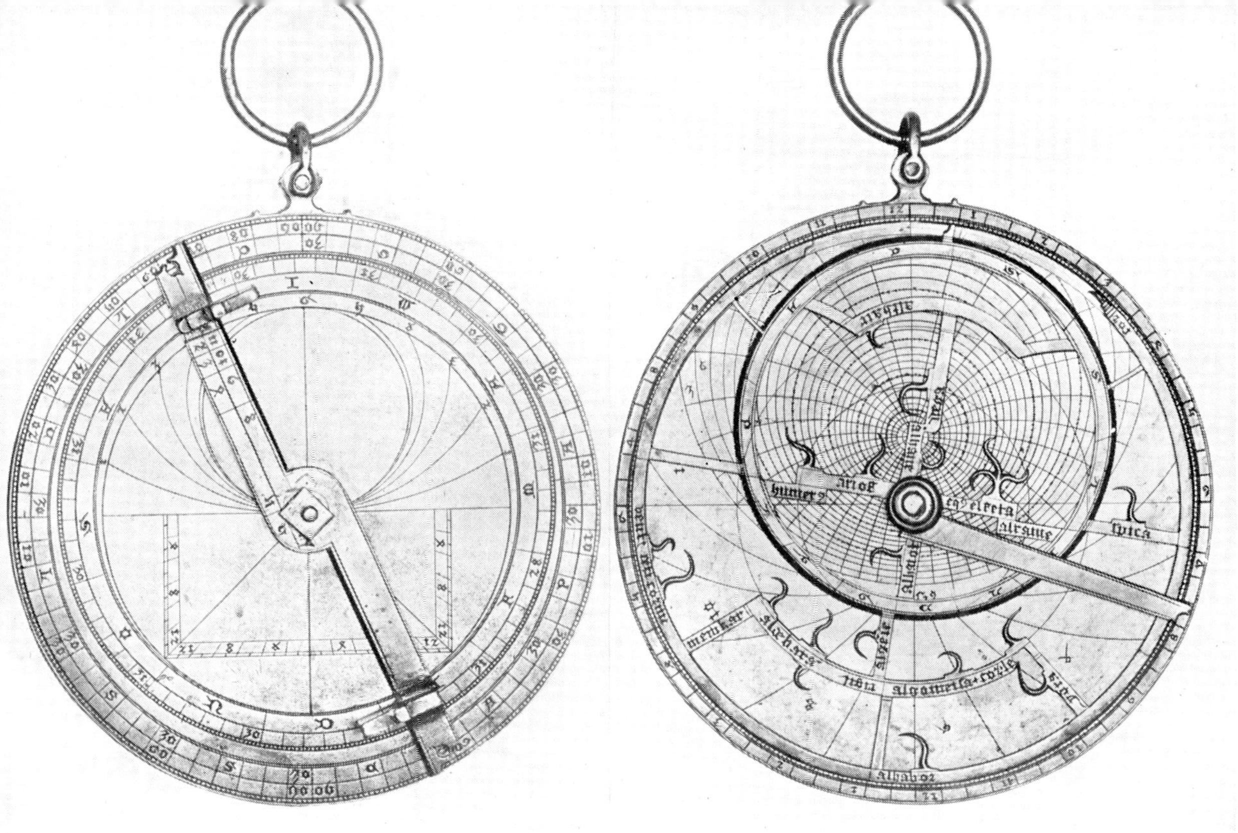

A FRENCH XIV-CENTURY ASTROLABE
From R. T. Gunther, *The Astrolabes of the World*, Oxford, 1932

PLATE I

PLATE 2 A PAGE FROM THE EMPEROR FREDERICK II's *DE ARTE VENANDI CUM AVIBUS*

Showing how various species of birds protect their young. From MS. Vaticano Palat. Latino 1071 (XIII cent.)

the diameter at right angles to the datum line, which was thus the horizon line, and, with this diameter always perpendicular to the earth, the *alidade* was rotated to point at a particular star whose altitude was read on the scale round the plate. With this information it was possible to calculate time and determine north. The advantage of the astrolabe was that these values could be read off the instrument itself. For any particular latitude the Pole Star always has approximately a constant altitude and the other stars go round it. On the plate of the astrolabe was a stereographic projection of the celestial sphere on to a plane parallel to the equator as observed at a particular latitude on the earth, showing the equinoctials, tropics of Cancer and Capricorn, meridian, azimuths and almucantars (Fig. 5). Thus a different plate was needed for each latitude. If the observed altitude of a particular star were set to the corresponding altitude as shown on the plate, every other star would be in its correct position. Above this plate was a second plate, the *rete*, which was elaborately cut away and formed a rotating star map. On the *rete* was marked a circle which represented the ecliptic and so showed the position of the sun relative to the stars for each day of the year. If the stars were in their correct position, the position of the sun could therefore be read off. The line connecting the position of the sun with the position of the Pole Star was given by turning the *label* (a pointer rotating about the point representing the Pole Star), to the position of the sun. This gave the direction of the sun in azimuth and marked off time. The astrolabe was most useful in tropical latitudes where the variation in the altitude of the sun is great, and for this reason it was mostly developed by the Arabs. Its great convenience as an instrument for telling the time was that it was portable. Sundials, which are instruments for showing the change in azimuth angle and must, therefore, be aligned north and south, could not be made portable until they could be combined with a compass. Such a combination was not produced until the end of the 15th century.

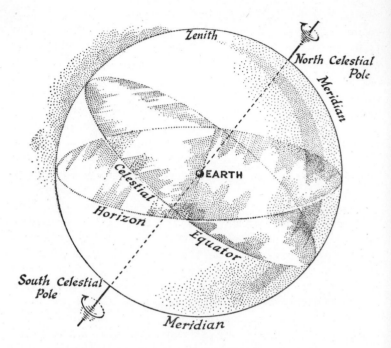

FIG. 5. The celestial sphere. The observer on the earth regards himself as being at the centre of the stellar sphere, of which he can see only half above the horizon. This horizon forms a great circle on the stellar sphere. The celestial poles are the points on the stellar sphere pierced by the axis about which this sphere seems to turn, which is the same as the axis of the earth. The circles of latitude and longitude and the tropics of Cancer and Capricorn are identical with those on the earth, the equator of the earth corresponding to the celestial equator. The position of a point on the celestial sphere can then be determined by means of two co-ordinates analogous to latitude and longitude on the earth, or by reference to another system of great circles related to the observer's zenith. These are the azimuthal circles passing through the zenith and cutting the horizon at right angles, and the almucantars, or circles of equal altitude parallel to the horizon. The ecliptic is the apparent path of the sun through the stars on the celestial sphere. The co-ordinates of a point on the celestial sphere referred to the ecliptic are the celestial latitude and longitude. The equinoctials are the two points at which the celestial equator cuts the ecliptic. The meridian is the great circle which passes through the celestial poles and the zenith.

Another instrument used in the 13th century was the quadrant, of which improved versions were made by an Italian, Johannes Campanus of Novara (d. after 1292), and by two Montpellier astronomers who lived about the same time. Another instrument which came into use at about this time was the mural quadrant, which had been used by Alexandrian, Arabian and Persian astronomers. This was mounted so that one end was level with a hole in the wall of the observatory. A travelling sight was swung round until it and the hole were aligned with the heavenly body under observation, and the angle was read on a scale. Another instrument constructed by Campanus was a sort of armillary sphere for determining the position of the planets. This consisted of an armilla, or ring, fixed in the plane of the equator, with other rings representing the horizon, the meridian and the ecliptic so that it was a sort of model of the celestial sphere.

It was with such instruments that Guillaume de St. Cloud, a follower of Roger Bacon and the founder of the Paris school of astronomy, determined from the solstitial altitudes of the sun the obliquity of the ecliptic in 1290 and the latitude of his place of observation at Paris. The obliquity he calculated as being 23° 34' and the latitude of Paris he made 68° 50'. The modern figure for the obliquity of 1290 is 23° 32' and his value for the latitude of Paris is that which is now accepted. Another of his observations was to note the meridian altitude of the sun when he himself was in a dark room with a small aperture to admit a beam of light, and from this he determined the epoch of the spring equinox. Another Frenchman, Jean de Murs, used a graduated arc of 15 feet radius to make the same determination at Evreux on 13 March, 1318.

The reform of the calendar, which had been urged by Grosseteste and Roger Bacon, again aroused attention when the *Alfonsine Tables* reached Paris about 1293. Pope Clement VI bade Jean de Murs and Firmin de Belleval to Avignon to report on the project, which they did in 1345. Another report was drawn up by Cardinal Pierre d'Ailly for the Council of Constance, 1414–18. The accuracy of the *Alfonsine Tables* was still mistrusted and the reform had to wait for nearly two centuries, though when at last it was made it was on the basis of numerical values very much the same as those arrived at in the 14th century.

Other instruments were invented or improved in France and observations were extended during the 14th century. Jean de Linières produced a catalogue of positions of 47 stars, the first attempt in Christendom to correct some of the star places given in the 2nd-century catalogue of Ptolemy. In 1342 a Jew, Levi ben Gerson of Montpellier, introduced the Baculus Jacobi, a cross-staff which had apparently been invented in the 13th century by Jacob ben Makir. Levi applied a diagonal scale to the instrument. The cross-staff was used for measuring the angular distance between two stars or, as a navigational instrument, for taking the elevation of a star or the sun above the horizon. It consisted of a graduated rod or staff with a cross-bar attached at right-angles to it. The cross-staff was held with the staff against the eye. The cross-bar was moved until the sight at one end was in line with the horizon and the sight at the other end in line with a star or the sun. From the reading on the graduated scale on the staff the angle of elevation of the star could be obtained from a table of angles.

During the first half of the 14th century an important school of astronomy grew up also at Oxford, in particular at Merton College. One of the results of the work there was the development of trigonometry. Tangents were used by John Maudith (1310) and Thomas Bradwardine (d. 1349), and by Richard of Wallingford (*c.* 1292–1335) who took the loose methods used in the trigonometry of al-Zarquali's *Toledo Tables* and applied to them Euclid's rigorous methods of demonstration. John Maudith and Richard of Wallingford are the initiators of Western trigonometry, though an important treatise on the subject was written about the same time in Provence by Levi ben Gerson (1288–1344) and translated into Latin in 1342. The great improvement introduced by these writers was to introduce the Hindu-Arabic practice of basing plane trigonometry on sines instead of chords, as had been done in the old Greco-Roman tradition dating from Hipparchus. Richard also adapted the *Alfonsine Tables* to Oxford and invented certain instruments for instance an elaborate rectangulus for measuring and comparing altitudes and an improved equatorium for showing the positions of the planets.

The lively interest in astronomy during the 13th and 14th centuries, of which this work was the outcome, is shown also by the astronomical models then constructed. In 1232 the Emperor Frederick II had received a planetarium from the Sultan of Damascus. About 1320 Richard of Wallingford constructed an elaborate astronomical clock, showing the positions of the sun, moon and stars and also the ebb and flow of the tides. He also left a handbook describing how this instrument was to be used. An elaborate planetarium driven by weights was also made by the clockmaker Giovanni de' Dondi (b. 1318), and such things became popular as scientific toys.

(3) METEOROLOGY AND OPTICS

Meteorology and optics formed a single heterogeneous subject in the 13th century, because these sciences were concerned with phenomena supposed to occur in the regions of the elements fire and air lying between the sphere of the moon and the terraqueous globe. These topics had been discussed by Aristotle in his *Meteorologica*, which was the chief source of 13th-century 'meteorology', and in this work Aristotle had attributed all the changes seen in the sky, except the movements of the heavenly bodies, to changes in those regions. The element fire was a sort of principle of combustion rather than actual flame and so was not itself visible, but it was easily set alight by movement, and agitation, brought about by hot dry exhalations rising up from the earth on which the sun's rays were falling, caused a number of phenomena to occur in the sphere of fire, as, for instance, comets, shooting stars and auroras. All these phenomena must occur in the region beneath the moon, because beyond it the heavens were ingenerable and incorruptible and could suffer no change but circular motion. In the sphere of the element air these hot dry exhalations caused wind, thunder and lightning, and thunderbolts, while cold moist exhalations produced by the sun's rays falling on water caused cloud, rain, mist, dew, snow and hail. A special group of phenomena associated with the moist exhalations were rainbows, halos and mock suns.

Throughout the Middle Ages comets and similar apparent changes in the heavens continued to be classed as 'meteorological' rather than astronomical phenomena, that is, as phenomena occurring in the sub-lunary region. In the 16th century more accurate measurements of their positions and orbits were to provide some of the most telling evidence against the truth of Aristotle's ideas on the structure of the universe. Comets were described several times in the 13th and 14th centuries, one of the most interesting references being made by Grosseteste to what may have been Halley's comet, which would have been due to appear in 1228. Another interesting reference was made by Roger Bacon, who held that the awesome comet of July, 1264 had bee generated under the influence of the planet Mars and had produced an increase of jaundice leading to bad temper, the result of which was the wars and disturbances in England, Spain and Italy at that time and afterwards!

Observations on weather and attempts, partly with an agricultural interest, to predict it by astrology had been made from the 12th century onwards. A most remarkable series of monthly weather records were kept during 1337–44 for the Oxford district by William Merlee. He based attempts to forecast the weather partly on the state of the heavenly bodies, and also on inferior signs such as the deliquescing of salt, the carrying of sound from distant bells, and the activity of fleas and the extra pain of their bites, all of which indicated greater humidity.

The subject which was to see the most remarkable progress during the 13th and 14th centuries was optics. The study of light attracted the attention in particular of those who tended to Augustinian-Platonism in philosophy, and this was for two reasons: light had been for St. Augustine and other Neoplatonists the analogy of Divine grace and of the illumination of the human intellect by Divine truth, and it was amenable to mathematical treatment. The first important medieval writer to take up the study of optics was Grosseteste, and he set the direction for future developments. Grosseteste gave particular importance to the study of optics because of his belief that light was the first 'corporeal form' of material things and was not only responsible for their dimensions in space but also was the first principle of motion and efficient causation. According to Grosseteste, all changes in the universe could be attributed ultimately to the activity of this fundamental corporeal form and the action at a distance of one thing on another was brought about by the propagation of rays of force or, as he called it, the 'multiplication of species' or 'virtue'. By this he meant the transmission of any form of efficient causality through a medium, the influence emanating from the source of the causality corresponding to a quality of the source, as, for instance, light emanated from a luminous body as a 'species' which multiplied itself from point to point through the medium in a movement that went in straight lines. All forms of efficient causality, as for instance, heat, astrological influence and mechanical action, Grosseteste held to be due to this propagation of 'species', though the most convenient form in which to study it was through visible light.

Thus the study of optics was of particular significance for the understanding of the physical world. Grosseteste's theory of the multiplication of species was adopted by Roger Bacon, Witelo, Pecham and other writers and they all made contributions to optics in the hope of elucidating not only the action of light but also the nature of efficient causality in general. For this purpose the use of mathematics was essential, for, as Aristotle had put it, optics was subordinate to geometry, and the progress made in medieval optics would certainly have been impossible without the knowledge of Euclid's *Elements* and Apollonius' *Conics*. Throughout the whole Middle Ages, and indeed much later, the Aristotelian distinction was maintained between the mathematical and the physical aspects of optics. As Grosseteste put it in discussing the law of reflection, geometry could give an account of what happened, but it could not explain why it happened. The cause of the observed behaviour of light, of the equality of the angles of incidence and reflection, was to be sought, he said, in the nature of light itself. Only a knowledge of this physical nature would make it possible to understand the cause of the movement.

The chief sources of 13th century optics were, besides Aristotle's *Meteorologica* and *De Anima*, the optical writings of Euclid, Ptolemy and Diocles (second century B.C.), and of the Arab writers Alkindi, Alhazen, Avicenna and Averroës. Aristotle, who was more concerned with the cause of vision than the laws by which it was exercised, had held that light (or colour) was not a movement but a state of transparency in a body and was produced by an instantaneous qualitative change in a potentially transparent medium. Other Greek philosophers had put forward other explanations, Empedocles asserting that light was a movement which took time to be transmitted and Plato that vision could be explained by a series of separate rays going out from the eye to the object seen (see above, p. 17). In contrast with this theory of extramission, the Stoics had suggested that vision was due to rays of light entering the eye from the object. It was one or other of these theories of rays, implying that light travelled in straight lines, that had been adopted by the Greek geometers, such as Euclid and Ptolemy, who had developed optics to a place equal to that of astronomy and mechanics among the most advanced physical sciences of Antiquity. These men discovered that the angle of reflection of rays from a surface was equal to the angle of incidence. Ptolemy, who measured the amount of refraction in rays passing from air into glass and into water, observed that the angle of refraction was always less than the angle of incidence but wrongly supposed that this was by a constant proportion. He concluded from this that the apparent position of a star did not always correspond to its real position because of refraction by the atmosphere.

This Greek work on optics was further developed by the Arabs and particularly by Alhazen (965–1039), whose work was the main source of what was known about optics in medieval Christendom. Alhazen achieved a better understanding not only of geometrical optics but also of vision, though he persisted in the erroneous belief that the lens of the eye was the sensitive part. He showed that the angle of refraction was not proportional to the angle of incidence and studied spherical and parabolic mirrors, spherical aberration, lenses and atmospheric refraction. He also held that the transmission of light was not instantaneous and rejected Plato's theory of extramission, which had been upheld by Euclid and Ptolemy, in favour of the view that light came from the object to the eye where it was 'transmuted' by the lens. Knowledge of the anatomy of the eye was also improved by the Arabs, whose chief source of information had been Rufus of Ephesus in the 1st century A.D. Outstanding work on this was done by Rhazes and Avicenna.

Among 13th century writers on optics, Grosseteste himself is remarkable chiefly for his attempt to explain the shape of the rainbow by means of a simple phenomenon which he could study experimentally, namely, the refraction of light by a spherical lens. Aristotle had held that the rainbow was caused by reflection from drops of water in the cloud, but Grosseteste attributed it definitely to refraction, though he thought that this was caused by the whole cloud acting as a large lens. Though his contribution to optics was more to emphasise the value of the experimental and mathematical methods than to add much to positive knowledge, he did make a few important additions. He was responsible for the theory of double refraction which remained the standard explanation of the spherical lens or burning glass until the sixteenth century. According to this theory light radiating out from the sun was refracted once on entering the lens, and again on passing out the farther side, the combined refractions bringing the rays to a focus at a point. In his *De Iride* he attempted also to formulate a quantitative law for refraction, on which he knew Ptolemy's work. This law, he claimed, 'experiments showed us' and he held that it was also in accordance with the principle of economy. Conceiving vision as being due to extramitted visual rays, he said that when rays passed from a rare to a dense medium the refracted ray halved the angle between the projection of the incident ray and the perpendicular to the common surface at the point of entry of the incident ray into the dense medium. When visual rays passed from a dense to a rare medium they were bent in the opposite direction. Simple experiments would have disproved Grosseteste's 'law', but he used it to try to explain the shape of the rainbow. He was also the first Latin writer to suggest using lenses to magnify small objects and bring distant objects closer. In fact, this work on optics did result in the invention of spectacles in northern Italy at the end of the 13th century (see below, pp. 196 and 205–6).

Grosseteste's chief disciple, Roger Bacon, made a number

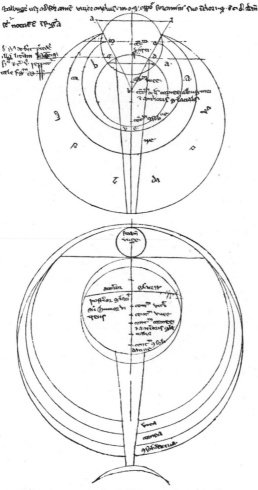

FIG. 6. Roger Bacon's geometrical diagram showing the curvatures of the refracting media in the eye. From the *Opus Majus*, British Museum MS. Royal 7. F.viii (XIII cent.).

of small contributions to knowledge of reflection and refraction, though many of the experiments he described were repetitions of those made by Alkindi and Alhazen. He continued Grosseteste's teaching about methodology. He made some original experimental determinations, for instance, of the focal length of a concave mirror illuminated by the sun, and he pointed out that the sun's rays reaching the earth might be treated as parallel instead of radiating out from a point, thus making possible a better explanation of burning lenses and parabolic mirrors. He firmly adopted the theory that in vision material light, travelling with enormous though finite velocity, passed from the object seen to the eye, but he pointed out that in the act of looking something psychological 'went forth', so to speak, from the eye. He gave a better description of the anatomy of the vertebrate eye (Fig. 6) and optic nerves than any previous Latin writer, and recommended that those who wished to study the subject should dissect cows or pigs. He discussed in detail the conditions necessary for vision and the effects of various kinds and arrangements of single lenses and, working on the theory that the apparent size of an object depends on the angle it subtends at the eye, he tried to improve vision. For this he used plano-convex lenses, the operation of which, however, he imperfectly understood. His scientific imagination played freely with the possibilities of indefinitely magnifying small objects, and bringing distant objects nearer, by suitable arrangements of mirrors or lenses. He held that Julius Cæsar had erected mirrors in Gaul with which he saw what was going on in England, and that lenses might be used to make the sun and moon descend and appear above the heads of enemies; the ignorant mob, he said, could not endure it.

Roger Bacon's attempt to discover the cause of the rainbow is a good example of his conception of the inductive method (see below, pp. 226 *et seq.*). He began by collecting phenomena similar to the rainbow, colours in crystals, in dew on the grass, in spray from mill wheels or oars when lit by the sun, or as seen through a cloth or through the eyebrows. He then examined the rainbow itself, noting that it appeared always in cloud or mist. By a combination of observation, astronomical theory and measurements with the astrolabe he was able to show that the bow was always opposite the sun, that the centre of the bow, the observer's eye and the sun were always in a straight line, and that there was a definite connection between the altitudes of the bow and of the sun. He showed that the rays returning from the rainbow to the eye made an angle of 42 degrees with the incident rays going from the sun to the bow. To explain these facts he then adopted the theory, put forward in Aristotle's *Meteorologica*, that the rainbow formed the base of a cone of which the apex is at the sun and the axis passed from the sun through the observer's eye to the centre of the bow. The base of the cone would become elevated and depressed, thus producing a larger or smaller rainbow, according to the altitude of the sun; if it could be sufficiently elevated the whole circle would appear above the horizon, as with rainbows in sprays. This theory he used to explain the height of the bow at different latitudes and different times of year. It would imply, among other things, that each observer would see a different bow and this he confirmed by the observation that when he moved towards, away from or parallel to the rainbow it moved with him relative to trees and houses; 1,000 men in a row, he asserted, would see 1,000 rainbows and the shadow of each would bisect the arc of his bow. The colours and form of the rainbow, therefore, bear to the observer a relation unlike those of fixed objects such as crystals. As to the colours, Bacon's discussion was as inconclusive as that of everyone else till Newton; the form he explained as due to the reflection of light from spherical water drops in the cloud, the rainbow of any particular observer appearing only in the drops from which the reflected rays went to his own eyes. This theory he extended to explain halos and mock suns; it was not in fact correct.

Among Grosseteste's successors later in the 13th century the Polish writer, Witelo (b. *c.* 1230), experimentally determined new values for the angles of refraction of light passing between air, water and glass. He also carried out experiments in which he produced the colours of the spectrum by passing white light through a hexagonal crystal, and understood, at least by implication, that the blue rays were refracted through a greater angle than the red. Also of considerable interest is his discussion of the psychology of vision. Another English writer, John Pecham (d. 1292), made a useful contribution by writing a lucid little text-book on optics, though he made few original advances. Some remarkable advances were made by the German writer Theodoric or Dietrich of Freiberg (d. 1311), whose work on refraction and on the rainbow is an outstanding example of the use of the experimental method in the Middle Ages.

Among those who had written on the rainbow before Theodoric composed his *De Iride et Radialibus Impressionibus*, Grosseteste had attributed the shape of the bow to refraction, and Albert Magnus and Witelo, writing with much greater knowledge, had pointed out the need to consider the refraction as well as the reflection of the rays by *individual* raindrops. Theodoric himself advanced the theory that the primary bow was caused by light falling on spherical drops of rain becoming refracted into each drop, reflected at its inner surface and refracted out again; and that the secondary bow was caused by a further reflection before the second refraction. This theory he supported by a number of experiments with crystal balls and spherical glass vessels filled with water, and he traced with great accuracy the course of the rays which produced both the primary and the secondary rainbows (Figs. 7, 8).

The colours of the rainbow Theodoric also tried to investigate experimentally. He showed that the same colours as those seen in the rainbow could be produced by passing light through crystal balls or glass balls filled with water, and through hexagonal crystals, if either the eye were applied to the far side of the ball or crystal or the light were projected on to an opaque screen. The colours of this spectrum were always in the same order, red being nearest the line of

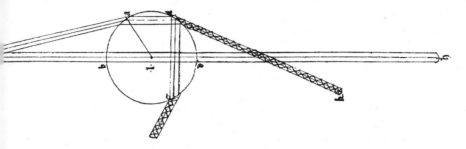

FIG. 7. Drawing from Theodoric of Freiberg's *De Iride* showing an experiment with the refraction of light. The rays enter the transparent ball at points a and b. The coloured refracted rays are indicated by cross-shading. From Basel University Library MS. F.iv.30 (XIV cent.).

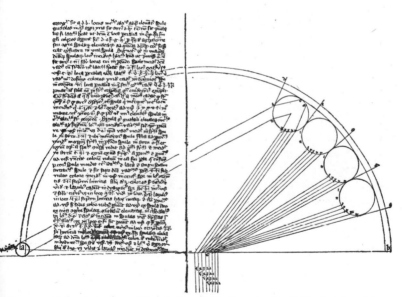

FIG. 8. Drawing from Theodoric of Freiberg's *De Iride* showing his explanation of the rainbow by double refraction and reflection within spherical raindrops. The paths of individual rays within each drop are not shown in this diagram. From Basel University Library MS. F.iv.30 (XIV cent.).

79

incidence and being followed by yellow, green and blue, the four principal colours which he distinguished. To explain the appearance of the spectrum Theodoric made use of the theory of colour which Averroës had developed in his commentaries on Aristotle, according to which colours were attributed to the presence in varying degrees of two pairs of opposite qualities: brightness and obscurity, boundedness and unboundedness. The first pair were formal and the second material causes, and the reason why a spectrum could be produced was that the light stream consisted not of geometrical lines but of 'columns' with breadth and depth, so that different parts of it could be affected differently on passing through a suitable medium. Thus, when light fell perpendicularly on to the surface of a hexagonal or spherical crystal, it passed straight through without refraction and remained fully bright and unbounded. Such light therefore remained white. But light falling at an angle to the surface of the crystal was refracted, its brightness was reduced by a positive amount of obscurity, and it was affected by the boundedness of the surface of the crystal. The different combinations of the qualities affecting the light stream then caused the range of colours emerging from the crystal from the brightest, red, to the darkest, blue, even though the crystal itself was not coloured as, for example, coloured glass was.

Theodoric carried out a number of experiments to demonstrate various points of his theory. He stated explicitly that in the rays refracted through a hexagonal crystal or glass flask filled with water, red appeared nearest the original line of incidence and blue farthest from it. He did not think of recombining the colours, so that they reformed white light, by passing them through a second crystal in a reverse position to the first, as Newton was to do. He did observe that if the screen were held very close to the crystal the light projected on to it showed no spectrum and appeared white, a fact which he explained by saying that at this distance the light was still too strong for the obscurity and boundedness

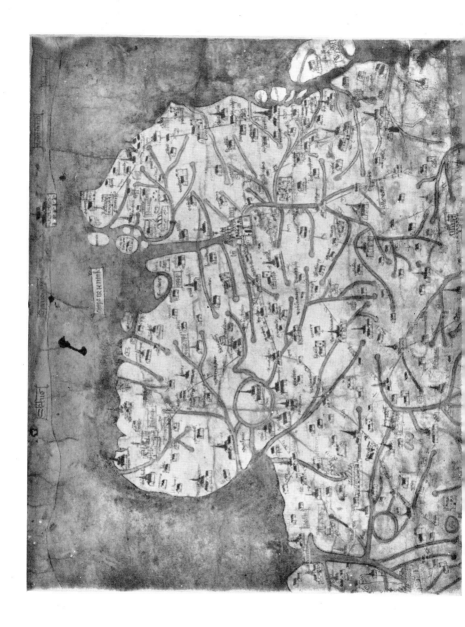

to produce their effects. Taken altogether, Theodoric made a remarkable advance both in optics and in the experimental method, and the technique of reducing a complicated phenomenon, like the shape and colours of the rainbow, to a series of simpler questions which could be investigated separately by specially-designed experiments was particularly pregnant for the future. Theodoric's theory was not forgotten; it was discussed by Themon Judæi later in the 14th century, by Regiomontanus in the 15th and in the University of Erfurt and perhaps elsewhere in the 16th. An explanation of the rainbow similar to Theodoric's was published by Marc Antonio de Dominis in 1611 and it was almost certainly the basis of the much fuller explanation published by Descartes in 1637.

By a curious coincidence an explanation of the rainbow similar to Theodoric's was given also by the contemporary Arabic writers, Qutb al-din al-Shirazi (1236–1311) and Kamal al-din al-Farisi (d. c. 1320). Western and Eastern writers seem to have worked quite independently of each other but used the same ultimate sources, principally Aristotle and Alhazen. Al-Farisi gave also an interesting explanation of refraction, which he attributed to the reduction of the speed of light passing through different media in inverse proportion to the 'optical density', an explanation suggestive of that advanced in the 17th century by the supporters of the wave theory of light. By another interesting coincidence he was also improving the theory of the *camera obscura*, or pin-hole camera, at the same time as similar work was being done by Levi ben Gerson. Both showed that the images formed were not affected by the shape of the hole and that an accurate image was formed when the aperture was a mere point, but that a multitude of only partially superimposed images appeared with a larger hole. They used this instrument to observe eclipses and other astronomical phenomena, and the movements of birds and clouds.

Another important development in medieval optics was the geometrical study of perspective in connection with painting. The beginnings of deliberate use of central projection dates from the paintings of Ambrogio Lorenzetti of Siena in the middle of the 14th century, and this was to revolutionise Italian painting in the 15th century.

(4) MECHANICS AND MAGNETISM

The only causes of local motion in the terrestrial region considered in the 13th century were mechanical action and magnetism, and the only natural mechanical cause was gravity. Mechanics was the part of physics, apart from astronomy and optics, to which mathematics was most effectively applied in the Middle Ages, and the chief sources of 13th-century mechanics were the most mathematical of all the treatises in the Aristotelian corpus, the *Mechanica*, generally but wrongly attributed to Aristotle himself in the Middle Ages, and a small number of late Greek and Arabic treatises. Aristotle's *Physics* was also important for mechanical ideas. Indeed the whole corpus of the mechanics that came down to the 13th century was based on the principle expounded in that work : the principle that local motion, like other kinds of change, was a process by which a potentiality towards motion was made actual. Such a process necessarily required the continued operation of a cause and when the cause ceased to operate, so did the effect. All moving bodies which were not alive thus received their motion from a mover distinct from themselves and the mover necessarily accompanied the body it moved. Further, the effect was proportional to the cause, so that the velocity of a moving body varied in direct proportion to the power or 'virtue'[1] of the motor and, for the same body and motor in different media, in inverse proportion to the resistance offered by the medium. Movement was thus the resultant of two forces outside the body itself, one impelling and the other resisting. Aristotle had no conception of mass, the intrinsic resistance which is a property of the moving body itself, which was to

(1) This power was generally called *virtus*, meaning power or ability to do something.

be the basis of 17th-century mechanics.[1] With falling bodies the force or power causing the movement was the weight, and so it followed from the above principles that in any given medium the velocity of a falling body was proportional to its weight and, further, that if a body were moving in a medium which offered no resistance its velocity would be infinite. Since this conclusion involved an impossibility Aristotle therefore saw in it an additional argument against the existence of void.

When Aristotle's mechanics became known in Western Christendom in the 13th century they were submitted, like the rest of his scientific ideas, to logical and empirical examination. This led, in the following century, to a radical criticism of his dynamical ideas and of their physical consequences, such as the impossibility of void, which prepared the way for the immense intellectual effort by which Galileo and his 17th-century followers escaped from Aristotelian principles and established the mathematical mechanics which was the central feature of the Scientific Revolution.

In the 13th century it was not dynamics but statics and to some extent kinematics, that is, the study of rates of motion, that underwent the most striking developments, particularly in the school of Jordanus Nemorarius. He is probably to be identified with Jordanus Saxo (d. 1237), the second master-general of the Order of Preachers, or Dominicans. It followed from the Aristotelian principle that velocity was proportional to motive power, that motive power could be estimated as proportional to velocity. Aristotle had stated that if a certain motive power moved a certain body with a certain velocity, then twice the motive power would be necessary to move the same body with twice the same velocity. Motive power was measured, therefore, by the product of the weight of the body moved multiplied by

(1) The concept of mass was deduced only in the 17th century from the supposition that in a vacuum or a medium whose resistance was small in comparison with the body's weight, all bodies fell with equal velocity.

the velocity impressed on it. This has been called 'Aristotle's axiom'. Dynamical and statical ideas were not clearly distinguished either by Aristotle, the author of the *Mechanica*, or by the writer of the Greek *Liber Euclidis de Ponderoso et Levi* and the derivative Arabic works which formed the basis of medieval Latin statics. But it would follow from the above dynamical statement, converted into statical terms, that motive power would be equal to the product of the weight of the body moved multiplied by the distance through which it was moved.

From these Aristotelian ideas and fragments of Alexandrian mechanics, containing only minor works of Archimedes, Jordanus Nemorarius and his school developed a number of important mechanical ideas which were to be taken over, in the 17th century, by Stevin, Galileo and Descartes. In the *Mechanica* it had been shown to follow from Aristotle's axiom that the two weights which balanced each other at opposite ends of a lever were inversely proportional to the velocities with which their points of attachment moved when the lever was displaced (Fig. 9).

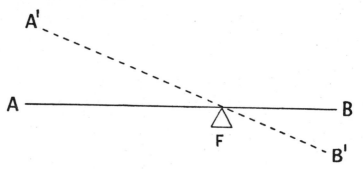

Fig. 9. The different weights A and B would balance if placed at such positions on the lever that when the lever turned on the fulcrum F the ratio of the velocities $\frac{A^1}{B^1}$ was proportional to the ratio of the weights $\frac{B}{A}$.

In his *Elementa Jordani Super Demonstrationem Ponderis* Jordanus gave a formal geometrical proof, beginning with Aristotle's axiom, that equal weights at equal distances from the fulcrum were in equilibrium. In the course of this he made use of what has been called the 'axiom of Jordanus', that the motive power which can lift a given weight a certain height can lift a weight k times heavier to $1/k$ times the height. This is the germ of the principle of virtual displacements.

The *Mechanica* also contained the idea of the composition of movements. It had been shown there that a body moving with two simultaneous velocities (V_1 and V_2) bearing a constant ratio to each other would move along the diagonal (V_r) of the rectangle made by lines proportional to these velocities (Fig. 10); and also that if the ratio of the velocities

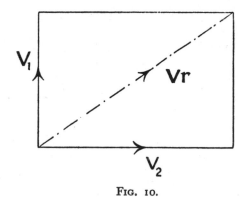

FIG. 10.

varied, the resultant motion would not be a straight line but a curve (Fig. 11).

Jordanus applied this idea to the movement of a body falling along an oblique trajectory. He showed that the one effective force or motive power by which the body was moved at any given moment could be dissociated into two, the natural gravity downwards towards the centre of the earth and a 'violent' horizontal force of projection. The component of gravity acting along the trajectory he called *gravitas secundum situm*, or 'gravity relative to position'; he showed that the more oblique the trajectory, that is the nearer to the horizontal, the smaller was this component. The obliquity of two trajectories could be compared, he said, by measuring the distance fallen in a given horizontal distance.

In another treatise belonging to this school, *De Ratione Ponderis* or *De Ponderositate* by an author whom Duhem, in his *Origines de la Statique*, has called 'the Forerunner of Leonardo', Jordanus' ideas were developed and applied to the study of the angular lever and of bodies on inclined planes. A faulty solution of the problem of the angular lever had been given

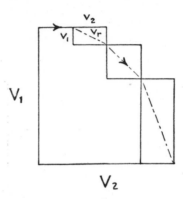

FIG. 11. The distances travelled due to V_1 increase in each successive interval of time while the horizontal distances travelled during the same intervals due to V_2 remain constant.

in the *Mechanica*, but the author of *De Ratione Ponderis* showed, again with the principle of virtual displacements at least implicit, that equilibrium was reached when the apex of the triangle formed by joining the point of support to each weight was on top. In developing this proof the author approached the fundamental idea of the statical moment, showing that two weights E and F on a lever would be in equilibrium when they were inversely proportional to their effective distances BL and BR from the fulcrum (B), that is, E : F : BR : BL (Fig. 12).

In discussing the component of gravity acting on bodies on inclined planes, the author of *De Ratione Ponderis* pointed out that the *gravitas secundum situm* of a body was the same at all points on the plane. He showed then, from the axiom of Jordanus, how to compare this value on planes of different inclination. He concluded that

if two weights descend on planes of different inclination and the weights are directly proportional to the lengths of the inclines, these two weights will have the same motive power in their descent. (Duhem, *Origines de la Statique*, 1905, p. 146.)

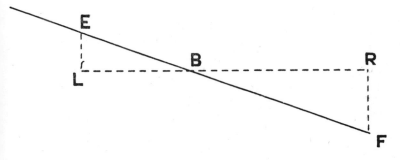

FIG. 12.

The same proof was later given by Stevin and Galileo, to whom *De Ratione Ponderis* would have been available in the printed text edited by Tartaglia (1565). This treatise also contained the hydrodynamical principle, apparently coming from Strato (*fl.c.* 288 B.C.), that the smaller the section of a liquid flowing with a given fall, the greater its velocity of flow.

This work of Jordanus Nemorarius and his school became widely known in the 13th and 14th centuries; it was summarised by Blasius of Parma in the 15th century and, as Duhem has shown, it was used extensively by Leonardo da Vinci and was to become the starting-point for some of the striking developments in mechanics that took place in the late 16th and 17th centuries.

      *   *   *   *

The other natural moving force or power besides gravity which chiefly engaged the attention of 13th-century physicists was magnetic attraction. This was the subject of what is one of the most striking examples of planned experimental research before the end of the 16th century, and William Gilbert, writing in 1600, acknowledged his debt to the little book completed on 8th August, 1269. The *Epistola de Magnete* of Petrus Peregrinus of Maricourt, in which much of Gilbert's work was anticipated, was written as a letter to a fellow countryman of its author in Picardy while Peregrinus waited in Charles of Anjou's besieging army outside the walls of the south Italian town of Lucera.

Certain properties of the lodestone were known before Petrus Peregrinus's researches. The fact that it attracted iron had been known to Thales and was later widely quoted as the classical example of occult 'virtue'. Its tendency to orientate itself north and south was known to the Chinese and adapted, perhaps by Moslems in maritime contact with them, for the invention of the compass. The earliest references to this instrument in medieval Latin literature occur in Alexander Nequam's *De Naturis Rerum* and other works round about 1200, but it is probable that its navigational use in the West preceded that date. Compasses with floating and later with pivoted needles were used from the end of the 13th century by both Arab and Christian sailors in the Mediterranean in conjunction with portolan maps or 'compass-charts' (see below, pp. 180 *et seq.*). At the end of his treatise Petrus Peregrinus described improved instruments with both types of needle. His floating needle was used with a reference scale divided into 360 degrees.

Peregrinus opened his observations on magnets with the following injunction:

You must realise, dearest friend, that the investigator in this subject must know the nature of things and not be ignorant of the celestial motions; and he must also make ready use of his own hands, so that through the operation of this stone he may show remarkable effects. For by his carefulness he will then in a short time be able to correct an error which by means of natural philosophy and mathematics alone he would never do in eternity, if he did not carefully use his hands. For in hidden operations we greatly need manual industry, without which we can usually accomplish nothing perfectly. Yet there are many things subject to the rule of reason which cannot be completely investigated by the hand.

He then passed to the consideration of how to recognise lodestones, how to determine their poles and distinguish north from south, the repulsion of like poles, the induction in iron of the opposite pole to that of the lodestone with which it was rubbed, inversion of poles, the breaking of a magnetic needle into smaller ones and the exertion of magnetic attraction through water and glass. One of the nicest experiments was made to determine the poles of a spherical lodestone or, as he called it, *magnes rotundus*, designed to illustrate the heavenly movements. A needle was held on the surface of the lodestone and a line drawn on the stone in the direction the needle took. The two points of junction of lines drawn from various positions would then be the poles of the lodestone.

The directive action on a magnet pointing north he attributed neither to the magnetic poles of the earth as Gilbert was to do in his theory that the earth was a large magnet, nor to the North Star as some of Petrus's contemporaries held. He pointed out that the lodestone did not always point directly at the North Star. Nor, he said, could its orientation be attributed to supposed deposits of lodestone in the northern regions of the earth, for lodestone was mined in many other places. He held that the magnet was directed towards the poles of the heavens on which the celestial sphere revolved, and he discussed the design of a *perpetuum mobile* based on this theory. But a contemporary, John of St. Amand, at the end of his *Antidotarium Nicolai*, approached the modern conception of magnetism. He said:

Wherefore I say that in the magnet is a trace of the world, wherefore there is in it one part having in itself the property of the west, another of the east, another of the south, another of the north. And I say that in the direction north and south it attracts most strongly, little in the direction east and west.[1]

(1) L. Thorndike, *Isis*, 1946, vol. 36, pp. 156–7.

Petrus Peregrinus's explanation of the induction of magnetism in a piece of iron was based on Aristotelian principles of causation. The lodestone was an active agent which assimilated the passive iron to itself, actualising its potential magnetism. This conception was elaborated by John of St. Amand. He held that when a magnet pointed to the earth's poles:

the southern part attracts that which has the property and nature of the north, albeit they have the same specific form, and this is not except by some property existing more complete in the southern part which the northern part has potentially and thereby its potentiality is completed.

The action of magnetic attraction at a distance had been explained by Averroës as a form of multiplication of species. The lodestone modified the parts of the medium touching it, for example air or water, and these then modified the parts next to them and so on until this *species magnetica* reached the iron, in which a motive virtue was produced causing it to approach the lodestone. The resemblance between this and Faraday's and Maxwell's tubes of force was brought even closer by John of St. Amand's description of a 'current from the magnet through the entire needle placed directly above it'.

(5) GEOLOGY

Geology in the 13th century was concerned mainly with the changes in the relative positions of the main masses of the elements earth and water forming the terraqueous globe in the centre of the universe, with the origin of continents and oceans and of mountains and rivers, and with the cause of the production of minerals and fossils. The three main sources of medieval geology were Aristotle's *Meteorologica* and two Arab treatises, the pseudo-Aristotelian *De Proprietatibus Elementorum* or *De Elementis*, written probably in the 10th century, and Avicenna's 10th-century *De Mineralibus*. Aristotle did not fully discuss all the geological questions which later arose out of his cosmological theories, but he recognised that parts of the land had once been under the sea and parts of the sea floor once dry. He attributed this mainly to water erosion. He also offered explanations of rivers and minerals. He held that rivers originated in springs formed for the most part from water which, after being evaporated from the sea by the sun, rose to form clouds, and these, on cooling, fell again as rain and percolated into spongy rock. Thence the water ran out as springs and returned by rivers to the sea. He also believed that water was produced inside the earth by the transformation of other elements. Minerals he believed were formed by exhalations arising inside the earth under the action of the sun's rays. Moist exhalations produced metals, dry exhalations 'fossils'.

Some later Greek writers had used erosion by water as evidence for the temporal origin of the earth, for, they argued, if the earth had existed from eternity all mountains and other features would by now have disappeared. This view was opposed in other Greek works such as *On the Cosmos* which some scholars have said was based on Theophrastus[1] (*c.* 372–287 B.C.). In this work it was maintained that there was a fluctuating balance between erosion by water and the elevation of new land caused by fire imprisoned in the earth trying to rise to its natural place. Against this a purely 'neptunic' theory was developed again from the *Meteorologica* by late Greek commentators, such as Alexander of Aphrodisias (. 193–217 A.D.), according to whom the earth had once been completely covered with water which the sun's heat had evaporated to expose the dry land. There was supposed to be a gradual destruction of the element water. This last conclusion had, in fact, been deduced by certain Greek philosophers of the 5th century B.C. from the presence of inland fossils; they alone in Antiquity seem to have understood that fossils were the remains of animals which had lived under the waves once covering the places where they were found. The presence of inland shells had also been widely attributed by later Greek geographers to a partial withdrawal of the sea, such as that caused by the silting up of the

(1) Theophrastus's only surviving geological work is *Concerning Stones*.

Nile, but shells on mountains were believed to have been carried there by temporary deluges. The explanation of mountains, according to the theory contained in the late Greek commentaries on the *Meteorologica*, was that once the land had been exposed its perfectly spherical shape was then carved into valleys by water, leaving the mountains projecting above them.

Sometime about the 10th century the author of the pseudo-Aristotelian *De Elementis* once more refuted this pure 'neptunism', and Avicenna in his *De Mineralibus* replaced it by a 'plutonic' explanation of mountains. He accepted the theory that the whole earth had once been covered with water and put forward the view that the emergence of dry land and the formation of mountains was due, sometimes to sedimentation under the sea, but more often to the eruption of the earth by earthquakes due to wind imprisoned under the earth. The mud thus raised was then transformed into rock partly by the hardening of clay in the sun and partly by the 'congelation' of water, either in the way stalactites and stalagmites are formed, or by some form of precipitation brought about by heat or by some unknown 'mineralising virtue' generated in the petrifying clay. Plants and animals imprisoned in the clay were there turned into fossils. Once formed, mountains were eroded by wind and water and went on being gradually destroyed.

Avicenna's theory was adopted in his *De Mineralibus et Rebus Metallicis* (*c.* 1260) by Albertus Magnus, who quoted volcanoes as evidence for imprisoned subterranean wind and attributed the generation of the 'mineralising virtue' to the influence of the sun and stars. The geology of Albertus was largely derived from the *Meteorologica*, *De Elementis*, perhaps *On the Cosmos*, and from Avicenna's *De Mineralibus*, but he worked his authorities into a coherent theory and made a number of observations of his own. He extended Avicenna's account of fossils, of which he said in his *De Mineralibus et Rebus Metallicis*, book 1, tract 2, chapter 8:

There is no-one who is not astonished to find stones which,

both externally and internally, bear the impressions of animals. Externally they show their outline and when they are broken open there is found the shape of the internal parts of these animals. Avicenna teaches us that the cause of this phenomenon is that animals can be entirely transformed into stones and particularly into salt stones. Just as earth and water are the usual matter of stones, he says, so animals can become the matter of certain stones. If the bodies of these animals are in places where a mineralising power (*vis lapidificativa*) is being exhaled, they are reduced to their elements and are seized by the qualities peculiar to those places. The elements which the bodies of these animals contained are transformed into the element which is the dominant element in them: that is the terrestrial element mixed with the aqueous element; then the mineralising power converts the terrestrial element into stone. The different external and internal parts of the animal keep the shape which they had beforehand.

He went on in another work, *De Causis Proprietatum Elementorum*, book 2, tract 4, chapter 5:

Of this we find evidence in the parts of aquatic animals and perhaps of naval gear that are found in mountain stones in hollow mountains, which water no doubt deposited there enveloped in sticky mud, and which were prevented by the coldness and dryness of the stone from total putrefaction. Very striking evidence of this kind is found in the stones of Paris, in which one very often meets round shells the shape of the moon.

Albertus gave original descriptions of many precious stones and minerals, although he derived the substance of his mineralogy from Marbode. He accepted many of the magical properties ascribed to stones. He also described an explanation of rivers widely held until the 17th century. Some early Greek writers, such as Anaxagoras and Plato, had held that there was an immense reservoir in the earth from which springs and rivers came. This gave rise to the theory, supported by certain passages of the Bible, of the continuous circulation of water from the sea through underground caverns and up inside mountains, from which it flowed as rivers back again to the sea. Albertus accepted this. Among his own geological observations, those he made near Bruges led him to deny sudden universal overflowings of oceans and to reduce changes in the figures of continents and seas to slow modifications in limited areas.

Other writers in the 13th century made observations on various other geological phenomena. The tides had been correlated with the phases of the moon by Stoic Posidonius (b. *c.* 135 B.C.), and, like the menstruation of women, were commonly attributed to astrological influences. In the 12th century Giraldus Cambrensis had combined some observation with a discussion of this and other theories. Grosseteste in the next century attributed the tides to attraction by the moon's 'virtue', which went in straight lines with its light. He said that the ebb and flow of the tides was caused by the moon drawing up from the sea floor mist, which pushed up the water when the moon was rising and was not yet strong enough to pull the mist through the water. When the moon had reached its highest point the mist was pulled through and the tide fell. The second, smaller monthly tide he attributed to lunar rays reflected from the crystalline sphere back to the opposite side of the earth, these being weaker than the direct rays. Roger Bacon took over this explanation. In another work associated with Grosseteste's circle, the *Summa Philosophiæ*, which scholars attributed to Grosseteste until this century, a good account was given of contemporary thought about geology generally. Another 13th-century work, the Norwegian encyclopædia, *Konungs Skuggsja* or *Speculum Regale*, contained descriptions of glaciers, icebergs, geysers, and other phenomena. These, like Michael Scot's descriptions of hot sulphur springs and of the volcanic phenomena of the Lipari Islands, are evidence of a wide interest in local geology, which increased in the following centuries.

The most important Italian writer on geology in the 13th century was Ristoro d'Arezzo. It is probable that he knew the work of Albertus Magnus, though he may simply have used the same sources. But certainly Italian geology in general was dominated for the next two centuries by

Albertus Magnus. In accordance with the Italian tradition Ristoro, in *La Composizione del Mondo* (1282), was very astrological. He attributed the elevation of dry land above the sea to attraction by the stars, as iron was attracted by magnets. He also recognised other influences, such as water erosion, sea waves throwing up sand and gravel, Noah's Flood depositing sediment, earthquakes, calcareous deposits from certain waters, and the activities of man. He made a number of observations, describing in the Apennines the eroded castellated strata containing iron which lay over the aqueous deposits of softer sandstones, shales and conglomerates. He recognised the marine origin of certain fossilised mollusc shells and discovered, apparently during a mountain expedition, a hot pool in which his hair became 'petrified' while bathing. He attributed the presence of these fossilised shells in mountains, not to their having been petrified where they had once lived, but to the Flood.

In the 14th century, the clockmaker Giovanni de' Dondi described the extraction of salt from hot springs and explained these as due to subterranean waters heated not, as Aristotle and Albertus Magnus had said, by flowing over sulphur, but by subterranean fire and gases produced by the heating action of celestial rays. The heating action of celestial virtue was also one explanation of the fire at the centre of the earth in which some alchemists believed and which they used to explain the presence of metallic ores, supposed to have been formed by condensation from metalligenous vapours, and also of volcanoes and similar phenomena. Geological matters were also discussed in Italy by such 14th-century writers as Dante (1265–1321), Boccaccio (1313–75) and Paulo Nicoletti of Venice (*d.* 1429) and in the 15th century by Leonardo Qualea (*c.* 1470) and Leo Battista Alberti (1404–72), who made observations on various local phenomena. All Italian writers who discussed the subject either accepted Ristoro's explanation of fossils in mountains as having been carried there by the Flood, or denied their organic origin altogether and regarded them either as having been spontaneously generated by a plastic or formative virtue produced by celestial influence or simply as accidents or 'sports' of nature.

In Paris in the 14th century, the nominalist Albert of Saxony or, as he was sometimes called, Albertus Parvus (*fl. c.* 1357), developed a new explanation of land and mountain formation from his theory of gravity (see below, p. 243). He held that the earth was in its natural place when its centre of gravity coincided with the centre of the universe. The centre of volume of the earth did not coincide with its centre of gravity, for the sun's heat caused part of the earth to expand and project above the enveloping water which, being fluid, remained with its centre of gravity at the centre of the universe. The shift of earth relative to water thus gave rise to dry land, leaving other parts submerged, and justified the hypothesis, later exploded by Christopher Columbus (1492), of a hemisphere of ocean balancing a hemisphere of land. The projecting land was then eroded by water into valleys, leaving the mountains. This was the only function Albert of Saxony ascribed to water and, together with the heat of the sun, it again displaced the centre of gravity of the earth, which thus underwent continuous little movements in order to coincide with the centre of the universe and caused continuous changes in the boundaries of land and sea. The erosion by water washed the land into the sea of which the floor, owing to the movements of the centre of gravity of the earth, gradually moved right through the middle of the earth eventually to reappear again as dry land on the other side. He made no mention of fossils. He used this theory of the shifting of the earth to explain the precession of the equinoxes.

Another northern successor of Albertus Magnus, Conrad von Megenburg (1309–74), put forward in his work *Das Buch der Natur* the view that springs and rivers were due to rain and rain alone. This had already been suggested by the Roman architect Vitruvius (1st century B.C.). This explanation, as well as Albert of Saxony's theory of mountains and Albertus Magnus's explanation of fossils, was accepted by Leonardo da

Vinci and passed, via Cardano and Bernard Palissy, to the 17th century.

(6) CHEMISTRY

Medieval chemistry began as an empirical art, but by the 13th century it had acquired a considerable body of theory, the purpose of which was to explain the particular kind of change with which chemistry was concerned, namely changes of quality and of substance in inanimate substances in the terrestrial region. This body of theory became inextricably interwoven with alchemy, and this association was to determine the character of chemical investigation for four centuries. Alchemy was empirical in spirit but was led up a blind theoretical alley by concentrating its attention rather on changes in colour and appearance than on changes in mass. So, while alchemical practice produced a large amount of useful information, alchemical theory had little to offer to the new chemistry that began to grow up in the 17th century.

The chief sources of practical chemistry in the 13th century were, apart from the practical experience handed down from generation to generation, the Latin translations of a number of Greek and Arabic treatises on dyeing, painting, glass making and other decorative processes, pyrotechnics, *materia medica*, mining and metallurgy, to which successive generations perhaps added one or two new recipes (see below, pp. 187–197). The few Latin chemical manuscripts which remain from before the 12th century are entirely practical, but from about 1144, when Robert of Chester translated the *Liber de Compositione Alchemiæ*, Arab alchemy began to enter western Europe.

The origin of alchemy seems to have been in the union of the practice of Egyptian metal workers with the theories of matter of Alexandrian Gnostics and Neoplatonists which, apart from a Timæan conception of *materia prima*, was fundamentally Aristotelian. The earliest alchemists, such as Zosimus and Synesius in the 3rd century A.D., who were Gnostics, thus combined descriptions of chemical apparatus and practical laboratory operations with an account of the visible universe as an expression of figures and symbols and a belief in sympathetic action, action at a distance, celestial influence, occult powers beneath manifest qualities and the powers of numbers. These ideas permeated chemistry from the 3rd century A.D. to the 17th and very often even practical laboratory operations were described in obscure symbolic language, perhaps to deceive others and keep the secrets hidden. It was Zosimus who first used the word *chemeia*, the Art of the Black Land, Egypt or *Khem*, which gave rise to the Arabic *alchemy* and the modern English *chemistry*. The main object of alchemy was the production of gold from the base metals. The possibility of doing so was based on the idea developed by Aristotle that one substance might be changed into another by changing its primary qualities.

Aristotle held that the generation and corruption of substantial forms in the sublunary region occurred at various levels in a hierarchy of substances. The simplest instances of perceptible matter were the four elements, but these were analysable in thought into *materia prima* determined by various combinations of the two pairs of primary contrary qualities or elementary principles acting as 'forms'. Perceptible substances differed from each other in many ways, for instance, in smell, taste or colour, but all, Aristotle said, were either hot or cold, wet or dry (fluid or solid). These four qualities were therefore primary and all others were secondary and derivative. The four elements were determined by the primary qualities as follows: Hot Dry=fire, Hot Wet= air, Cold Wet=water, Cold Dry=earth. The four elements of Empedocles had been unchangeable but with Aristotle, by interchanging members of the two pairs of primary contrary qualities, one element might be transformed into another. The old form (*e.g.*, Cold Wet) was then said to have been corrupted and the new one (*e.g.*, Hot Wet) generated. Such substantial changes might involve a change of one or both qualities, or two elements might come together and interchange their qualities to produce the two others, as, for instance: Water (Cold Wet) +Fire (Hot Dry)⇄Earth (Cold Dry) +Air (Hot Wet) (Fig. 13). The second kind of change could not, of course, occur between consecutive elements, for this would bring together either two identical or two contrary qualities, which was *ipso facto* impossible. In chemical change and combination the combining substances thus disappeared with their properties, although they remained

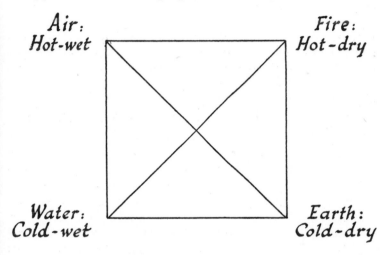

Air:
Hot-wet

Fire:
Hot-dry

Water:
Cold-wet

Earth:
Cold-dry

FIG. 13. The chemical elements.

potentially regenerable, and new substances with new properties arose from their union. In a mixture, on the other hand, all the substances retained their properties and no new 'substantial form' arose. This Aristotelian idea that the elements might be transformed suggested that by depriving metals of certain attributes, or perhaps of all their attributes and thus reducing them to *materia prima*, they could subsequently be given the attributes of gold. For this purpose alchemists tried to discover an elixir, the 'Philosopher's Stone', which would act as a catalyst or as a ferment as yeast acted on dough.

By the 7th century, when the Arabs captured Alexandria,

the magical element in Greek alchemy had gone far beyond the practical. Arab alchemy derived mainly from Greek sources, but the leading exponents gave it once again a more practical turn. The first of these was Jabir ibn Hayyan (8th century), who made important developments in both theory and practice. 'The first essential in chemistry', he said, as rendered by E. J. Holmyard in his *Makers of Chemistry* (Oxford, 1931, p. 60),

is that thou shouldst perform practical work and conduct experiments, for he who performs not practical work nor makes experiments will never attain to the least degree of mastery. But thou, O my son, do thou experiment so that thou mayest acquire knowledge.

He accepted the Aristotelian theory that minerals were generated from exhalations in the earth, but held that in the formation of metals the dry exhalations first produced sulphur and the moist exhalations mercury, and that metals were formed by the subsequent combination of these two substances. He discovered, however, that ordinary sulphur and mercury combined to form not metals but a 'red stone' or cinnabar (mercuric sulphide), and he therefore concluded that it was not these which formed metals but hypothetical substances to which they were the nearest approach. The most perfect natural harmony of combination produced gold; other metals were the result of defects in either purity or proportion of the two ingredients. The object of alchemy was therefore to remove these defects. As regards practical chemistry, the Arab manuscripts attributed to Jabir contain descriptions of such processes as distillation and the use of sand-baths and water-baths, crystallisation, calcination, solution, sublimation, and reduction, and of such practical applications as the preparation of steel, dyes, varnishes and hair-dyes.

Among the other Arab alchemists who influenced Western Christendom, the most important were Rhazes (d. *c.* 924) and Avicenna (980–1037). Rhazes gave both a clear account of apparatus for melting metals, distilling and other operations, and a systematic classification of chemical substances and reactions. He also combined Aristotle's theory of *materia prima* with a form of atomism. Avicenna, in his *De Mineralibus*, the geological and alchemical part of the *Sanatio* (*Kitabal-Shifa*), made few fundamental chemical advances on his predecessors, but gave a clear account of the accepted theories. One aspect of chemical theory which caused difficulty was to explain how, in chemical combination, elements which no longer existed in the compound could be regenerated. Avicenna held that the elements were present in the compound not merely potentially but actually, but the question continued to trouble the medieval scholastics. Avicenna also made an attack on the makers of gold. Disbelief in transmutation had existed since Jabir's time and Avicenna, while accepting the theory of matter on which the claim was based, denied that alchemists had ever brought about more than accidental changes as, for instance, in colour. In spite of the practical spirit of Rhazes, through which the Arab chemists developed such processes as the refinement of metals by cupellation, that is, refining in a shallow vessel or cupel, and solution in acids and assays of gold and silver alloys by weighing and determining specific gravity, and in spite of Avicenna's criticism, the esoteric and magical art of alchemy continued to flourish vigorously. The earliest Arab works translated into Latin thus included not only Rhazes's treatise on alums (or vitriols) and salts and Avicenna's *De Mineralibus*, but also the magical *Emerald Table*.

Both aspects of alchemy became popular in Western Christendom from the 13th century onwards, though such writers as Albertus Magnus usually adopted Avicenna's scepticism about transmutation. The encyclopædias of writers like Bartholomew the Englishman (fl. *c.* 1230–40), Vincent of Beauvais, Albertus Magnus and Roger Bacon contained a large amount of chemical information derived from both Latin and Arabic sources, and the last two seem to show some practical acquaintance with laboratory techniques. No fundamental advance was made on the Arabs in chemical theory before Paracelsus in the early 16th century, but in practical chemistry some important additions were made in the later Middle Ages.

Perhaps the most important Western contribution to practical chemistry was in methods of distillation. The traditional form of the still had been developed in Greco-Roman Egypt and was described by Zosimus and other early alchemical writers. This consisted of the curcurbite or vessel in which was placed the matter to be distilled, the alembic or still-head in which condensation occurred, and the receiver which received the distilled fraction after it had condensed. The curcurbite was heated over a fire or in a sand-bath or water-bath. Modifications of this standard design were made for various purposes and were taken over by the Arabs, through whom they became known in the West, and some of these early designs, including the turk's-head type, in which the still-head was partly immersed in water to give more rapid condensation, remained in use as late as the 18th century. The Greco-Egyptian still was used at relatively high temperatures and was useful for distilling or sublimating substances like mercury, arsenic and sulphur. The Arabs improved it in various ways and introduced the gallery with several stills heated in one oven for producing substances like oil of roses and naphtha on a large scale, but neither the Greeks nor the Arabs developed efficient methods of cooling the alembic that would permit the condensation of volatile substances like alcohol. This seems to have been the contribution of the West (Fig. 14).

The earliest known account of the preparation of alcohol is described in the following paragraph translated from an early 12th-century manuscript of the technical treatise *Mappæ Clavicula* discussed by Berthelot in *La Chimie au Moyen Age*, vol. 1, p. 61:

On mixing a pure and very strong wine with three parts of salt, and heating it in vessels suitable for the purpose, an inflam-

mable water is obtained which burns away without consuming
the material [on which it is poured].

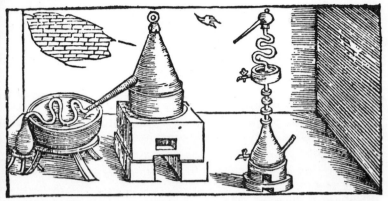

FIG. 14. Still with *canale serpentium* or *serpentes* condensing tube. From
V. Biringuccio, *Pirotechnia*, Venice, 1558 (1st edn. 1540).

In early 12th-century Italy, *aqua ardens*, containing about 60
per cent. alcohol, was prepared by one distillation, and *aqua
vitæ*, with about 96 per cent. alcohol, by redistillation. The
method of cooling as described in the 13th century by the
Florentine doctor, Taddeo Alderotti (1223–1303), was to
extend the length of the tube leading from the alembic to the
receiver and pass it horizontally through a vessel of water.
The introduction of rectification by distillation with lime-
stone or calx is attributed to Raymond Lull (*c.* 1232–1315)
and further improvements to the cooling apparatus in the
14th century are attributed to the Franciscan alchemist,
John of Rupescissa (d. after 1356). Most of the early stills
were probably of metal or pottery but in the early 15th
century the Italian doctor, Michael Savonarola (1384–1464),
speaks of distilling apparatus made of glass, which would be
an obvious advantage in distilling substances like the mineral
acids. By the end of the 13th century alcohol had become an
important substance: it was used as a solvent in the preparation of perfumes and for extracting medicines, was prescribed
as a medicine by doctors like Arnald of Villanova (*c.* 1235–

1311), and spirits were beginning to take their place with wine and beer as a drink. By the 15th century distillers had become incorporated as a guild.

The still was used to prepare a number of other substances as well as alcohol. The earliest descriptions of the preparation of nitric and sulphuric acids are contained in a late 13th-century Latin manuscript of a work entitled *Liber de Investigatione Perfectionis*, which was attributed to Geber (the Latinised form of Jabir) and is probably based on Arabic sources but with Latin additions. In the 13th century a new type of still appeared for preparing concentrated acids, in which the neck of the curcurbite was extended and bent over to form a 'retort' and so prevent the distilling acids from attacking the *lutæ* or cements used in making the join between it and the alembic air-tight. Mineral acids were prepared in fairly large quantities for assaying in metallurgy and good descriptions of their manufacture as well as that of sulphur, mercury and other substances obtained by distillation were given in the 16th century by metallurgical writers like Agricola and Biringuccio. The ' waters' or 'essences' of organic substances like plants and dried herbs and even ants and frogs were also obtained by steam-distillation, as well as by solution in alcohol, for use as medicines; and at least by the 16th century, with Hieronymus Brunschwig, it was recognised that these 'essences' were the active principles of drugs.

Some other improvements in practical chemistry appear in another late 13th-century Latin alchemical treatise attributed to Geber, the well-known *Summa Perfectionis*. This also was probably of Arabic origin but with Latin additions. It contains very clear and complete descriptions of chemical npparatus and practices used in trying to make gold. Beginaing with a discussion of the arguments against transmutation and their refutation, it passes on to the theory that metals are composed of sulphur and mercury and to a description of the definition and qualities of each of the six metals, gold, silver, lead, tin, copper, iron. Then there is a description of chemical methods such as sublimation, distillation, calcination, solution, coagulation and fixation, of the nature of different substances, and of the preparation of each towards its transmutation by elixirs. Finally, there is a description of methods of analysis to ascertain whether the transmutation has succeeded. These include cupellation, ignition, fusion, exposition over vapours, admixture of burning sulphur, calcination and reduction. The *Summa Perfectionis* shows the considerable knowledge of chemical apparatus and processes in the possession of Western alchemists by the end of the 13th century and not least in interest is the evidence it gives of the use of the balance (Fig. 15), as in the observation that lead gains weight when calcined because 'spirit is united with the

FIG. 15. Chemical balance and furnace. From V. Biringuccio, *Pirotechnia*.

body'. Thus if alchemical theory went astray because it was based on too exclusive an attention to changes in colour and appearance, the alchemists' familiarity with the balance at least prepared the way for the concentration on mass on which modern chemistry is based.

The magical as well as the practical side of alchemy flourished vigorously in the West during the later Middle Ages. The search by alchemists for a formula that would give health and eternal youth, riches and power, is the origin of legends like that of Dr. Faustus, and the wide publicity given to the more scientific alchemy by the great 13th-century encyclopædists gave rise, from the 13th to the 17th century, to an enormous number of manuscripts claiming the production of gold. These were at first written by men of some learning, but later, during the 14th and 15th centuries, by members of all classes; as Thomas Norton put it in *The Ordinall of Alchimy* (*c.* 1477) by 'Free *Masons* and *Tinkers* with poore *Parish Clerks; Tailors* and *Glasiers* . . . And eke Sely Tinkers'; and often they were fathered on such names as Albertus Magnus, Roger Bacon, Arnald of Villanova and Raymond Lull. Indeed, at times the practice became so common that it was condemned by princes and prelates alarmed for its effect on the value of money.

(7) BIOLOGY

The common characteristic which distinguished all living from non-living things, according to Aristotle and to 13th-century ways of thought, was the ability to initiate movement and change without an external mover, that is, the power of self-movement or self-change. The kinds of movement or change common to all living things were growth, the assimilation of diverse matter under the form of the organism, and the continuation of this process in the reproduction of the species. These were the only kinds of living activity displayed by plants. Their substantial form was thus a 'nutritive soul' (or vital principle), which was not, of course, something separate and distinct from the material plant itself, but an inherent principle causing the observed behaviour. Animals added to nutrition the power of sensitivity, that is, the power to respond to environmental stimuli by local motion, and theirs was therefore a 'sensitive soul'. Men were distinguished again by the power of abstract reflection and the exercise of the will, which were the marks of a 'rational soul'. Men were also capable of sensation and nutrition, and animals of nutrition, the higher forms of soul including the activities of all those below them. Aristotle thus recognised a hierarchy of living forms stretching, as he said in the *Historia Animalium* (588 b 4), 'little by little from things lifeless to animal life', from the first manifestations of life in the lower plants, through the plants to sponges and other sessile animals scarcely distinguishable from plants, and again through invertebrate and vertebrate animals, apes and pygmies to man. Each type was distinct and unchanging, its substantial form being both the efficient and final cause of its particular bodily activity, whether in nutrition, reproduction, locomotion, sensation or reasoning.

The subject of 13th-century biology, then, was these activities of the different beings making up the scale of living nature, and the way in which they were conceived of opened the way naturally for teleological as well as mechanical explanations. Aristotle and Galen had both taken a teleological view of the existence and functioning of organic structures, and this had led them to make valuable discoveries about the adaptation of the parts of organisms to each other and of the whole to the environment. Certainly, in the 13th century and later, the search for the purpose or function of organs often led to valuable conclusions. It was certainly also sometimes abused, as in what have been described as the wearisomely reiterated reasons for the existence of imperfectly described structures given by a writer like Guy de Chauliac.

Until the 13th century, the chief interest of the Latins in botany had been medical and in zoology moral and didactic. The same attitudes, in fact, characterised much of natural history down to the 17th century. When, in the 13th century, biology became a science combining observation with a system of natural explanations, this was largely due to the translations of Aristotle's own biological works, of the pseudo-Aristotelian *De Plantis*, (a compilation from Aristotle and Theophrastus believed in the Middle Ages to be an original work of the former), and of various treatises by Galen. Robert of Cricklade's (Prior of St. Frideswide's, Oxford, *c.* 1141–71) anthology of extracts from the *Natural History* witnesses to a revival of interest also in Pliny in the middle of the 12th century, and what the Arabs and, in particular,

Avicenna and Averroës had to teach was quickly assimilated as it became available.

FIG. 16. Drawing of an ant's nest among wheat. From British Museum MS. Royal 12. C. xix (late XII cent.).

The early encyclopædias deriving from this movement included many incredible stories. Alexander Nequam (1157–1217) dismissed, as a ridiculous popular notion, the legend that the beaver, of which the testicles were the source of a certain medicine, castrated itself to escape its hunters, but he accepted the basilisk as the progeny of a cock's egg brooded by a toad and the common belief that an animal knew the medicinal value of herbs. For, as he said in his *De Naturis Rerum*, book 2, chapter 123:

educated by nature, it knows the virtues of herbs, although it has neither studied medicine at Salerno nor been drilled in the schools at Montpellier.

But Nequam made no claim to be a scientist. Like Hildegarde of Bingen (1098–1179), who, besides expounding mystical cosmology, in another work perhaps wrongly attributed to her, named nearly a thousand plants and animals in German, he believed that man's Fall had had physical effects on nature, causing spots on the moon, wildness in animals, insect pests, animal venoms and disease, and his purpose was frankly didactic.

This didactic attitude was continued in many of the later encyclopædias, but other activities provided opportunities for observation. Some of these were associated with agriculture (see below, pp. 158 *et seq.*) and produced the treatises on husbandry of Walter of Henley (*c.* 1250?) and Peter of Crescenzi (*c.* 1306) and the sections on agriculture in the encyclopædias of Albertus Magnus (*De Vegetabilibus et Plantis*) and Vincent of Beauvais (*Speculum Doctrinale*). Crescenzi's treatise remained the standard European work on the subject until the end of the 16th century. Also, Thomas of Cantimpré's *De Natura Rerum* (*c.* 1228–44) contains a description of herring fisheries, the *Konungs Skuggsja* of seals, walruses and whales, and Albertus Magnus, whose duties as provincial of the German Dominican province took him long distances on foot, gave an account in his *De Animalibus* of whaling and fishing and of German agricultural life. Travellers such as Marco Polo and William of Rubruck also brought back descriptions of new creatures, of the wild asses of Central Asia and of rice, ginger and fat-tailed sheep.

The circle of natural philosophers and magicians which the Emperor Frederick II (1194–1250) kept at his court can claim a treatise on horse diseases, and the *De Arte Venandi cum Avibus* of Frederick himself is one of the most important medieval works on zoology. *The Art of Falconry*, based on Aristotle and various Moslem sources, began with a zoological introduction on the anatomy and habits of birds and passed to the rearing and feeding of falcons, the training of dogs for hunting with them, various types of falcons and the cranes, herons and other birds which they were used to hunt. When Frederick made use of other practical treatises on falconry he did not hesitate to describe them as 'lying and inadequate', nor did he hesitate to call Aristotle a man of books. The Emperor's book contains 900 pictures of individual birds, some of them possibly by Frederick himself, which are accurate even down to details of plumage, and the representations of birds in flight are obviously based on close and careful observation (Plate 2). He watched and questioned Saracen falconers, observed the nests of herons, cuckoos and vultures and exploded the popular legend that barnacle geese were hatched from barnacles on trees. He had barnacles brought to him and, seeing that they contained nothing in any shape like a bird, concluded that the story had grown up simply because the geese bred in such remote parts that no-one had been there to see. He was interested in the mechanical conditions of flight and bird migrations, made experiments on the artificial incubation of eggs and showed that vultures did not go for meat if their eyes were covered. He also noted various other points of bird behaviour, as, for example, how the mother falcon gave half-dead birds to her young to teach them how to hunt and how the mother duck and other non-predatory birds feigned to be wounded and decoyed approaching strangers from their nests. He also described the air-cavities of the bones, the structure of the lungs and other previously unrecorded facts of avian anatomy.

Other works on falconry, both in Latin and in the vernacular, witness to its wide popularity, but it was not the only sport that rendered service to zoology. The menageries which kings, princes and even towns kept for amusements such as bear-baiting or out of curiosity were in Italy and the East descended from those of antiquity. That which Frederick II carted about with him on his travels and even across the Alps, included elephants, dromedaries, camels, panthers, lions, leopards, falcons, bearded owls, monkeys and the first recorded giraffe to appear in Europe. The first large menagerie in the north was that established in the 11th century, at Woodstock, by the Norman kings. In the 14th century a large collection of exotic animals was kept by the Popes at Avignon. These forerunners of modern zoological gardens could satisfy the curiosity of the rich, and the charm exercised by animals over the minds of poorer people is shown by the well-known description of the domestic cat in Bartholomew the Englishman's *On the Properties of Things*, the reputed source of Shakespeare's natural history.

A similar interest in nature is shown by the hounds, foxes, hares and above all the foliage covering the capitals, bosses and misericords of York, Ely or Southwell cathedrals. There one may see, fresh and resilient, the leaves, flowers or fruit of the pine, oak, maple, buttercup, potentilla, hop, bryony, ivy and hawthorn. Emile Mâle, in his *Religious Art in France in the Thirteenth Century* (English translation, 1913, p. 52), has recognised in French Gothic cathedrals 'the plantain, arum, ranunculus, fern, clover, coladine, hepatica, columbine, cress, parsley, strawberry-plant, ivy, snapdragon, the flower of the broom and the leaf of the oak'. Even the conception of nature as symbolic of spiritual truths led, in the 12th and 13th centuries, to a special intensity of observation.

> 'The holly bears a bark
> As bitter as any gall
> And Mary bore sweet Jesus Christ
> For to redeem us all.'

The same interest in nature is seen in the illustrations of certain manuscripts. Matthew Paris in his *Chronica Majora* (*c.* 1250) described an immigration of the crossbills (*cancellatas*) and illustrated the bird. The borders of manuscripts from the 13th century onwards were frequently illuminated with naturalistic drawings of flowers and many kinds of animals, prawns, shells and insects. The 13th-century French architect, Villard de Honnecourt, interspersed his architectural drawings, studies in perspective and designs for engines of war and perpetual motion with illustrations of a lobster, a fly, a dragon-fly, a grasshopper, two parrots on a perch, two ostriches, a rabbit, a sheep, a cat, dogs, a bear and a lion 'copied from life'. He also gave a recipe to preserve the natural colours of dried flowers (*d'un herbier*). The progress that was made in naturalistic illustration in the century after Villard de Honnecourt may be estimated by comparing his drawings with those in the late 14th-century Ligurian manuscript attributed to a certain Cybo, monk of Hyères. The borders of this manuscript contain illustrations of plants, quadrupeds, birds, molluscs and crustacea, spiders, butterflies and wasps, beetles and other insects, caterpillars as well as adults often being shown. A point of particular interest is the tendency to put together on the same page animals now classified as belonging to the same group (Plate 3).

In contrast with the naturalistic spirit of these manuscripts stands the conventional iconography of many of the encyclopædias and herbals. Singer has divided the illustrations of plants in the latter into what he calls the Naturalistic and the Romanesque traditions. Botanical iconography may be traced through the 6th-century Byzantine *Codex Aniciæ Iulianæ* back to Dioscorides himself, whose own work was based on the herbal of Cratevas (1st century B.C.). He, according to Pliny, made coloured drawings of plants. The Benedictine monasteries not only cultivated extensive fields, but also planted kitchen and physic gardens, and the object of the herbal writer, who had little idea of the geographical distribution of plants, was usually to try to identify in his own garden the plants mentioned by Dioscorides and the *Herbarium* of pseudo-Apuleius (4th century A.D.), the main text-books. Since the Mediterranean plants mentioned in these books were frequently absent or at best represented by other species of the same genus, neither the drawings nor the descriptions given in them corresponded to anything the Northern herbalist might see. In new herbals or new copies of the old texts, text and illustrations were usually made by a different hand, and in the Romanesque tradition the drawings made in the spaces left by the scribe became a matter of increasingly stylised copying. This tradition, which emanated from northern France and seems to have descended from a debased style of Roman art, reached its limit at the end of the 12th century.

Naturalistic representations of plants and animals were also made throughout the Dark Ages, for example, in the mosaics in many churches in Rome, Ravenna and Venice. Some Latin herbals of the 11th and 12th centuries were also illustrated in this naturalistic tradition, of which the 12th century Bury St. Edmunds herbal is a striking example (Fig. 17). From the 13th century onwards naturalistic

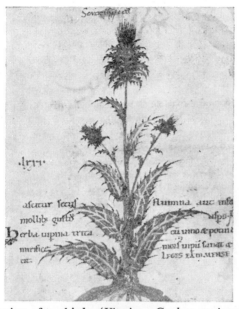

FIG. 17. Drawing of a thistle (*Viperina=Carduus marianus*), from *The Herbal of Apuleius Barbarus* executed at Bury St. Edmunds. From Oxford MS. Bodley 130 (XII cent.).

illustrations steadily increased. Outside the herbals, naturalistic representations of plants and animals appear in the paintings of artists like Giotto (*c*. 1276–1336) and Spinello Aretino (*c*. 1333–1410) and, in the 15th century, herbal illustrators learnt from the three-dimensional realism of the art of Italy and Flanders, reaching perfection in the drawings of Leonardo da Vinci and Albrecht Dürer. An outstanding example is the herbal of Benedetto Rinio, completed in 1410, which was illustrated with 440 magnificent plates by the Venetian artist, Andrea Amodio (Fig. 18). Both the naturalistic and the romanesque traditions continued without a break into the early printed herbals with which histories of botany usually begin.

FIG. 18. Drawing of *Eryngium maritimum* ('de iringo') from Benedetto Rinio's *Liber de Simplicibus*. From MS. Marciano Latino vi. 59 (1410) in the Bibl. Naz. di S. Marco, Venice.

Considering the way they were composed it is not surprising that text and illustrations sometimes had little relation to each other, the former often describing a Mediterranean species known to the authority from whom it was copied and the latter being either purely formal or drawn from a native species known to the artist. But medical men relied on the herbals to identify plants with given pharmaceutical properties and some attempt had to be made to improve verbal descriptions. These were almost always clumsy and frequently inaccurate and the synonyms given by writers of botanical lexicons or pandects, as, for instance, in the 13th century by Simon of Genoa and in the 14th century by Matthæus Sylvaticus (see below, p. 126), sometimes did not all correspond to the same object, even though considerable personal observation went into drawing them up. A clear, accurate and unambiguous nomenclature is, indeed, to be found nowhere before the 17th century and only imperfectly before Linnæus.

Not all medieval herbals restricted their interest wholly to pharmacy, nor were their descriptions all inaccurate. The *Herbal* (*c.* 1287) of Rufinus, which Thorndike has recently published, was not only a medical herbal but a book of botany for plants' sake. Rufinus' authorities were Dioscorides, the *Macer Floridus* attributed to Odo of Meung who flourished at the end of the 11th century, the *Circa Instans* of the Salernitan doctor Matthæus Platearius, the leading contribution to 12th-century botany, and several other works. As Thorndike has pointed out, Rufinus added to his authorities

careful, detailed description of the plant itself—its stalk, leaves, and flower—and an equally painstaking distinguishing of its different varieties or a comparison of it with, and differentiation of it from, other similar or related flora. He further takes care to inform us as to other names applied to a given herb or other plants indicated by the same name.

As in other herbals, the plants were nearly all in alphabetical order. Dioscorides had sometimes roughly grouped together plants of similar form and presented a series belonging to the Labiateæ, Compositæ, or Leguminosæ. The same tendency is seen in the Anglo-Saxon *Herbal* of about 1000 A.D. extracted from Dioscorides and pseudo-Apuleius; there was a real grouping of umbelliferous plants. Serious attempts at classification belonged to the natural scientific tradition of the North, whereas Rufinus, who had been brought up in the Italian medical tradition of Naples and Bologna, seems to have known nothing, in those days of expensive manuscripts, even of the *De Vegetabilibus et Plantis* of Albertus Magnus.

The botanical and zoological sections of the 13th-century encyclopædias of Bartholomew the Englishman, Thomas of Cantimpré and Vincent of Beauvais were by no means devoid of observation, but in this respect they cannot be compared with the digressions in which Albertus Magnus described his own personal researches when writing commentaries on Aristotle's works. The commentary, in which the text of the original might be either clearly distinguished from or included in the body of critical discussion, was the common medieval form of presentation of scientific work inherited by the 13th-century Latins from the Arabs. The *De Vegetabilibus et Plantis* (*c.* 1250) was a commentary on the pseudo-Aristotelian *De Plantis*, which in Alfred of Sareshel's translation was the chief source of botanical theory down to the 16th century. 'In this sixth book', Albertus remarked at the beginning of a discussion of native plants known to him, we will satisfy the curiosity of the students rather than philosophy. For philosophy cannot discuss particulars . . . Syllogisms cannot be made about particular natures, of which experience (*experimentum*) alone gives certainty.

Albertus' disgressions show a sense of morphology and ecology unsurpassed from Aristotle and Theophrastus to Cesalpino and Jung. His comparative study of plants extended to all their parts, root, stem, leaf, flower, fruit, bark, pith, etc., and to their form. He observed that trees growing in the shade were taller, slimmer and had less branches than others, and that in cold and shady places the wood was harder. Both effects he attributed not to lack of light, but to lack of the warmth which favoured the activity of the roots in absorbing nourishment from the soil. The heat of the soil, which according to Aristotle served as the stomach of plants, was supposed to elaborate their food for them and therefore it was supposed that they needed to produce no excrement. Albertus claimed that the sap, potentially all parts of the plant because it supplied them with this nourishment, was carried in the veins which were like blood-vessels but had no pulse. The winter sleep of plants was caused by the retreat of the sap inwards.

He drew a distinction between thorns, which were of the nature of the stem, and prickles which were merely developed from the surface. Because in the vine a tendril sometimes grew in the place of a bunch of grapes he inferred that a tendril was an imperfect form of a bunch of grapes. In the flower of the borage he distinguished, though without understanding their functions in reproduction, the green calyx, the corolla with its ligular outgrowths, the five stamens (*vingulæ*) and the central pistil. He classified floral forms into three types, bird-form as in the columbine, violet and dead nettle, pyramid- or bell-form as in the convolvulus and star-form as in the rose. He also made an extensive comparative study of fruits, distinguishing between 'dry' and fleshy fruits, and described various types differing in the structure and relations of seed, pericarp and receptacle, in whether the pods burst or the flesh dried in ripening, and so on. He showed that in fleshy fruits the flesh did not nourish the seed, and in the seed he recognised the embryo. He also remarked in book 6, tract 1, chapter 31:

On the leaves of the oak often form certain round ball-like objects called galls, which after remaining some time on the tree produce within themselves a small worm bred by the corruption of the leaf.

Theophrastus had suggested in his *Inquiry into Plants* that the vegetable kingdom should be classified into trees, shrubs, under-shrubs, and herbs, with further distinctions such as those between cultivated and wild, flowering and flowerless, fruit-bearing and fruitless, deciduous and evergreen, or terrestrial, marshy and aquatic plants within these groups. His suggestions were rather indefinite and tentative. Albertus' general classification follows the main outlines of this scheme. Though not set out in detail, Dr. Agnes Arber, in her book on *Herbals*, has suggested that the following system might have been in his mind. His plants form a scale from the fungi to the flowering plants, though in the last group he did not explicitly recognise the distinction between monocotyledons and dicotyledons.

I Leafless plants (mostly our cryptogams, that is, plants with no true flower).

II Leafy plants (our phanerogams or flowering plants and certain cryptogams).

    1. Corticate plants with stiff outer covering (our monocotyledons, having only one seed lobe).

    2. Tunicate plants, with annular rings, *ex ligneis tunicis* (our dicotyledons, having two seed lobes).

      a Herbaceous.

      b Woody.

The appearance of new species had received an explanation from a number of natural philosophers before Albertus Magnus. In the cosmogonies of several of the early Greeks attempts were made to account for the origin of life and the variety of living things. Thus Anaximander held that all life had originated by spontaneous generation from water and that man had developed from fish. Xenophanes quoted fossil fish and seaweed as evidence that life arose from mud. Empedocles believed that life arose by spontaneous generation from earth: first plants appeared and then parts of animals (including man), heads, arms, eyes, etc., which united by chance and produced forms of all sorts, monstrous or proper. The proper forms extinguished the monstrous and, when the sexes had become differentiated, reproduced themselves, and the earth then ceased its generation. Similar views were adopted by Lucretius, and the notion of 'seeds' in the earth, to which Adelard of Bath alluded, received an explanation in the Stoic conception of *logoi spermatikoi*, which tended to produce new species of both animate and inanimate things from indeterminate matter. St. Augustine's theory of the creation of things in their *rationes seminales,* or 'seminal causes' (see above, p. 16), which had a wide influence in the Middle Ages, was derived from this conception. It was paralleled among the Arabs by the 9th-century al-Nazzam and his pupil al-Jahiz, who speculated on adaptation and the struggle for existence.

Apart from Anaximander's, all these theories accounted for the succession of new species not by modification from living ancestors but by generation from a common source such as the earth. But some ancient writers, such as Theophrastus, had believed that existing types were sometimes mutable. Albertus accepted this belief and illustrated it by the domestication of wild plants and the running wild of cultivated plants. He described five ways of transforming one plant into another. Some of these did not involve a change of species but merely the actualisation of potential attributes, such as when rye increased in size over three years and became wheat. Others involved the corruption of one substantial form and the generation of another, such as occurred when aspens and poplars sprang up in place of a felled oak or beech wood, or when mistletoe was generated from a sickening tree. Like Peter of Crescenzi later, he also believed that new species could be produced by grafting.

Speculations about the origin of new species and the mutation of those now existing continued in the next century with Henry of Hesse (1325–97), who referred to the appearance of new diseases and the new herbs which would be needed to cure them. Later they entered the natural philosophies of Bruno, who was indebted also to the Stoics, and of Francis Bacon, Leibniz, and the evolutionists of the 18th century. The reflections of Albertus Magnus and of Henry of Hesse on the mutation of species were not related to any concept of an evolving, developing and progressing universe, animal kingdom or human race, an idea which is characteristically modern and had no place in medieval thought. Aristotle had described a scale of nature in his biological works, but in this there was no movement upwards, and when Albertus made this Aristotelian scale the basis of his botanical and zoological system he accepted, apart from accidents and the causes of mutation just mentioned, the continuance of breeding true to type.

Albertus' *De Animalibus*, and particularly the sections on reproduction and embryology, is one of the best examples of the way the system of facts and natural explanations provided by the translations of Aristotle's and other Greek works stimulated the natural philosophers of the 13th century to make similar observations of their own and to modify the explanations in their light. The first 19 books of the 26 books of the *De Animalibus* are a commentary embodying the text of Michael Scot's translation of Aristotle's *History of Animals*, *Parts of Animals* and *Generation of Animals*. In his commentary Albertus also made use of Avicenna's own commentary on these works, of Avicenna's *Canon*, which was based on Galen, and of Latin translations of some of Galen's own works. The remaining 7 of Albertus' 26 books consist of original discussions of various biological topics and descriptions of particular animals, taken partly from Thomas of Cantimpré.

For Aristotle, the reproduction of the specific form was an extension of growth, for, as growth was the realisation of the form in one individual, reproduction was its realisation in the new individual to which that gave rise. Albertus followed Aristotle in distinguishing four types of reproduction: sexual reproduction, in which male and female principles were either separate in different individuals, as in higher animals and in general those with local motion, or united as in plants and sessile animals and some others such as bees; reproduction by budding, as in some mussels; and spontaneous generation, as in some insects, eels and the lower creatures generally. The sexes of plants were clearly distinguished only by Camerarius (1694), though the point had been suggested by Theophrastus, Pliny and Thomas Aquinas. Like Aristotle, Albertus rejected the Hippocratic theory, also maintained by Galen, that both parents contributed to the form. Aristotle had held that the female provided merely the material (which he believed to be the catamenia (*menstruum*) in mammals and the yolk of the egg in birds) out of which the immaterial male form constructed the embryo. Albertus agreed with this but followed Avicenna in maintaining that the material produced by the female was a seed, or *humor seminalis*, separate from the catamenia or yolk, which he said was simply food. He incorrectly identified this seed with the white of the egg. The spermatozoon was not, of course, discovered until the invention of the microscope and he identified the cock's seed with the chalazea. The cause of the differentiation of sex, he held, was that the male 'vital heat' was able to 'concoct' the surplus blood into semen, informing it with the form of the species, while the female was too cold to effect this substantial change. All other differences between the sexes were secondary to this.

The efficacy of vital heat derived from the fact that, of the two pairs of primary qualities, hot-cold were active and dry-wet passive. The heart was the centre of vital heat and the central organ of the body. To it, and not to the brain, which Aristotle had said was a cooling organ, ran the nerves. Vital heat was the source of all vital activity. It was the cause of the ripening of fruit, of digestion which was a kind of cooking, and it determined the degree to which an animal would approach the adult form on being extruded from the parent. The facts of heredity Aristotle had explained by the degree of dominance of the male form over the female matter, female characteristics prevailing where the vital heat of the male was low. Monstrosities were produced where the female matter was defective for the purpose in hand and resisted the determining form. Vital heat, which Aristotle described in the *De Generatione Animalium* (736 b 36) as 'the spiritus [pneuma] included in the semen and the foam-like, and the natural principle in the spiritus, being analogous to the element of the stars', Albertus said was also the cause of spontaneous generation. The corruption of the form of a dead organism generated the forms of lower creatures which then organised the available matter, as worms generated in dung. The vital heat of the sun also caused spontaneous generation, and the Arabs and scholastics generally supposed that such forms were supplied by celestial virtue.

Just as Aristotle was in opposition to Hippocrates and Galen over the question whether the male seed alone formed the embryo, so he was over the question whether in embryology any new characters arose or all were already preformed in the seed which simply had to expand. Hippocrates had held a form of this preformation theory combined with pangenesis, that is, he held that the sperm was derived from all parts of the parent's body, and therefore gave rise to the same parts in the offspring. Aristotle showed that the theory that the embryo was an adult in miniature, which had only to unfold, implied that the parts developing later already existed in the earlier and all in the sperm, whose parts already existed in its parent and therefore in the sperm which produced the parent, and so on to infinity. He considered such *emboîtement*, or encasement, an absurd conclusion, and therefore maintained the epigenetic theory that the parts arose *de novo* as the immaterial form determined and differentiated the matter of the embryo. After the male seed had acted on the female matter by curdling it, he said that the embryo developed like a complicated machine whose wheels, once set going, followed their appointed motions. He described the development of a number of animals and made this comparative study the basis for a classification of animals. His observation that development was faster at the head end foreshadows the modern theory of axial gradients, and by showing that the more general preceded the more specific characters he anticipated von Baer. He also correctly understood the functions of the placenta and umbilical cord.

Albertus' own researches into embryology were guided by Aristotle.[1] He never hesitated to accept the evidence of his eyes but, while he was ready to adopt the theories of alternative authorities and, for instance, like Avicenna combined

(1) In the text of Albertus' *De Animalibus* edited by H. Stadler it is possible to follow the original text with Albertus' amplifications.

epigenesis with a theory of pangenesis, he usually attributed errors of fact to copyists rather than to Aristotle. Following Aristotle's example, he opened hens' eggs after various intervals and added *per anathomyam*, and with considerable understanding, to Aristotle's description of what was going on, from the appearance of the pulsating red speck of the heart to hatching. He also studied the development of fish and mammals, of which he understood the foetal nutrition. And while Aristotle had thought that the pupa was the egg of the insect, of which he supposed the life history to be from maternal female to larva to pupa (his egg) to adult, Albertus recognised the true insect egg, as well as that of the louse. In book 17, tract 2, chapter 1 of the *De Animalibus* he amplified Aristotle's text to say:

at first, eggs are something very small, and from them worms are generated, which in their turn are converted into the matter of ova [*i.e.*, pupæ], and then from them the flying form emerges; and so there is a triple change from the egg.

He said, in fact 'that the generation of all animals is first from eggs'. At the same time he believed in spontaneous generation. He gave an excellent description of insect mating, and his description in book 5, tract 1, chapter 4 of the life history of a butterfly represents a remarkable piece of sustained observation.

A certain kind of caterpillar is hidden in cracks after the sun has begun to recede from the summer tropic and it putrefies internally and becomes surrounded by a hard, horny, annular skin. In this is born a flying worm which has in front a long coiled tongue which it thrusts into flowers and it sucks out the nectar. It develops four wings, two in front and two behind, and flies and becomes multi-coloured and develops several legs, but not as many as it had when it was a caterpillar. The colours vary in two ways, either according to genus or in one individual. Some genera are white, some black and some of other intermediate colours. But there is a certain kind belonging to the last genus in which many different colours are found in the same individual. This animal, thus winged and generated from a caterpillar, is called by some people in Latin by the common name *verviscella*. It flies at the end of autumn and emits many eggs, for the whole lower part of its body below the thorax is converted into eggs, and in laying eggs it dies. And then again from these eggs caterpillars hatch next spring. But certain grubs do not become *verviscellæ* but gather at the ends of the branches of trees and there make nests and lay eggs, and from these arise grubs in the next spring. Those of this sort always extend the nest towards the sun at midday. But the sort that are generated from the flying forms place all their eggs in walls and cracks in wood and walls of houses near gardens.

Albertus' personal observations extended to many other zoological phenomena besides reproduction. Thomas of Cantimpré, though a good observer, had included a whole book of fabulous animals in his *De Natura Rerum* (*c.* 1228–44), but Albertus criticised the stories of the salamander, the beaver and the barnacle goose from personal observation. He said of the phœnix, the symbol of the resurrection, that it was studied more by mystical theologians than by natural philosophers. He gave excellent descriptions of a large number of northern animals unknown to Aristotle and noted the colour varieties of the squirrel (*pirolus*), which passed from red to grey as one went from Germany to Russia, and the lightening of colour in falcons (*falcones*), jackdaws (*monedulae*) and ravens (*corvi*) in cold climates. He considered colour as compared to form as of little importance as a specific character. He noted the relation of build to method of locomotion and applied Aristotle's principle of 'homology' to the correspondence between the bones in the forefoot of the horse and the dog. He showed that ants whose antennæ had been removed lost their sense of direction, and he concluded (wrongly) that the antennæ bore eyes. His knowledge of internal anatomy was sometimes meagre, but he dissected crickets and observed the ovarian follicles and tracheæ. He seems to have recognised the brain and nerve cord of crabs and something of their function in movement. He observed that the moulting of crabs included their limbs, and showed that these regenerated if amputated. 'But', he said in book 7, tract 3, chapter 4:

such animals are rarely regenerated in the abdomen, because in the bridge above which the soft parts are placed, the organs of their movement are fixed; and a motive virtue goes down that bridge from the part of them which corresponds to the brain. Therefore since it is the seat of a more noble power, it cannot be removed without danger.

The system by which Albertus classified the animals he described in Books 23–6 followed the main lines of that suggested by Aristotle, which to some extent he elaborated. Aristotle had recognised three degrees of likeness within the animal kingdom: the 'species', in which there was complete identity of type and in which differences between individuals were accidental and not perpetuated in reproduction; the 'genus', which consisted of such groups as fishes or birds; and the 'great genus', which involved the morphological correspondence or homology between scale and feather, fish-bone and bone, hand and claw, nail and hoof, and of which the whole group of sanguineous animals (the modern vertebrates) was an example. Though no classification was actually set out by Aristotle, the main lines of his system are easily recognised, as they were by Albertus. As each species and genus had many differentiæ they might be grouped in many ways, and, again like Aristotle, Albertus did not keep to one system, but put animals sometimes into groups based on morphological or reproductive similarity, and sometimes into ecological groups such as flying (*volatilia*), swimming (*natatilia*), walking (*gressibilia*) and crawling (*reptilia*) animals. Here he advanced on Aristotle by proposing the division of water animals into ten genera: *malachye* (cephalopods), *animalia mollis testæ* (crabs), *animalia duris testæ* (shell fish), *yricii marini* (sea urchins), *mastuc* (sea anemones), *lignei* (sea-stars, sea-cucumbers), *veretrale* (pennatulide or gephyra?), *serpentini* (polychæte worms?), *flecmatici* (medusæ) and *spongia marina* (sponges). With some animals he repeated or aggravated Aristotle's mistakes, putting whales with fish and bats with birds, although he observed the bat's teeth and said in Book I (tr. 2, c. 4), that 'she approaches the nature of quadrupeds'.

The main system of classification which Albertus derived from Aristotle was that based on the mode of generation, that is, on the degree of development, itself depending on the parents' vital heat and moisture, reached by the offspring at the time of extrusion from the parent's body. Thus, mammals were the hottest animals and produced viviparously young which were perfect likenesses to their parents, although smaller; vipers and cartilaginous fishes were internally oviparous, externally viviparous; birds and reptiles produced perfect eggs, that is eggs which did not increase in size after being laid; fish, cephalopods and crustacea produced imperfect eggs; insects produced a scolex (larva or premature 'egg') which then developed into the 'egg' (pupa); testacea produced generative slime or reproduced by budding; and in general members of the lower groups might be generated spontaneously. The complete 'Aristotelian' scale of living nature as recognised and modified by Albertus, is set out in Table 2 (p. 127).

After the 13th century, descriptive botany and zoology was carried on by herbalists and naturalists having a variety of interests. Of the herbalists, Matthæus Sylvaticus included in his dictionary of medical 'simples', or *Pandectæ*, in 1317, a large amount of information based on personal observation of plants in various places he had visited or in the collection of domestic and foreign plants he kept in his botanical garden at Salerno. This is the earliest known non-monastic botanical garden and from this time others appear, particularly in connection with the medical faculties of Universities, the first of this kind being established at Prague in 1350. A number of surgeons and physicians such as John of Milano in Italy, John Arderne in England and Thomas of Sarepta in Silesia wrote herbals in the 14th century. John of Milano illustrated his herbal, the *Flos Medicinæ* completed before 1328, with 210 drawings of plants and Thomas of

Man (rational soul)
Animals (sensitive soul)

    Enaima (sanguineous: modern vertebrates).

1. Man.
2. Hairy quadrupeds (land mammals, classified by cloven-hoof, teeth, etc.).
3. Cetacea (sea mammals, included by Albertus with fish).
4. Birds (classified by raptorial and webbed feet, etc.).
5. Scaly quadrupeds and apoda (reptiles and amphibia).
6. Fishes (bony and cartilaginous).

    Anaima (bloodless: modern invertebrates).

7. Malacia (cephalopods).
8. Malacostraca (crustacea).
9. Entoma (insects, millipedes, spiders, intestinal worms, etc., Albertus' *animalia corpora annulosa vel rugosa habentia*).
10. Ostracoderma or testacea (molluscs, except cephalopods; sea-urchins, ascidians).
11. Zoophyta (sea-cucumbers, sea-anemones, jelly-fish, sponges).

    Plants (nutritive soul).

A. Viviparous

a. with perfect egg

B. Oviparous (sometimes internally oviparous, externally viviparous, as in some vipers and in cartilaginous fish)

b. with imperfect egg

c. with imperfect egg

Oviparous

C. Vermiparous, with scales

Produced by generative slime, budding or spontaneous generation

Produced by spontaneous generation

Produced without sexual differentiation from seeds, or by budding (classified as above, p. 118).
(A to C represents the scale of egg or embryo types depending on vital heat.)

127

Sarepta, who died as a bishop about 1378, is of particular interest for having in his youth made a herbarium of dried plants collected in various places, including England. An anonymous French herbal compiled in Vaud about 1380 is of interest for containing fresh information about Swiss plants, but the most outstanding herbal of this period was the *Liber de Simplicibus* completed by Benedetto Rinio in Venice in 1410 (see above, p. 114). Besides the magnificent paintings of 450 domestic and foreign plants, this herbal contained brief botanical notes indicating collecting seasons, the part of the plant containing the drug, the authorities used and the name of each plant in Latin, Greek, Arabic, German, the various Italian dialects and Slavonic. Venice at that time had a vigorous trade in drugs with both East and West, and Rinio's herbal was kept in one of the main apothecary's shops, where it could be used for the practical purpose of identifying plants. The same medical interest was responsible for the printed herbals that began to appear later in the 15th century (see below, pp. 361 *et seq.*)

Of the other naturalists of the 14th century, Crescenzi included in his *Ruralia Commoda* a large amount of information about varieties of domestic plants and animals of all kinds and devoted a special section to gardens (see below, pp. 161 *et seq.*). His main agricultural authorities were the Roman writers Cato the Elder, Varro, Pliny and the part of the *Geoponica* dealing with vines, which had been translated by Burgundio of Pisa, while for scientific biology he went to Albertus Magnus and Avicenna. The German naturalist, Conrad von Megenburg, is distinguished for having written about 1350 the first important scientific work in German, *Das Buch der Natur*. This was basically a free translation of Thomas of Cantimpré's *De Rerum Natura*, but it contained some fresh observations on rainbows, plague and various animals and plants. It was very popular, and the first printed edition of 1475 was the earliest work in which woodcuts representing plants were used with the definite intention of illustrating the text and not merely for decoration. These illustrations probably did not much antedate the printing, but a late 14th-century naturalist whose illustrations showed very great powers of observation was Cybo of Hyères (see above, p. 112). Gaston de Foix, who in 1387 began to write his celebrated French treatise, *Le Miroir de Phœbus*, which did for hunting what the Emperor Frederick II had done for falconry, also showed himself to be an excellent naturalist. This work, which was very popular and was translated into English in the early 15th century, contained very good and practical descriptions of how to keep hounds, falcons and other hunting animals and also a large amount of information about the habits of the hunted animals such as the hart, wolf, badger, and otter. Another French writer, Jehan de Brie, in a book of 'shepherdry' written in 1379 for Charles V, showed that even in court circles there could be an interest in nature. In England a series of treatises on various country sports culminated with the *Boke of St. Albans* in two editions in 1486 and 1496, the second containing the first full account in English of fishing. An Italian zoological writer of the 15th century was Petrus Candidus who, in 1460, wrote a series of descriptions of animals, to which some excellent illustrations of birds, ants and other creatures were added in the 16th century.

A large number of theoretical works on biology were also written in the 14th and 15th centuries, mainly in the form of commentaries on various books by Aristotle, Galen, Averroës or Avicenna. In the 13th century Giles of Rome (*c.* 1247–1316) had written a treatise on embryology, *De Formatione Corporis Humani in Utero*, based largely on Averroës, in which he discussed the development of the fœtus and the time at which the soul entered. On this last point there was much controversy and among those to discuss it was Dante, who put forward the view of St. Augustine and of Averroës that the soul was generated together with the body, but manifested itself only with the first movement of the fœtus. Another 14th century writer, the Italian doctor Dino del Garbo (d. 1327), ascribed the birth and development of plants and animals from seeds to a kind of fermentation and tried to prove that the seeds of hereditary diseases lay in the heart. His compatriot, Gentile da Foligno, tried to work out the mathematical relation between the times of formation and movement of the fœtus and birth of the infant. Another subject that attracted the attention of scholastic writers of the 14th century was the origin and nature of the movement of animals, and writers like Walter Burley, Jean de Jandun and Jean Buridan discussed this question in commentaries on Aristotle's *De Motu Animalium*. Other parts of Aristotle's *De Animalibus* were commented on by writers from the early 14th-century John Didneshale in England to the mid-15th-century Agostino Nifo in Padua. Another long series of treatises, beginning with that of Alfred of Sareschel, was written under the title *De Motu Cordis*. The problem whether, in generation, seed was contributed by both sexes was also argued out by theoretical writers, particularly with the popularity in the 15th century of Lucretius, who had upheld the double seed theory. This discussion went on into the 17th and 18th centuries in the dispute between the animalculists and ovists. At the end of the 15th century Leonardo da Vinci tried to bring some of these theoretical questions within reach of experiment, but it was not until the 19th century that experimental embryology got properly under way.

The branch of biology in which the most interesting developments took place in the 14th and 15th centuries was neither botany, zoology nor embryology but human anatomy. The chief motive for the study of anatomy was its practical value for the surgeon and physician (see below, pp. 206 *et seq.*, 371 *et seq.*) and the chief sources of anatomical knowledge were Galen (129–200 A.D.) and Avicenna, the anatomical sections of whose *Canon of Medicine* were themselves based largely on Galen. Certain alternative ideas about anatomy were also known from Aristotle, as seen, for example, in the early 13th-century *Anatomia Vivorum* of Roger of Wendover, which was used by Albertus Magnus. By the end of the 13th century the preference was most commonly given to the usually more accurate Galen.

Galen's anatomical ideas, based on dissections of human and animal bodies, were intimately connected with a system of physiology. According to Galen, the brain (and not the heart as Aristotle had said) was the centre of the nervous system, and the vital functions were explained by means of the three spirits (*spiritus* or pneuma) and the four Hippocratic humours, corresponding to the four

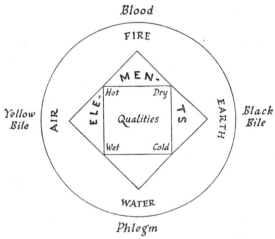

FIG. 19. The four humours.

elements (Fig. 19). The balance of these four humours—blood, phlegm (or *pituita*, found in the pituitary body), black bile (or *melancholia*, found in the spleen) and yellow bile (or *chole*, found in the gall bladder)—was necessary for the healthy functioning of the body, but the vital functions themselves were brought about by the production and movements of the three spirits (Fig. 20). The principle of life in Galen's physiology, which he partly derived from the 3rd-century B.C. Erasistratus, was the *spiritus* or pneuma drawn in by the act of respiration. It entered the body through the trachea and passed to the lung and thence,

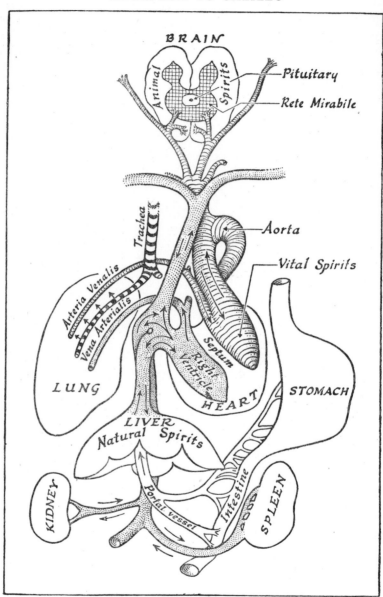

FIG. 20. Galen's system of physiology.

through the vein-like artery (*i.e.*, pulmonary vein), to the left ventricle of the heart, where it encountered the blood. The blood was manufactured in the liver from the chyle formed, during digestion, by the 'transformative power' of the stomach. The useless parts of the food were absorbed by the spleen and converted into black bile, which was excreted through the bowel. The chyle itself was carried in the portal vein from the alimentary canal to the liver, where it was elaborated into venous blood and imbued with a pneuma innate in all living substances, 'natural spirit', the principle of growth. This was the 'first concoction'.

Galen maintained that the liver was the centre of the venous system, though Aristotle had correctly held the veins to be related to the heart. From the liver Galen said that the blood, charged with natural spirit and nutriment, was distributed all over the body, ebbing and flowing in the veins. One great vein passed to the right side of the heart. This organ, Galen held, was not a muscle, for, unlike somatic muscle it was never static and could not be moved at will. It was the centre of innate heat produced by slow combustion, its temperature being controlled by the lungs during respiration. He held also that the heart had only two chambers, the auricles being simply dilations of the great veins.

The main action of the heart, according to Galen, was its expansion during diastole, when blood was drawn into it (*cf.* below, pp. 330 *et seq.*). The blood entering the right side of the heart had two possible fates. The bulk of it, after the 'soot' of combustion had been removed in the right ventricle and carried in the artery-like vein (*i.e.*, pulmonary artery) to the lungs and exhaled, ebbed back into the general venous system. Some blood, however, trickled through minute pores in the inter-ventricular septum and entered the left ventricle. There it encountered the pneuma brought from the lungs by the vein-like artery and, in the 'second concoction', became elaborated into 'vital spirit', the principle of movement and muscular activity. Vital spirit was distributed throughout the body in the arteries with the arterial blood, which expanded under the influence of innate heat and caused the dilation of the heart (diastole) and, when it reached the peripheræ of the body, the pulse. Some of the arteries went to the head, where, in the *rete mirabile*[1] at the base of the brain, the blood was finely divided and in the 'third concoction' was charged with a third pneuma, 'animal spirit'. This animal spirit was contained in the ventricles of the brain and distributed by the nerves, which were supposed to be hollow, and was the basis of all nervous function.

The three principal organs of the body were thus the liver, the centre of the venous system and of the vegetative or nutritive faculty; the heart, the origin of vital heat and the centre of the arterial system and the animal faculty (power of movement); and the brain, the centre of the nervous system and the psychic faculty. The animal spirit was the liaison between the immaterial soul and the material body.

Like the Alexandrian physiologists and anatomists going back to Herophilus and Erasistratus in the 3rd century B.C., in whose teaching he had been brought up, Galen had been a good observer. He studied the anatomy of bones and muscles, though in the latter, like Vesalius later, he sometimes drew conclusions about man from the dissection of such animals as the Barbary ape. He seems, in fact, to have worked largely with animals. He distinguished between sensory ('soft') nerves entering the spinal cord from the body and motor ('hard') nerves going out from the spinal cord. He recognised many of the cranial nerves and made experiments on the spinal cord, showing that sectioning between different vertebræ of living animals had different effects: instantaneous death when the cut was made between first and second vertebræ and arrest of respiration, paralysis of the thoracic muscles, and paralysis of the lower limbs, bladder and intestines when made at different points further down. He also had a fairly good idea of the general course

(1) A structure at the base of the brain which is well developed in some animals, for instance, the calf, but not in man.

of the veins and arteries, on the functions of which he made experiments. Erasistratus had thought that the latter contained only air, but Galen showed that when a length of artery was ligatured at both ends and punctured, blood came out of it. Thus, if his mistakes, such as his theory of the movements of blood, misled anatomists and physiologists until the 16th or 17th century, it was by his experimental method, with which he investigated problems ranging from the production of the voice by the larynx and the functioning of the kidney to the medicinal properties of herbs, that men learnt to correct them.

The medieval scholars who first read Galen's works were able to add little that was original, but, from the 12th-century, it was recognised, as it was put in the Salernitan *Anatomia Ricardi Anglici*, that 'a knowledge of anatomy is necessary to physicians, in order that they may understand how the human body is constructed to perform different movements and operations'. The great 13th- and 14th-century surgeons insisted that some practical knowledge of anatomy was essential to their craft, Henry of Mondeville (d. 1320), for example, declaring that the mind must inform the hand in its operation and the hand in its turn instruct the mind to interpret the general proposition by the particular instance. In 12th-century Salerno the dissection of animal and human bodies seems to have been a part of medical training; the earliest Western work on anatomy is the early 12th-century *Anatomia Porci* attributed to a certain Copho of Salerno, which described the public dissection of a pig. This work was followed during the 12th century by four others from Salerno, the fourth of which, the *Anatomia Ricardi*, was the first to describe human anatomy. This was based largely on literary sources and contained descriptions of the eye, motor and sensory nerves, fœtal membranes and other structures similar to those given by Aristotle and Galen.

In the 13th century, the practice of dissection was continued at Bologna, where the first evidence of human dissection is found in the *Chirurgia* of the surgeon William of Saliceto, completed in 1275. This work was the first Western topo-graphical anatomy and, though based largely on earlier Latin sources, it contained the observations of a practical surgeon such as on the thoracic organs of a man wounded in the chest and on the veins in joints and in the lower abdomen as seen in cases of hernia. Another Italian surgeon, Lanfranchi (d. before 1306), who worked in Paris, gave anatomical details associated with wounds in many different parts of the body. Further opportunities for human dissection were given at Bologna by the practice of making *post mortem* examinations to determine the cause of death for legal pur-poses. This practice was mentioned at the end of the 13th century by Taddeo Alderotti (d. 1303), who also attended dissections of animals, and the first formal account of a *post mortem* examination was given by Bartolommeo da Varignana in 1302. A manuscript of about the same date in the Bodleian Library at Oxford has an illustration of a dissection scene and, later in the 14th century, many *post mortem* dissections were made during the Black Death.

The man who 'restored' anatomy by introducing the regular practice of public dissections of corpses for teaching purposes was Mondino of Luzzi (*c.* 1275–1326), who was a pupil of Alderotti and became professor at Bologna. Mondino's *Anatomia*, completed in 1316, was the most popular text-book of anatomy before that of Vesalius in the 16th century and it exists in a large number of manuscripts and printed editions. Mondino himself dissected male and female human corpses and also, on one occasion, a pregnant sow. His book was the first work specifically devoted to anatomy and not merely an appendage to a work on surgery. It was, in fact, a practical manual of dissection in which the organs were described as they were to be opened: first those of the abdomen, then of the thorax and of the head, and finally the bones, spinal column and extremities. This arrangement was imposed by the need, in the absence of good preservatives, to dissect the most perishable parts first and to complete the dissection within a few days.

Mondino also used preparations dried in the sun to show the general structure of tendons and ligaments and macerated bodies to trace the nerves to their extremities. A good account of the general procedure is given by Guy de Chauliac in his *Chirurgia Magna* completed in 1360.

In spite of his personal observations Mondino's *Anatomia* was very largely based on Galen, the 7th-century Byzantine writer, Theophilus, and on Arabic authorities. The influence of the last can be seen in his Latinised Arabic terminology. Among the non-Arabic terms which he used two have survived to the present day, namely, matrix and mesentery. Mondino did not, in fact, dissect to make discoveries but, like a modern medical student, to gain some practical acquaintance with the teaching of the text-book authority. In his own manual he preserved both the mistakes and the correct observations of his authorities. He believed the stomach to be spherical, the liver five-lobed, the uterus seven-chambered, and the heart to have a middle ventricle in the septum. Yet he gave a good description of the muscles of the abdomen and may have been the first to describe the pancreatic duct. In at least one of his ideas, his attempt to establish the correspondence between the male and female generative organs, he was to be followed by Vesalius. Of particular interest are certain of his physiological ideas. He held that the production of urine was due to the filtering of the blood by the kidneys and attributed to the brain the old Aristotelian function of cooling the heart. In addition to this, the brain acted as the centre of the nervous system, and he held that its psychological functions were localised in three ventricles, as follows: the anterior ventricle, which was double, was the seat of the *sensus communis* or 'common sense' which, according to contemporary psychology, represented man's ability to make comparisons between different senses; the middle ventricle was the seat of the imagination; the posterior, of memory. Mental operations were controlled by the movement of the 'red worm' (that is the *choroid plexus* of the third cerebral ventricle), which opened and closed the passages between the ventricles and directed the flow of the animal spirits (Fig. 43, p. 339).

After Mondino's time anatomical teaching, with public dissections of human bodies and even research, was carried on at Bologna and elsewhere in northern Italy by a series of distinguished physicians, Guido da Vigevano, Niccolò

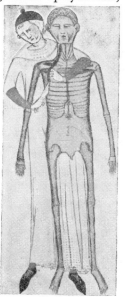

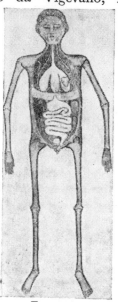

FIG. 21A.   FIG. 21B.

Two illustrations from Guido da Vigevano's *Anatomia*, showing, respectively, a surgeon beginning a dissection, and the thoracic and abdominal viscera. From MS. Chantilly 569 (XIV cent.).

Bertruccio, Alberto de' Zancari, Pietro Torrigiano and Gentile da Foligno. Guido da Vigevano, who worked both at Pavia and in France, wrote a treatise in 1345 which was based partly on Mondino and other authorities and partly on his own dissections. It is of interest for its excellent illustrations, which show a considerable advance in the technique of dissection over that of the early 14th century (Figs. 21A and B). One notable feature is that the corpse was slung from a gibbet, as later in many of Vesalius's illustrations.

Of the other Paduan physicians, Gentile da Foligno is of particular interest for being possibly the first to describe gallstones and Niccolò Bertruccio for his description of the brain. In 14th-century France, Henry of Mondeville, a fellow student of Mondino at Bologna, had already, by 1308, made systematic dissections and used charts and a model of the skull for teaching at Montpellier. In the anatomical section of his medical compendium he gave a good account of the system of the portal vein. Mondeville's definition of nerves includes tendons and ligaments, and it is of interest that another famous Montpellier teacher, Bernard of Gordon (d. *c.* 1320), seems to have suggested that nerves exerted a mechanical pull on the muscles. Bernard followed Greek authorities in believing that epilepsy was caused by the humours blocking the passages of the brain and interfering with the supply of air to the limbs. Guy de Chauliac, who had studied at Bologna under Bertruccio, carried on the teaching by public dissections at Montpellier, and one manuscript of his surgical treatise contains some excellent illustrations showing dissections in progress. In the 15th century public dissections began in other centres, in Vienna in 1405 and in Paris in 1407. There are further anatomical illustrations in a manuscript of about 1420 of a treatise by the English physician John Arderne and in a German manuscript, written between 1452 and 1465, of the *Chirurgia* of the 13th-century Paduan physician, Bruno of Longoburgo. In the mid-15th century for about fifty years there seems to have been a decrease of interest in anatomy, possibly because of an over-concentration on purely practical and immediate surgical requirements and possibly because of the custom, prevalent in the northern universities where surgery was held in low esteem and anatomy was taught by professors of medicine, of the anatomical teachers leaving dissection to a menial while a demonstrator pointed out the parts, instead of the anatomist doing the dissection himself (see below, pp. 206–9). This slackening of progress did not last long, for already by the end of the 15th century Leonardo da Vinci had begun to make his brilliant anatomical drawings based on his own dissections and, early in the 16th century, Achillini made some fresh discoveries. By 1543, when Vesalius published his great work, the progress of anatomical research was already well under way (see below, pp. 368, 371–3).

The position of man in the 13th-century universe was a special one: he was both the purpose and the final product of the material creation, and the centre of the complete scale of creatures. Man, 'who by reason of his nobleness falls under a special science called medicine', stood at the apex of the scale of material beings and at the base of the scale of spiritual beings: his body was the product of generation and fated to suffer corruption in the former realm; his soul was received at conception, or, according to some authorities, at some later period of gestation, direct from God who created it and destined it for eternal life. Thus man occupied a central position between two orders of being, the purely material order of the other animals, descending through plants to inanimate things, and the purely spiritual order of the angels, ascending to God.

One effect of this view of the special position of man in the universe was to emphasise the sacramental aspect of his scientific activities, to show that he, before all other creatures, was in a position to worship the Creator of this great chain of being stretching above and below him, in which each thing existed to fulfil its own nature in its special place and all to praise the Lord. The sentiment that was to inspire much of 13th-century science had, in fact, been expressed at the beginning of the century by the founder of an order which was to give so many great innovators to Western scientific thought, particularly in England.

'Be Thou praised, O Lord,' St. Francis of Assisi began his *Cantico del Sole*, 'for all Thy creatures, especially for our brother the sun, who brings the day and with it gives light. For he is glorious and splendid in his radiance and, Most High, signifies Thee.'

This was certainly the sentiment of Grosseteste, Roger Bacon and Pecham in Oxford; and in Paris, Germany and Italy also, and among the other great order of friars to whom 13th-century science owes its chief progress, the belief was certainly not wanting that *amor intellectualis dei* included the study of nature, of the immense revolving spheres of the heavens and of the smallest living creature, of the laws of astronomy, optics and mechanics, of the laws of biological reproduction and of chemical change. The feeling expressed by Vincent of Beauvais in his *Speculum Majus*, prologue, chapter 6, might equally well have come from the pen of Albertus Magnus or many another 13th-century scientific writer:

I am moved with spiritual sweetness towards the Creator and Ruler of this World, because I follow Him with greater veneration and reverence, when I behold the magnitude and beauty and permanence of His creation.

Another effect of the idea of man's nature held in 13th-century Christendom has already been touched upon, namely, the effect of the idea that man is rational and free-willed in leading to the rejection of Greek and Arabic determinism, and this was to be even more important in the sequel. Few people at the end of the 13th century apart from the Averroïsts, believed that Aristotle had said the last word on philosophy and natural science and, though all would have admitted that he had provided them with the framework of their system of scientific thought, the theologians were careful to preserve both man and God from constraint within any particular system. The free speculation which resulted led to radical criticisms of many of the fundamental principles accepted in the 13th century, even of propositions whose acceptance then seemed necessary to the Christian religion itself (though most of these lay outside natural science); even, indeed, though radical views led to an occasional brush with ecclesiastical authority. Within natural science perhaps the most fundamental advance made as a result of these criticisms was in scientific method and the conception of scientific explanation and this, together with the development of technology, formed the double track that led across the watershed of the 14th century and with many turns to the 16th- and 17th-century world.

IV

TECHNICS AND SCIENCE IN THE
MIDDLE AGES

(1) TECHNICS AND EDUCATION

IT HAS OFTEN BEEN POINTED out that science develops
best when the speculative reasoning of the philosopher and
mathematician is in closest touch with the manual skill of the
craftsman. It has been said also that the absence of this
association in the Greco-Roman world and in medieval
Christendom was one reason for the supposed backwardness
of science in those societies. The practical arts were certainly despised by the majority of the most highly educated
people in Classical Antiquity, and were held to be the work
of slaves. In view of such works as the long series of Greek
medical writings, stretching from the first members of the
so-called Hippocratic corpus to the works of Galen, the
military devices and the 'screw' attributed to Archimedes,
the treatises on building, engineering and other branches of
applied mechanics written during Hellenistic and Roman
times by Ctesibius of Alexandria, Athenæus, Apollodorus,
Hero of Alexandria, Vitruvius, Frontinus and Pappus of
Alexandria, and the works on agriculture by the elder
Cato, Varro and Columella, it may be doubted whether
even in Classical Antiquity the separation of technics and
science was as complete as has been sometimes supposed. In
the Middle Ages there is much evidence to show that these
two activities were at no period totally divorced and that
their association became more intimate as time went on. This
active, practical interest of educated people may be one
reason why the Middle Ages was a period of technical innovation, though most of the advances were probably made by

unlettered craftsmen. And certainly it was this interest of many theoretical scientists in practical results that encouraged them to ask concrete and precise questions, to try to get answers by experiment and, with the aid of technics, to develop more accurate measuring instruments and special apparatus.

From the Dark Ages, Western scholars showed an interest in getting certain kinds of results for which some technical knowledge was necessary. Medicine was studied in the earliest Benedictine monasteries, and the long series of medical works, written during the Middle Ages, and continuing without a break into the 16th century and modern times, is one of the best examples of a tradition in which empirical observations were increasingly combined with attempts at rational and theoretical explanation, with the result that definite medical and surgical problems were solved. Another long series of treatises was written on astronomy by scholars from the time of Bede in the 7th century for purely practical purposes such as determining the date of Easter, fixing latitude and showing how to determine true North and tell the time with an astrolabe. Even a poet such as Chaucer could write an excellent practical treatise on the astrolabe. Another series of practical treatises is that on the preparation of pigments and other chemical substances, which includes the 8th-century *Compositiones ad Tigenda* and *Mappæ Clavicula*, of which Adelard of Bath later produced an edition, the early 12th-century *Diversarum Artium Schedula* of Theophilus the Priest, who lived probably in Germany, the late 13th-century *Liber de Coloribus Faciendis* by Peter of Saint Omer, and the early 15th-century treatises of Cennino Cennini and John Alcherius. Technical treatises were among the first to be translated out of Arabic and Greek into Latin and this was the work of educated men. It was, in fact, chiefly for their practical knowledge that Western scholars, from the time of Gerbert at the end of the 10th century, first began to take an interest in Arab learning. The 13th-century encyclopædias of Alexander Nequam, Albertus Magnus and Roger Bacon contained a great deal of accurate information about the compass, chemistry, the calendar, agriculture and other technical matters. Other contemporary writers composed special treatises on these subjects: Grosseteste and later writers on the calendar; Giles of Rome in *De Regimine Principum* on the art of war; Walter of Henley and Peter of Crescenzi on agriculture; Peregrinus, in the second part of *De Magnete*, on the determination of azimuths. It took a scholar to write about arithmetic, yet most of the advances that followed Fibonacci's treatise on the Hindu numerals were made in the interests of commerce.

In the 14th century, the Italian Dominican friar, Giovanni da San Gimignano (d. 1323), wrote an encyclopædia for preachers in which he gave for use as examples in sermons descriptions of numerous technical subjects: agriculture, fishing, cultivation of herbs, windmills and watermills, ships, painting and limning, fortifications, arms, Greek fire, smithing, glass-making and weights and measures. The names of two other Dominicans, Alessandro della Spina (d. 1313), and Salvino degl' Armati (d. 1317), are associated with the invention of spectacles. In the 15th century, a most interesting series of treatises was written on military technology. Beginning with Konrad Kyeser's *Bellifortis*, written between 1396 and 1405, this included a treatise by Giovanni de' Fontana (*c.* 1410–20), the *Feuerwerksbuch* (*c.* 1422), a treatise by an anonymous engineer in the Hussite wars (*c.* 1430), the so-called 'Mittelalterliches Hausbuch' (*c.* 1480). The series went on in the 16th century with the treatises of Biringuccio and Tartaglia. These contained descriptions of how to make guns and gunpowder as well as problems of military engineering, which were discussed also by other contemporary writers such as Alberti and Leonardo da Vinci. Some of these treatises dealt also with general technical matters such as the construction of ships, dams and spinning-wheels. The series of practical chemical treatises which, in the earlier Middle Ages, had consisted mainly of recipes for pigments, continued in the 14th and 15th

L

centuries with accounts of distillation and other practical techniques and went on in the 16th century with Hieronymus Brunschwig's books on distillation, the metallurgical *Probierbüchlein* and Agricola's *De Re Metallica* (see above, p. 97 *et seq.*; below, pp. 187 *et seq.*). Examples of the interest shown by medieval scholars in technics could, in fact, be multiplied almost indefinitely. They show not only that they had an abstract desire for power over nature such as Roger Bacon had expressed, but also that they were capable of getting the kind of knowledge that would lead to results useful in practice.

One reason for this interest of the learned in technics is to be found in the education they received. The popular handbook on the sciences by Hugh of St. Victor (d. 1141), *Didascalicon de Studio Legendi*, shows that by the 12th century the seven liberal arts had been extended and specialised so as to include various kinds of technical knowledge. The mathematical subjects forming the *quadrivium* had, of course, had a practical object at least since the time of Bede, but from the early 12th century there was a tendency to increasing specialisation. In the *Didascalicon* Hugh of St. Victor followed a modified version of the classification of science in the tradition coming from Aristotle and Boethius; he divided knowledge in general into theory, practice, mechanics and logic. Giving a pseudo-historical account of the origin of the sciences, he said that they arose first in response to human needs as a set of customary practices which were later reduced to formal rules. These practices began by man imitating Nature: for example, he made his own clothes in imitation of the bark with which Nature covered trees or the shell with which she covered shellfish. Each of the 'mechanical' arts, forming the 'adulterine' science of mechanics which provided for those things necessary because of the weakness of the human body, arose in this way. In mechanics Hugh included seven sciences: the manufacture of cloth and of arms, and navigation, which ministered to the extrinsic needs of the body; and agriculture, hunting,

146

medicine and the science of theatrical performances, which ministered to intrinsic needs. He gave a brief description of each of these activities.

Later in the 12th century another popular classification of the sciences was written by Dominicus Gundissalinus, his *De Divisione Philosophiæ*. This was based partly on Arab sources, in particular on Alfarabi, whereas Hugh had used only the traditional Latin sources. Gundissalinus, following another form of the Aristotelian tradition, classified the sciences into theoretical and practical. He subdivided the former into physics, mathematics and metaphysics and the latter into politics, or the art of civil government, the art of family government, which included giving instruction in the liberal and mechanical arts, and ethics or the art of self-government. The 'fabrile' or 'mechanical' arts were those concerned with making out of matter something useful to man and the matter used could come either from living things, for example, wood, wool, linen or bones, or from dead things, for example, gold, silver, lead, iron, marble or precious stones. Through the mechanical arts resources were acquired which provided for the needs of the family. To each of the mechanical arts there corresponded a theoretical science which studied the basic principles which the mechanical art put into practice. Thus theoretical arithmetic studied the basic principles of numbers used in reckoning by the abacus, as in commerce; theoretical music studied in the abstract the harmonies produced by voices and instruments; theoretical geometry considered the basic principles put into practice in measuring bodies, in surveying, and in using the results of observing the motions of the heavenly bodies with the astrolabe and other astronomical instruments; the science of weights considered the basic principles of the balance and lever. Finally, the science of 'mathematical devices' turned the results of all the other mathematical sciences to useful purposes, for stone-masonry, for instruments for measuring and lifting bodies, for musical and optical instruments and for carpentry.

In the 13th century, these ideas were taken up by a number of well-known writers, for example, Roger Bacon, Thomas Aquinas and Giles of Rome. The treatises of Michael Scot and Robert Kilwardby are of special interest. Michael Scot held that each of the practical sciences was related to a theoretical science and was the practical manifestation of the corresponding theoretical science. Thus to different branches of theoretical 'physics' there corresponded such practical sciences as medicine, agriculture, alchemy, the study of mirrors and navigation; to the different branches of theoretical mathematics there corresponded such practical arts as business concerned with money, carpentry, smithing and stone-masonry, weaving, shoemaking. Robert Kilwardby's treatise, *De Ortu Scientiarum*, very widely read for generations, expressed the same conviction of the importance of the practical side of science concerned with getting useful results. Of special significance is Kilwardby's pseudo-historical account of the theoretical sciences as arising out of particular, concrete problems encountered in attempting to satisfy the physical needs of the body as, for example, his version of the ancient Greek tradition that geometry arose first as a practical art among the Egyptians because they had to survey the land after the flooding of the Nile, and was transformed into a theoretical and demonstrative science by Pythagoras. Among the 'mechanical' sciences he included agriculture, viticulture, medicine, cloth-making, armouring, architecture and commerce. Roger Bacon gave elaborate descriptions of various practical sciences, asserted emphatically that the justification of the theoretical sciences was their useful results, and stressed the need to include the study of the practices of artisans and of practical alchemists in any scheme of education.

Though it was only in guilds of artisans that any sort of practical training in the mechanical arts was received, the utilitarian aims of medieval writers on education were reflected, often to a surprising extent, in the courses that might be taken at a university. This was the case, for example, in the 12th-century medical school at Salerno, where the regulations of King Roger II of Sicily and the Emperor Frederick II required that the medical student should take a course lasting five years and including human anatomy and surgery. After passing an examination at the end of this course he was not allowed to practise until he had spent a further year learning from a trained practitioner. From the end of the 13th century, attendance at an 'anatomy' at least once a year was prescribed for medical students at Bologna, and in the 14th century the medical school in the university devoted itself increasingly to surgery. Some practical instruction in anatomy seems, in fact, to have been required in most medical schools from the end of the 13th century (see above, pp. 130 *et seq.*; below, pp. 206 *et seq.*).

In the 'arts' courses in most universities the mathematical subjects very often had some practical object in view. In 12th-century Chartres a list of books recommended for study by Thierry of Chartres included a high proportion of works on surveying, measurement and practical astronomy; a list of text-books in use at Paris at the end of the 12th century shows that the same utilitarian tradition was continued there. At the beginning of the 13th century the arts course at Paris took six years, a Licence in Arts not being granted before the age of 20, though at Paris and most other universities the six years were later reduced, sometimes to as little as four. The course usually consisted of a study of the seven liberal arts followed by the 'three philosophies', natural philosophy (that is, natural science), ethics and metaphysics. At Paris during the 13th century there was a tendency to reduce the time spent on mathematical subjects in favour of the other arts subjects such as metaphysics; at Oxford a considerable emphasis was placed on the mathematical subjects, the text-books prescribed including, for example, not only Boethius's *Arithmetic* and Euclid's *Elements*, but also Alhazen's *Optica*, Witelo's *Perspectiva* and Ptolemy's *Almagesta*. The arts course at Oxford is also of interest for including the study of Aristotle's *De Animalibus* as well as the more usual *Physica, Meteorologica, De Cælo* and other works on 'natural philosophy'. A similar emphasis on mathematics is seen in the arts course at Bologna, where the subjects prescribed included a book on arithmetic known as *Algorismi de Minutis et Integris*, Euclid, Ptolemy, the *Alphonsine Tables*, a book of rules by Jean de Linières for using astronomical tables to determine the motions of the heavenly bodies, and a work on the use of the quadrant. Some of the German universities seem also seriously to have cultivated the study of arithmetic, algebra, astronomy, optics, music and other mathematical sciences. It seems unlikely that any actual practical or laboratory instruction was included in the arts course at any medieval university, but there is evidence that special courses in astronomy were given at Oxford in the 14th century. Chaucer wrote his treatise on the astrolabe to explain to his son how to use the instrument which he sent him when he went up to Oxford. Certainly the Fellows of Merton College made astronomical observations and in at least one case, that of Richard of Wallingford and his planetarium, a scholar is known actually to have made his own instruments.

An important result of this mathematical training received in medieval education was that it encouraged the habit of expressing physical events in terms of abstract units and emphasised the need for the standardisation of systems of measurement. Without this habit of thought mathematical physics would be impossible. Lewis Mumford has vividly described how it developed first in connection with the purely practical regulation of affairs. The need to measure time for the orderly institutions of the Church and the routine of the monastery led to the sustained medieval interest in the calendar and to the division of the day into the unequal canonical hours, while the secular requirements of government and commerce led to the prevalence in civil life of the system of 24 equal hours in the day. The invention at the end of the 13th century of the mechanical clock, in which the hands translated time into units of space on the dial, completed the replacement of 'organic', growing, irreversible time as experienced by the abstract mathematical time of units on a scale, belonging to the world of science. Space also underwent abstraction during the later Middle Ages. The symbolic arrangement of subjects in paintings according to their importance in the Christian hierarchy gave way from the middle of the 14th century in Italy to the division of the canvas into an abstract checkerboard according to the rules of perspective. Besides the symbolic maps, like the Hereford *Mappa Mundi* of 1314, there appeared maps by cartographers in which the traveller or mariner could find his position on an abstract system of co-ordinates of latitude and longitude. Commerce changed during the Middle Ages from a barter economy based on goods and services to a money economy based on abstract units, first of gold or silver coinage and, later, also of letters of credit and bills of exchange. The problems arising from the dissolution of partnerships (some discussed in Italy as early as the 12th century) and in connection with interest, discount and exchange were one of the chief incentives to mathematical research. Problems of currency reform became the subject of treatises by academic mathematicians like Nicole Oresme in the 14th century and Copernicus two centuries later. This process of abstraction concentrated attention on the systems of units used. Attempts were made from as early as Anglo-Saxon times in England to standardise weights and measures and later (in legislation during the reign of Richard I) to replace units based on the human body like the foot and span by standard measures made of iron. Attempts were made also to establish the relationship between the different systems existing in different countries and even within the same country. A series of treatises was written by doctors interested in standardising units of weight and volume for drugs.

One of the most interesting examples of a mathematical art developing an abstract language of its own in order to communicate knowledge of how to produce a precise practical effect is music. In the Middle Ages the theory of music was studied as part of the *quadrivium*, chants were sung and instruments played in church, secular music is known from about 1100, and some universities like 14th-century Salamanca and 15th-century Oxford even gave degrees in music: so for several centuries men of learning were closely acquainted with both the theoretical and practical aspects of the art. The basis of medieval music was the Greek system of modes, of which the major scale of C is the only one that sounds familiar in the 20th century. Greek music consisted entirely of melody. Though the Greeks used choirs of men's and boys' voices singing at intervals of an octave, a practice known as 'megadizing', and also harps with which they played in simultaneous octaves, this hardly amounted to harmony, of which they had no real conception. To write down a melodic line the Greeks had used letters to indicate the rise and fall of pitch and by the 7th century A.D., in Church music, this was done by strokes over the words, which themselves controlled rhythm. From these developed the system of 'neumes' written on a staff of parallel horizontal lines to indicate pitch, as in the *Micrologus de Disciplina Artis Musicæ*, written about 1030 by Guido d'Arezzo, who is of interest also as the originator of the system of designating the notes of the scale by the first syllables of six lines of a hymn to St. John the Baptist: *ut, re, mi, fa, so, la.*

Early medieval Church music was all plainchant, in which the notes had fluid time-values; mensural or measured music in which the durations of the notes had an exact ratio among themselves seems to have been invented in Islam. A number of Arabic writers, of whom Alfarabi was one of the most distinguished, wrote on mensural music and, during the 11th and 12th centuries, knowledge of mensural music entered Christendom through Spain and through the translations of Arabic musical works by Christian scholars like Adelard of Bath and Gundissalinus. In the 12th century appeared in Christendom the system of notation in which the exact time-value of each note was indicated by black lozenges and diamonds on little poles, as explained in a treatise by John of Garland, who studied at Oxford early in the 13th century, and more fully in the *Ars Cantus Mensurabilis* attributed to Franco of Cologne, living during the second half of the 13th century. Hooks were attached to the black diamonds to serve the purpose of the modern crotchet, white notes were added and, eventually, the so-called Franconian notation was developed into the modern system, completed with bar-lines about 1600 and key-signatures about 1700. The new system of mensural notation made it possible to have firmly defined rhythms, to sing and, with the introduction of special notations for instruments, to play two different rhythms concurrently. With the last came also the beginning of the realisation of the full potentialities of harmony.

Harmony began in the West with the practice of singing concurrently the same tune at two different pitches, usually in fourths or fifths. This system had been developed in Christendom by about 900 A.D. and was known as the *organum* or 'diaphony'. It is possible that something similar had been developed independently in Islam where, for example, the 10th-century Alfarabi recognised the major third and the minor third as concords. In the 10th century several Latin treatises were written on the *organum*, one of the best-known being written in the Low Countries by a certain Hucbald. About 1100 the Englishman, John Cotton, and the author, probably French, of the anonymous treatise, *Ad Organum Faciendum*, explained a new *organum*, in which the voices periodically changed from singing the same melody at different pitches to singing different melodies in such a way as to produce a carefully varied set of accepted concords. By the end of the 12th century the descant had appeared, then both parts began to be moved in counterpoint. About a century later the 'new art' had developed enough to see the appearance of the well-known English six-part round, 'Sumer is icumen in', one of the earliest canons. By the mid-14th century quite complicated polyphony had been developed, as seen in the *Mass* for four voices composed by Guillaume de Machaut for the coronation of Charles V at Reims in 1364. Polyphony was elaborated still further by composers like John Dunstable and Josquin des Prés in the 15th century and Palestrina in the 16th. Besides developing vocal music these late medieval composers began to realise the possibilities of instruments. Pipes, trumpets, and plucked stringed instruments were known from early times and the organ, which had been known to the Greeks,

FIG. 22. Playing a stringed instrument with a bow. From British Museum MS. Additional 11695 (XII cent.).

reappeared in the West in the 9th century, when it seems to have been tuned in the modern major scale with the keys named after the letters of the alphabet. About the same date the introduction of the bow made it possible to produce a sustained note on a stringed instrument (Fig. 22), and in the 14th century stringed instruments began to be played with a fixed keyboard.

Throughout all these developments the musical theorist and composer worked closely together and musicians were often distinguished in other branches of science. Typical results of this close contact between theorist and practitioner are the writings of the early-14th-century English mathematician and astronomer, Walter of Odington, who illustrated his important theoretical treatise on music with examples from his own compositions. The contemporary mathematician, Jean de Murs, tried to order the mensural system according to a single rule relating the lengths of successive notes in the system, and experimented with new instruments foreshadowing the clavicord. The most outstanding 14th-century musical theorist was Philippe de Vitri (1291–1361), who made contributions to the methods and notation for establishing the relations between notes of varying length then recognised (*maxima* or *duplex longa, longa, brevis, semibrevis, minima* and *semiminima*), and to such notions as augmentation and diminution. Most of Philippe de Vitri's own compositions are now lost, but Guillaume de Machaut's *Mass* contains practical illustrations of many of his theoretical innovations. It was through this combination of theory and practice in the later Middle Ages that modern rhythmic and harmonic music realised the possibilities of the *organum* and the *Ars Cantus Mensurabilis*, and developed into an art which can be said to characterise the modern civilisation of the West as much as the natural science developing at the same time.

*   *   *   *

Most of the fundamental techniques on which both classical and medieval economic life were based had been invented in prehistoric times. Prehistoric man discovered the use of fire, tools and agriculture, bred, domesticated, and harnessed animals, invented the plough, pottery, spinning and weaving and the use of organic and inorganic pigments, worked metals, made ships and wheeled carts, invented the arch in building, devised such machines as the windlass, pulley, lever, rotary quern, bow-drill and lathe, invented numbers and laid the empirical foundations of astronomy and of medicine.

To this basic practical knowledge some important additions were made in the Greco-Roman world. Though the chief contribution of classical civilisation to science was not in technics but in speculative thought, one of the most important contributions ever made to technology was made by the Greeks. This was their attempt to give rational explanations of the machines and other inventions and discoveries of their predecessors, which made it possible to generalise and extend their use. Thus it was the Greeks who first developed the primitive methods of reckoning and measuring into the abstract sciences of arithmetic and geometry, and who first attempted to give rational explanations of the facts observed in astronomy and medicine. By combining observation and theory they greatly extended the practical use of these sciences. Greek writers, from the author or authors of the Aristotelian *Mechanica* and Archimedes down to Hero of Alexandria, attempted to explain the lever and other mechanisms. Hero gave a full account of the five 'simple' machines by which a given weight might be moved by a given force and of some of their combinations: the wheel and axle, lever, pulley, wedge and endless screw. These were held to be the basis of all machinery until the 19th century. The Greeks developed also the elementary principles of hydrostatics. Some Hellenistic and Roman writers were the first to give descriptions of the various kinds of machinery then in practical use. Some of the most important of these were the crossbow, catapults and other ballistic devices, watermills involving the important method of transmitting power through geared wheels and perhaps a windmill, the screw press and trip hammer, syphons, vacuum pumps, force pumps and Archimedes' screw, the bellows organ and water organ, a steam turbine and a puppet theatre driven by falling weights, the water clock and such important measuring instruments as the cyclometer or hodometer, surveying instruments such as the dioptra (a theodolite without telescope described by Hero), and the cross-staff, astrolabe and quadrant which remained the basic astronomical instruments until the invention of the telescope in the 17th century. Most of these devices were, in fact, Greek inventions. In other technical fields as, for example, in medicine and in agriculture (where the Romans seem to have introduced legume rotation), important improvements were introduced in the classical world. But whether they were describing new techniques or simply ones inherited from the less expressive Egyptian, Babylonian and Assyrian civilisations, these Greco-Roman technical writings were to have a very important influence as a source of technical knowledge in both the Mohammedan and the Christian worlds in the Middle Ages. In Western Christendom these classical technical works exerted an influence right down into the 17th century.

In the Dark Ages which followed the collapse of the Roman Empire in the West there was a considerable loss of technical knowledge, though this was compensated to a slight extent by some new techniques introduced by the invading Germanic tribes. From about the 10th century, however, there was a gradual improvement of technical knowledge in Western Christendom. This was brought about partly by learning from the practices and writings (often of classical origin) of the Byzantine and Arabic worlds, and partly by a slow but increasing activity of invention and innovation within Western Christendom itself. The gains thus made during the Middle Ages were never lost, and it is characteristic of medieval Christendom that it put to industrial use technical devices which in classical society had been known but left almost unused or regarded simply as toys. The result was that, as early as 1300, Western Christendom was using many techniques either unknown or undeveloped in the Roman Empire. By the year 1500 the most advanced countries of the West were in most aspects of technics distinctly superior to any earlier society.

(2) AGRICULTURE

The basic occupation throughout the Middle Ages and, in fact, till the end of the 18th century was agriculture, and it was in agriculture that the first medieval improvements on classical techniques were introduced. Roman agriculture as described by Cato and Varro in the 2nd and 1st centuries B.C. had, in certain respects, reached a high level; such crops as vines and olives were intensively cultivated and the increased yields obtained by growing a leguminous crop alternately with a cereal were well understood. With the fall of the Roman Empire agricultural methods at first declined, but from the 9th or 10th century improvement began and has continued steadily into modern times. The first outstanding achievement of the medieval agricultural population was the great business of agricultural colonisation. Rulers of the Dark Ages like Theodoric the Great in Italy, the Lombard kings of the 7th and 8th centuries, Alfred the Great and Charlemagne had as their policy, in the words of Orosius, 'to turn the barbarians to the ploughshare', to lead them 'to hate the sword'. The agricultural colonisation of Europe sketched in the Carolingian period, the eastward felling of the German forests, the work of clearing, draining and cultivation from woody England and the flooded marshes of the Low Countries to the dry hills of Sicily and Christian Spain, which went on under the leadership of Cistercians and Carthusians, feudal rulers and urban communes, had been practically completed by the 14th century. During that time, not only was Europe occupied and civilised, but agricultural productivity increased enormously as a result of improved methods. These maintained a steady increase in population at least until the Black Death in the 14th century and the growth of towns. As a result different regions became specialised for different crops and animals and for the production of wool and silk, hemp, flax and dye-plants and other materials to supply the growing needs of industry.

The first improvements in agriculture were brought about

by the introduction of the heavy Saxon wheeled plough and a new system of crop rotation, both of which had come into operation in north-western Europe by the 9th and 10th centuries. The use of the heavy wheeled plough equipped with coulter, horizontal share and mouldboard (Fig. 23), instead of the light Roman plough, made it possible to culti-

FIG. 23. Saxon ox-plough. From British Museum MS. Julius A. vi (VIII cent.).

vate heavier and richer soils, saved labour by making cross-ploughing superfluous and thus gave rise to the strip system of land division in northern Europe as distinct from the older Mediterranean block system. Because it needed six or eight oxen to draw it, the use of this plough perhaps led to the grouping of the farming population in north-western Europe into villages and the organisation of agriculture on communal lines as seen in the manorial system. At the same time as the heavy plough was coming into use, the system of crop rotation in north-western Europe was improved by having three fields, instead of two, of which one lay fallow. In the two-field system, one half of the land was left fallow while the other half was planted with grain. In the three-field system, one field was fallow, the second was planted with winter grain (wheat or rye), and the third with a spring crop (barley, oats, beans, peas, vetches). A complete rotation thus occurred every three years. The three-field system did not spread south of the Alps and the Loire, apparently because it was only in the north that summers were wet enough to make spring sowing, the chief novelty of this system, profitable. Even in the north the two systems continued side by side till the end of the Middle Ages. The three-field system did distinctly increase productivity and, when combined with the superior plough, it may have been one of the reasons for the shift of the centre of European civilisation to the northern plains in Charlemagne's time. Certainly one of its effects seems to have been to make possible the increasing use of the faster but more extravagant grain-fed horse instead of the hay-fed ox as the plough and draft animal.

Further improvements were introduced in methods of cultivation later in the Middle Ages. The ploughshare was made of iron, and the horse-drawn harrow with iron teeth replaced the older methods of breaking the clods with rakes or mattocks. Methods of draining low-lying land were also improved by the use of pumps and networks of sluices and canals; the lower reaches of the Rhine and the Rhône were confined to their courses by dykes; and along the coasts of the Netherlands large areas were reclaimed from the sea. Sand dunes were arrested by means of osier plantations along the North Sea coast and forests of pines were planted on the dunes of Leiria in Portugal by King Dinis of Lavrador who ruled until 1325. In Spain and Italy hydraulic science was used to construct works for irrigation. The most remarkable of these were the dams and reservoirs of Eastern Spain and the famous Lombard 'Naviglio Grande', built between 1179 and 1258, which carried water from Lake Maggiore over 35,000 hectares to irrigate the lands on the banks of the Oglio, Adda and Po. Under the guidance of enlightened agriculturalists, monastic, royal or urban methods of restoring and enriching the soil were also improved. Thierry d'Hireçon, who managed the estates of Mahout, Countess of Artois and Burgundy, and who died in 1328 as Bishop of Arras, is an outstanding example.

A record of contemporary agricultural theory is found in the writings of Albertus Magnus, with his botanical approach, of Walter of Henley in England and Peter of Crescenzi in

Italy, and of several other writers who attempted to reach rational methods by combining the study of ancient Roman sources and Arabic science with contemporary practice in Christendom. Thus Walter of Henley discussed marling and weeding, and Albertus Magnus discussed manuring. Walter of Henley's *Hosebondrie* (*c.* 1250) remained the standard work on the subject in England until the appearance of Sir Anthony Fitzherbert's *Husbandrie* in 1523. The best of the medieval treatises on agriculture was certainly Crescenzi's *Ruralia Commoda* (*c.* 1306). This was enormously popular on the continent; it was translated into several European languages and it exists in a large number of manuscripts and was printed many times. Crescenzi had studied at Bologna logic, natural science, medicine and finally law. After holding a series of legal and political offices, he settled on his estate near Bologna and wrote his *Ruralia Commoda* late in life. This work was a critical compilation from books and observation, written with the object of giving the intelligent farmer a rational and practical account of all aspects of his occupation, from the biology of plants (taken from Albertus Magnus) to the arrangement of farm buildings and water supply. It treated such subjects as the cultivation of cereals, peas and beans; of vines and their wines, their varieties, their diseases and their remedies; of fruit trees, vegetables, medicinal plants and flowers; the care of woods; the rearing of all kinds of farm animals, large and small; horses and their ailments; and hunting and fishing. Perhaps the most original parts of his treatise are his elaborate discussion of the grafting of vines and trees and his account of the insect larvae which destroy plants. His description of bee-culture shows that Roman methods had not been forgotten.

Of the methods of enriching the soil, the use of animal manures was fully appreciated in the Middle Ages: cattle were turned on to the stubble of arable fields; sheep were folded and the manure collected and spread. Lime, marl, ash, turf and calcareous sand were also used. And though, in most of Western Christendom, extensive cultivation with triennial rotation and fallow persisted, in the Netherlands, northern France and southern Italy it had become common by the 14th century to abandon the fallow year and plant instead root crops and legumes. Apart from the enrichment of exhausted soil, this had the advantage that it made it possible to maintain more animals through the winter; in the earlier Middle Ages most of the stock had to be killed off at the beginning of winter and the meat salted, the plough teams that were kept being fed on hay and straw. Yet in spite of these improvements, the expected yields in most parts of medieval Christendom remained low compared with those in the 20th century. For two bushels of wheat sown per acre in England the yield expected was 10 bushels; and for four bushels of oats sown the yield expected was 12 to 16 bushels. A marked improvement in yield came only with the 'scientific rotation' of the 18th-century agricultural revolution.

In other ways than in methods of cultivating and fertilising the soil medieval agriculture made steady progress. Increasing attention was paid to the cultivation of fruit trees, vegetables and flowers in gardens and new crops were introduced for special purposes: buckwheat or 'Saracen corn', hops, rice and sugarcane were grown for food and drink; oil plants for food and lighting; hemp and flax, teazles, the dye-plants, woad, madder and saffron, and in Sicily and Calabria even cotton and indigo, were grown for textile manufacture. Linen became the source of paper making which spread gradually northward for two centuries after entering southern Europe from the East in the 12th century. By the 13th century mulberries were being cultivated and silkworms raised in industrial quantities in southern Italy and eastern Spain. From the 14th century large tracts of Italy, England and Spain were given over to raising sheep for the wool trade, so that already Prussia, Poland and Hungary were replacing them as grain growers. Sheep were in many ways the most important stock in the Middle Ages: they provided the most important raw material for textiles; they gave meat and were the most important source of animal manure for the fields. Different breeds were kept for different purposes and there was some attempt to improve breeds by crossing and the selection of rams. Of the other livestock, cattle were valued mainly as draft animals, though also for leather, meat and the milk which was made into butter and cheese. With the introduction of fodder plants in the Netherlands in the 14th century the first experiments were made in crossing. Pigs were the chief source of meat but were kept also for lard and tallow used for candles. Poultry was abundant, the common guinea fowl or Indian fowl having been introduced in the 13th century. Bees were kept for honey, used in place of sugar, and for wax used for lighting.

Another very important source of food in the Middle Ages was fish, especially the herring, fished and marketed by the maritime peoples living round the North Sea. Herrings were the staple food of poorer people. The herring industry was much improved by a new method of preserving and packing in kegs invented in the 14th century. By the 13th century whales were being hunted by North Sea sailors and, on the shore, beds of oysters and mussels were organised.

Of all the animals in which an interest was taken in the Middle Ages the horse was the one to whose breeding the greatest care was devoted. The horse was one of the chief sources of non-human power: it drew the plough; it was used with saddle or cart for transport on land; it was ridden to the chase and for hawking; and above all it was a primary engine of war. In classical times cavalry had been of secondary importance because of inefficient methods of harnessing, but by the 9th century the stirrup seems to have made its appearance in western Europe, brought perhaps from the Arabs. Certainly stirrups are shown in the chessmen which are supposed to have been sent to Charlemagne by Haroun al Raschid. By the 11th century stirrups were common, saddles were becoming deeper, and prick spurs and the curb were coming into use. With these methods of controlling the mount the cavalry charge with lances became possible and remained the basis of tactics for several centuries. Armour became heavier and one of the chief points for breeding was to get a strong animal capable of carrying the enormous weight. Horse breeding was much influenced by Arab practices and the best works on the subject and on veterinary medicine relating to the horse were written in Arabic as late as the 14th century. Horse studs were set up in Christendom by rulers such as the counts of Flanders, the dukes of Normandy and the kings of the two Sicilies. The kings of Castile introduced laws regulating stock breeding generally. The Arabs had traced pedigrees through the dam, but the Western practice from as early as the 12th century seems to have been to trace them through the sire, and certainly Arab stallions were imported from time to time. In the 13th century several Spanish works were written on horse breeding and veterinary science; another was written by one of Frederick II's advisers in Sicily. In the 14th century Crescenzi's treatise had a section on the horse and further veterinary works were written in Italy and Germany later in the century.

The value of the horse as a draft animal depended on the introduction of a new kind of harness which allowed the animal to take the weight on its shoulders by means of a rigid stuffed collar instead of on its neck as hitherto (Fig. 24). In Greek and Roman times, to judge by sculpture, vase paintings and medals, horses were harnessed in such a way that the pull was taken on a strap passing round the neck so that the harder they pulled the closer they came to strangulation. The modern horse collar appeared in the West in the late 9th or early 10th century, introduced perhaps from China. At the same time two other inventions appeared: the nailed horseshoe which improved traction, and the extension of the lateral traces for the tandem harness, allowing horses to be harnessed one in front of the other so that an indefinite number could be used to move heavy weights. This had not been possible with the classical method of harnessing horses side by side. Another improvement which came in during the same period was the invention of a multiple yoke for oxen. These inventions transformed life in the West in the 11th and 12th centuries, much as the steam engine did in the 19th. They made it possible to use the horse to pull the heavy, wheeled plough, the first picture of a horse so

FIG. 24. Harnessing with collar and lateral traces, and shoeing with nailed shoes. From the *Luttrell Psalter*, British Museum MS. Additional 42130 (XIV cent.).

engaged appearing in the Bayeux tapestry. Perhaps because of changed economic conditions, perhaps because of the opposition of the Church, slave labour, the basis of classical industry, had become increasingly scarce in the Dark Ages. The new methods of harnessing animal power, and the increasing exploitation of water- and wind-power, came to make slavery unnecessary.

(3) THE MECHANISATION OF INDUSTRY

The great expansion of the use of watermills and windmills that took place during the later Middle Ages in association with the growth of manufacturing brought in an essentially new stage in mechanical technique. From this period must be dated that increasing mechanisation of life and industry, based on the ever-increasing exploitation of new forms of mechanical power, which characterises modern civilisation. The initial stages of the industrial revolution, before the use of steam, were brought about by the power of the horse and ox, water and wind. The mechanical devices and instruments invented in classical times, pumps, presses and catapults, driving wheels, geared wheels and trip hammers, and the five kinematic 'chains' (screw, wheel, cam, ratchet and pulley) were applied in the later Middle Ages on a scale unknown in earlier societies. The remaining kinematic 'chain', the crank, apparently unknown in classical times, appears first in the Dark Ages in such simple mechanisms as the rotary grindstone depicted in the mid-9th-century *Utrecht Psalter*. Though it is difficult to trace its later history, the crank mechanism had certainly come into general use by the 15th century. With the crank it became possible for the first time to convert reciprocating into rotary motion and *vice versa*, a technique without which modern machinery is inconceivable.

The earliest water-driven mills were used for grinding corn, though before them waterwheels operating chains of pots had been used in ancient Sumeria for raising water. These early cornmills were of three kinds. Horizontal millstones on a vertical shaft turned by water flowing past vanes attached to the bottom of the shaft are known from the 5th century A.D. from Ireland, Norway, Greece and other places, though there is no direct evidence for this kind of mill in Antiquity. A second type of mill, in which a vertical undershot waterwheel operated a pestle by a trip hammer mechanism, is described by Pliny. An undershot waterwheel driving a millstone by means of geared wheels is described by Vitruvius. This is the first instance known of the use of geared wheels for transmitting power. Four centuries later Pappus of Alexandria described a toothed wheel rotating on a helix or worm gearing. There is evidence that the Romans used also overshot wheels, which had the mechanical advantage that they were driven by the weight of the water as well as the force of the current. From the Mediterranean, watermills spread north-westward and, by the 4th century A.D., they were in general use throughout Europe for grinding corn and pressing olives. In the 4th century Ausonius describes a water-driven saw in use on the Moselle for cutting marble. In the 11th century Domesday Book records 5,000 watermills in England alone. The first evidence as to the type of mill in use in medieval Christendom comes from the 12th century, by which time the vertical undershot wheel was the common type. Overshot wheels do

Fig. 25.   Watermill. From the *Luttrell Psalter*.

not appear in illustrations before the 14th century (Fig. 25) and even by the end of the 16th century they had by no means entirely displaced the undershot type.

With the spread of watermills came improvements in methods of transmitting power and of converting their rotary motion for special purposes. As early as the 12th century, illustrations show that the proportions of the crown and pinion wheels forming the gear were adjusted to give the millstone a high speed of rotation even in slow streams, and the general mechanism of the geared wheel was adapted to mills worked by other forms of power. Illustrations from the end of the 13th century to the 16th show such mechanisms in mills worked by horses or oxen or by hand, and 15th-century illustrations show them in windmills. By the 12th century the rotary motion of the water wheel was being converted to operate trip hammers for fulling[1] and for crushing woad, oak bark (for tanning leather) and other substances, and by the 14th century the same mechanism was used for forge hammers. In the 14th century the treadle hammer, the English 'oliver', appeared, and in the 15th century a stamping mill was described for crushing ore. In the late 13th century the waterwheel was adapted also to

FIG. 26. Windmill. From Oxford MS. Bodley 264 (XIV cent.).

drive forge bellows (Fig. 31) and, if a device sketched by Villard de Honnecourt represents something actually used, sawmills for cutting wood. Water-driven sawmills certainly existed in the next century. By the 14th century waterwheels and also horse-driven wheels were used to drive grindstones for making edged tools; by the 15th century they were in use for pumping in mines and salt pits, for hoisting in mines with crank or windlass, and for driving iron-rolling mills and wire-drawing mills; by the 16th century they were used to drive silk mills.

Windmills came into use much later than watermills. The first certain knowledge of windmills comes from the writings

(1) 'When a little farther, at the doubling of the Point of a Rock, they plainly discover'd . . . Six huge Fulling-Mill Hammers, which interchangeably thumping several Pieces of Cloth, made the terrible Noise that caus'd all Don *Quixote's* Anxieties and *Sancho's* Tribulation that night.' (*Don Quixote*, 1603, part i, book 3, section 6).

of Arab geographers travelling in Persia in the 10th century, though mills may have existed there before that time. These writings describe windmills with horizontal sails operating a vertical axle to the lower end of which was attached a horizontal millstone. Windmills may have come to the West from Persia through the Arabs of Spain, through the Crusades, or through trade between Persia and the Baltic known to have passed through Russia. Certainly when windmills first appear in Christendom in the 12th century it is in the north-west, though these had vertical sails driving a horizontal axle. But whatever its early history in the West, by the end of the 12th century the windmill was widespread in England, the Netherlands and northern France; it was used especially in those regions where there was no water. The chief mechanical problem introduced by the windmill arose out of the need to present the sails to the wind, and in the earlier mills the whole structure was rotated about a pivot or post (Fig. 26). This meant that mills had to remain small and only from the end of the 15th century did the windmill increase in size and develop in a really efficient form. The axle was then set at a slight angle to the ground, the sails adjusted to catch every breath of wind, a brake was fitted and there were levers to adjust the position of the millstones. The 'turret' type of windmill with only the top section rotating, which was developed in Italy towards the end of the 15th century, was the last significant addition to the list of prime movers before the invention of the steam engine.

The development and application of these forms of power produced the same kind of social and economic changes and dislocations in the Middle Ages as were to occur again on a larger scale in the 18th and 19th centuries. As early as the 10th century the lords of the manor began to claim a monopoly for their cornmills, which were a source of money-income, and this led to a long struggle between the lords and the commune. The monks of Jumièges, as lords of the manor, destroyed the hand mills at Viville in 1207; the monks of St. Albans carried on a campaign against hand mills from the end of the 13th century until the so-called Peasants' Revolt, the great rising of the English communities led by Wat Tyler in 1381. The mechanisation of fulling in the 13th century led to a wholesale shift of the English cloth industry from the plains of the south-east into the hills of the north-west where water was available. Colonies of weavers settled round the fulling mills in the Lake District, the West Riding and the Stroud valley, and the cloth industry decayed in towns like York, Lincoln, London and Winchester which had provided the broadcloth that was the staple of English industry in the 12th century. The insistence of the land-owners who erected these mills that cloth should be brought to them and not fulled by hand or foot at home led to a long struggle, aspects of which are vividly described in *Piers Plowman*, and this action by the owners of mills was certainly also one of the causes of the Peasants' Revolt.

Though the other processes involved in the manufacture of cloth did not, until the 18th century, reach the complete mechanisation achieved in fulling in the 13th, the first steps towards this also were made during the Middle Ages. The main stages in early cloth making were carding and combing by hand, spinning by hand from a distaff on to a loose spindle, and weaving of the yarn thus prepared into a loose 'web' on a loom worked by hand and foot. The 'web' was then fulled in water and so felted. After fulling the cloth went to the 'rower' who raised the nap with teasles and to the shearsman who cut off the loose threads after which, when small blemishes had been repaired, it was ready for sale[1]. The mechanisation of spinning began in the 13th century when the spinning wheel turned by hand made its appearance (Fig. 27). The processes of twisting silk and winding it on reels are said to have been mechanised in Bologna in 1272. Certainly

(1) *Piers Plowman* (*c.* 1362) has a description of the cloth trade (ed. W. W. Skeat, Oxford, 1886, p. 466, B Text, Passus xv, ll. 444 *et seq.*): Cloth that cometh fro the wevying is nought comly to were, Tyl it is fulled under fote or in fullyng-strokkes, Wasshen wel with water and with taseles cracched, ytouked, and ytented and under tailloures hande.

various kinds of thread were being spun with wheels by the end of the 13th century and about the same time the quilling wheel came in, by means of which the spun yarn was wound regularly on to the quill or bobbin which was set in the shuttle for weaving. There are several 14th-century illustrations of this wheel in use. It is interesting from the mechanical point of view as one of the earliest attempts to use continuous rotary motion. At the end of the 15th century further improvements in mechanisms for spinning and

FIG. 27. Spinning wheel. From British Museum MS. Royal 10.E.iv (XIV cent.).

winding were envisaged by Leonardo da Vinci, who drew a sketch of a 'flyer' by means of which these two processes could go on simultaneously; he seems to have had in mind large-scale machinery driven by water power or a horse winch. He designed also a power-driven gig mill for raising the nap on cloth with teasles. In fact no satisfactory substitute has ever been discovered for teasles, though unsuccessful attempts to use iron combs were made as early as the mid-15th century. The flyer actually came into use about 1530 in a wheel incorporating also another innovation, the drive by treadle and crank. Power-driven spinning mills and gig mills seem to have been used on a considerable scale in the Italian silk industry from the end of the 16th century and full descriptions of them are given by Zonca (1607) (Figs. 28A and B).

In weaving, the improvements that took place between the end of the Roman Empire and the revival of Western silk manufacture in the 14th century occurred mainly out-

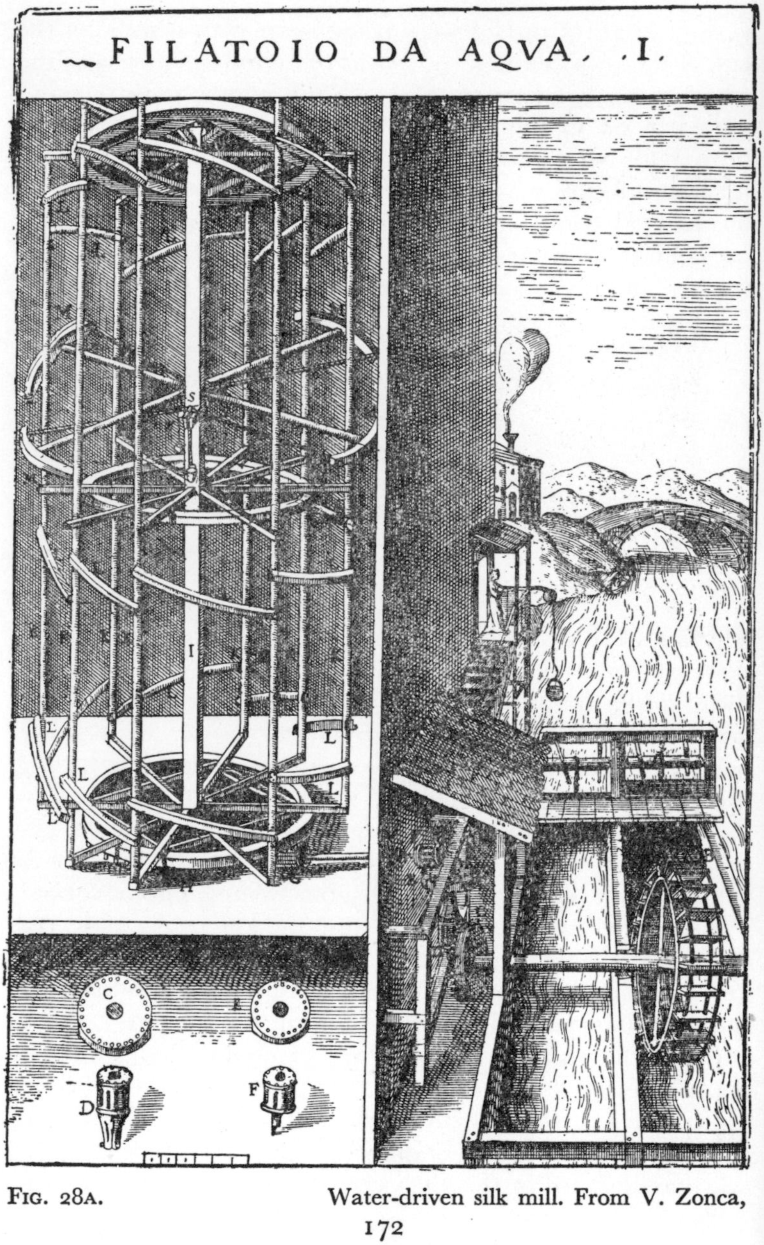

FIG. 28A.   Water-driven silk mill. From V. Zonca,

172

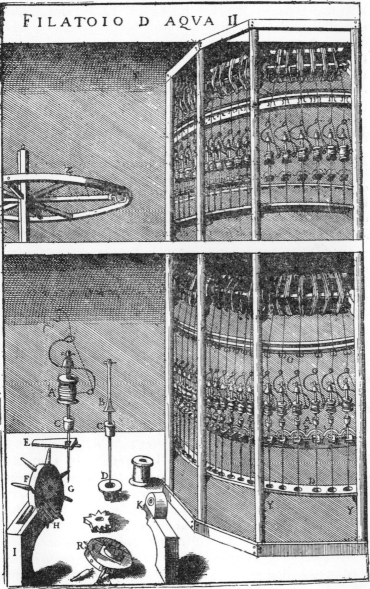

FILATOIO D AQVA II

Novo Teatro di Machine et Edificii, Padua, 1607.

Fig. 28b.

side the West in Byzantium, Egypt, Persia and China, though they were rapidly taken over in the West in the later Middle Ages. These improvements were introduced mainly to make possible the weaving of patterned silk materials, for which it was necessary to be able to select the particular threads of the warp to be moved. This was done by two distinct improvements to the loom: first, a loom worked by pedals with better heddles and, later, with a reed frame to provide a runway for the shuttle; and secondly, the draw loom. Both these devices seem to have been in existence in Egypt by about the 6th century A.D. and they probably entered Christendom through Italy, perhaps as early as the 11th century. From the silk industry their use spread to other branches of textile manufacture. Some further minor improvements were made in weaving technique in Europe in the 14th and 15th centuries; a knitting machine or stocking frame was invented in the 16th century, hand knitting having been invented a century earlier; and a ribbon loom was introduced about 1621. But the major improvements in weaving were not to come until the invention of the flying shuttle and power loom which, with the contemporaneous advances in the mechanisation of spinning, were to transform the textile industry, particularly in England, in the 18th and early 19th centuries.

Another industry which became rapidly mechanised at the end of the Middle Ages was the production of books. Of the different elements involved in printing, the manufacture of linen paper seems to have begun in China in the 1st century A.D., whence it spread westwards through the countries dominated by Islam, to enter Christendom through Spain and southern France in the 12th century. This was a more suitable material for printing than the older costly parchment and brittle papyrus. The inks with an oil base used in printing were developed first by painters rather than calligraphers. Presses were already known in the manufacture of wine and the printing of cloth. The most essential element, the type itself, was made possible by skills acquired by wood engravers and by goldsmiths who had developed a technique for casting metal. Type developed in three main stages, first in China and then in Europe, though since the techniques used in these two regions were very different it is difficult to say to what extent the one influenced the other. In China, printing from wooden blocks, a separate block being cut for each page, appeared in the 6th century A.D., printing from movable wooden characters in the 11th century and from movable metal type (in Korea) in the 14th century. In Europe, the use of wood cuts for the elaborate initial letters of manuscripts first appeared in a monastery at Engelberg in 1147; block printing appeared at Ravenna in 1289 and was common throughout Europe by the 15th century; movable metal type came in at the end of the 14th century, appearing at Limoges in 1381, Antwerp in 1417 and Avignon in 1444. The advantage of cast metal type was that hundreds of copies of each letter could be cast from a single mould instead of having to be carved separately as with wooden type. Though the first record of it in Europe is in the Netherlands, it was at Mainz that the use of accurately set movable metal type was brought to perfection. At Mainz, between 1447 and 1455, Gutenberg and his associates introduced, in place of the older method of casting type in sand, first the adjustable metal type-mould for making lead type, then the improvement of punches and the preparation of copper type. These were the strategic inventions in printing and with them the multiplication of books on a large scale became possible.

Perhaps the most spectacular result of medieval mechanical techniques is to be seen in the buildings, and many of the devices employed by the medieval mason to solve the statical problems arising in the construction of large churches were altogether original. It is impossible to say to what extent the medieval builder was being purely empirical and to what extent he was able to use the results of theoretical work in statics, but it is significant that during the late 12th and 13th centuries, just when the erection of the great

cathedrals was producing the most difficult practical problems, Jordanus Nemorarius and others were making important
additions to theoretical statics; at least one 13th-century
architect, Villard de Honnecourt, showed a knowledge of
geometry. The original developments in Gothic architecture
arose from the attempt to put a stone roof on the thin walls
of the central aisle of a basilica, the usual form of Christian
church since Roman times. The Romans never had to face
the problems which arose for the medieval mason because
they built the barrel or groined vaults over their baths in
concrete, and domes, like that of the Pantheon, in horizontally coursed brickwork with mortar; when the concrete or
mortar had set the thrust of the roof on the wall was very
small. This was not the case with medieval building, in
which no such concrete or mortar was used.

The masons of 10th- and 11th-century Burgundy tried to
roof their naves with barrel vaults in the Roman style, but
they found that the enormous thrust on the side walls tended
to push them out even though they were made very thick.
The first attempt to overcome this difficulty was to make the
side aisles nearly the same height as the nave and roof them
by means of groined vaults formed by two barrel vaults
intersecting at right angles. These groined vaults of the aisles
counteracted the thrust of the barrel vault of the nave and
themselves exerted very little thrust except at the corners,
which could be supported by massive pillars. This arrangement had the disadvantage that it left the church lighted
only by the aisle windows, and when, as in many Clunaic
churches, the roof of the nave was raised to get windows
above the aisles, the walls collapsed from lack of support.
A solution was found at Vézelay and Langres by using
groined vaults for the nave, two semicircular wooden
centrings being used on which to construct the diagonals of
the vault. By this means the 11th-century builder could
construct a vaulted roof to cover any space, square or
oblong, with a separate vault over each bay resting on semi-
circular transverse arches separating the bays.

This arrangement still had serious defects. The form of the semicircular arch, in which the height must be half the span, was quite inelastic and there was still a formidable outward thrust so that the transverse arches tended to drop. Considerable elasticity of design was introduced and the outward thrust reduced by adopting the pointed arch which appeared in Christendom first in Vézelay and other Cluniac churches in the late 11th century, and later in the Île de France. It is thought to have been brought to Europe from Asia Minor, where it had become common by the 9th century. Half-arches of this kind were used in the 12th century to buttress the walls of several French churches, flying buttresses, in fact, in all respects except that they were hidden under the triforium roof.

A further step which completed the change from the Roman to the Gothic vaulted roof was to build diagonal arches over the wooden centrings used in constructing the groins and to use these as permanent ribs (sprung from columns) on which to build the vault surface. This seems to have been done in various parts of Europe during the 11th and early 12th centuries and it was this invention which gave rise to the wonderful Gothic of the Île de France in the 12th century. It gave great elasticity of design to the vault and meant that any space of any shape could be vaulted with ease so long as it could be divided up into triangles, and that the summits of all the arches and vaults could be kept at any level desired. This freedom was increased still further when it was realised that the diagonal ribs need not be complete arches, but that three or more half-ribs could be used butting against each other at the summit of a pointed roof. Following the introduction of the permanent rib, differences in the method of filling in the vault surface led to a striking divergence in roof design between France and England. The French method was to make each vaulting panel arched and self-supporting. The English, on the other hand, did not make their panels self-supporting, so that further ribs had to be added to keep them up and this led to the fan vaulting of

N 177

which good examples are Exeter Cathedral and the Chapel of King's College, Cambridge.

Perhaps the most striking of all the devices invented to solve the problems created by stone vaulting was the flying buttress introduced in the Île de France in the 12th century. In contrast with English builders, who at first retained the Norman tradition of thick walls, the French reduced their walls to little else than frames for stained-glass windows, and in so doing they had to devise some means of counteracting the thrust of the nave roof. This they did, at Poissy in 1135 and later at Sens and St. Germain des Près, by carrying up a half-arch above the roof of the side aisle to the junction of the roof and wall of the nave. Later it was realised that the roof thrust extended some way down the wall and the flying buttress was doubled to meet this thrust as at Chartres and Amiens. This method of counteracting roof thrust created another problem, for it exposed the building to a considerable strain from east to west. To tie it together in this direction the wall arches and the gables over the windows were made specially strong. This gave the windows in French churches like La Sainte Chapelle in Paris a prominence they never had in England.

Probably many of the devices invented by the 12th- and 13th-century architects were based on rule of thumb, and the great period of medieval building is singularly lacking in treatises on the subject. But the notebook of Villard de Honnecourt, who designed parts of Laon, Reims, Chartres and other French cathedrals, shows that the 13th-century architect could possess a greater ability to generalise the problems of stress and weight lifting involved than the poverty of theoretical writings might suggest. The *Architettura* of Alberti shows that certainly by the 15th century architects had a good knowledge of mechanics. This knowledge becomes even more evident in the late 15th and early 16th centuries, when Leonardo da Vinci calculated the weight that a pillar or cluster of pillars of any given diameter could safely carry and tried also to determine the greatest weight that could be borne by a beam of any given span. By the 16th century, Vitruvius had begun to have a great influence on building, but his admirers, such as Palladio, who published his *Architettura* in 1570, far surpassed him in scientific knowledge. By the 17th century, problems such as the strength of materials and the stability of arches had become a subject of research by professional mathematicians like Galileo, Wren and Hooke; Wren and Hooke were also employed as architects.

FIG. 29. Ships showing construction, rig and rudder. From the *Luttrell Psalter*.

Another branch of construction in which considerable progress was made during the Middle Ages with the object of making better use of wind-power was ship-building. The two common types of medieval European ship derived, respectively, from the Roman galley and the Norse long ship. They had a number of features in common: both were long, narrow and flat-bottomed with a single mast and a square sail; both were steered by an oar on the side at the stern of the ship. The first improvement on this arrangement was the fore-and-aft rig as seen in the lateen sail which appears suddenly in Greek miniatures in the 9th century. By the 12th century lateen sails were common in the Mediterranean, and from there they spread to northern Europe. At the same time ships grew larger, got higher out of the water, the number of masts increased and, in the

13th century, the modern rudder fixed to the stern post, itself an extension of the keel, made its appearance (Fig. 29). These improvements made it possible to tack effectively against the wind, made oarsmen unnecessary, and extended the range of exploration. An early exercise in the mechanisation of ships, not necessarily representing anything actually built, appeared at the beginning of the 15th century with the drawings of ships with paddle-wheels by Konrad Kyeser and by the Sienese engineer, Jacopo Mariano Taccola. Ramelli also gave an illustration of a paddle boat in 1588 and another innovation, a submarine, was actually built and successfully used in the Thames in 1614.

An improvement to inland water transport was brought about in the 14th century by the introduction of lock gates on canals; new possibilities for transport on land were introduced by making roads of stone cubes set in a bed of loose earth or sand and by improvements in wheeled vehicles including (in the 13th century) the invention of the wheelbarrow. Mechanisation was attempted also with land vehicles as early as 1420, when Fontana described a velocipede. At the end of the 16th century wagons propelled by man-driven machinery and by sails were apparently constructed in the Low Countries. Flight had attracted attention in the West at least since the 11th century, when Oliver of Malmesbury is said to have broken his legs in an attempt to glide from a tower with wings fitted to his hands and feet. Roger Bacon was also interested in flight. Leonardo da Vinci actually designed a mechanical flying-machine which flapped its wings like a bird.

An important advance associated with these improvements in methods of transport was the appearance of the first good maps in the West since Roman times. When accurate maps were added to the rudder and the compass, which came into use in the 12th century (see above, pp. 88 *et seq.*), ships could be navigated effectively away from sight of land and, as Mumford has put it, exploration was encouraged in an attempt to fill in the gaps suggested by the rational expecta-

tions of space. The first true medieval maps were the
portolani, or compass-charts, for mariners. The earliest known
portolano is the late 13th-century *Carte Pisane*, but its relative
technical excellence suggests that others which have disappeared were made before it. Genoese sailors are said to
have shown St. Louis of France his position on a map when
he was crossing to Tunis in 1270. Some of the evidence might
seem to suggest a Scandinavian origin for *portolani*, but the
Arabs certainly had charts from an early date and charts were
developed also by the Byzantines, Catalans and Genoese.
The use of the Catalan *legua* for distances in all the known
portolani perhaps supports the Catalan claim to primacy, but
this use may have come in later as a matter of convenience
and, in fact, the question of the origin of *portolani* is undecided.
The novel feature of the *portolani*, as compared with the old
traditional symbolic *mappæ mundi*, is that they were made for
use as guides to a specific area. Made by practical men
and based on the direct determination of distances and
azimuths by using log and compass, they were generally
restricted to the coastline. They contained no indications of
longitude and latitude. They were covered with networks
of rhumb-lines giving the compass bearing of the places
on the map. The rhumb-lines radiated from a number of
points arranged in a circle and corresponding to the points
marked on a compass-card.

Other accurate maps showing inland regions as well as the
coastline were produced by men of education from the
13th century, by which time scholars like Roger Bacon were
taking an interest in real geography. Bacon himself made no
practical contributions to cartography, though his belief that
there was no great width of ocean between Europe and China
is said to have influenced Columbus, who found it repeated
in works by Pierre d'Ailly and Aeneas Sylvius. As early
as about 1250 Matthew Paris drew four recognisable maps
of Great Britain showing details such as the Roman Wall,
roads and towns. Between 1325 and 1350 an unknown
cartographer produced a remarkably detailed and accurate

map of England, the so-called 'Gough map', now in the Bodleian Library in Oxford, which shows roads with mileages probably as estimated by travellers (Plate 4). About the same time good maps showing northern Italy were made by Opicinus de Canistris, who died about 1352, and in 1375 the so-called Majorcan school of cartographers produced for Charles V of France the famous *Catalan Mappemonde*, which combined the virtues of the *portolani* and the land maps and included North Africa and parts of Asia (*cf.* Plate 5). This Majorcan centre had collected an enormous amount of marine and commercial information and was the forerunner of the colonial and naval institute founded by Prince Henry the Navigator at Sagres about 1437. These early maps showed no indication of latitude and longitude, though the latitude of many towns had been determined with the astrolabe (see above, pp. 63 *et seq.*). But in his *Geographia* Ptolemy had drawn maps on a complete network of parallels and meridians. This work was recovered and translated into Latin by Giacomo d'Angelo, who dedicated his translation, with some excellent maps redrawn from the Greek original by a Florentine artist, to Pope Gregory XII in 1406 and Pope Alexander V in 1409. After this, cartographers began to adopt Ptolemy's practice. Good examples are Andrea Bianco's map of Europe in 1436, and the map of Central Europe found among the manuscripts of Nicholas of Cusa (1401–64) and printed in 1491. Ptolemy's own atlas of the world was printed in numerous editions from about 1477. It gradually transformed cartography by emphasising the need for an accurate linear measure of the arc of the meridian, the essential requirement for accurate terrestrial cartography.

Until the end of the 18th century the most important material for machinery and construction generally was wood. Most of the parts of watermills and windmills, spinning wheels, looms, presses, ships and vehicles were of wood, and wood was used for geared wheels in much machinery as late as the 19th century. Thus it was that the first machine tools were developed for working wood, and even in the tools themselves only the cutting edge was of metal. Of the boring machines, the bow-drill known since Neolithic times, in which the drill was driven rapidly by a string wound round it and attached at each end to a bow which was moved back and forth, was replaced during the later Middle Ages by the brace and bit, and a machine for boring pump barrels from solid tree trunks was also known. The most important of the machine tools for accurate work, the lathe, may have been known in some form in Antiquity, but the pole-lathe was probably a medieval invention. The first known illustrations of pole-lathes appear only in sketches by Leonardo da Vinci, but they must have been in use before that time. The spindle was driven by a cord wound round it as in the bow-drill and attached at the bottom to a treadle, at the top to a springy pole which flexed the cord back on taking the foot off the treadle. Leonardo shows also a rotary lathe driven by bands from a wheel, though rotary lathes with crank and treadle drive became common only from the 17th century. In these early lathes the work was turned between fixed centres, but in the mid-16th century Besson designed a mandrel lathe in which the work was fixed to a chuck to which power was applied. Besson designed also a crude screw-cutting lathe (Fig. 30), to which further improvements were made in the 17th century, in particular the change introduced by the clockmakers from traversing the work over a stationary tool to traversing the tool itself while the work merely rotated. Thus, from the early machine tools designed for working wood, were developed tools capable of accurate work with metals.

The earliest machines made entirely of metal were firearms and the mechanical clock, and the mechanical clock in particular is the prototype of modern automatic machinery in which all the parts are precisely designed to produce an accurately-controlled result. In the mechanical clock the use of geared wheels, the main point of interest in early machinery, was completely mastered.

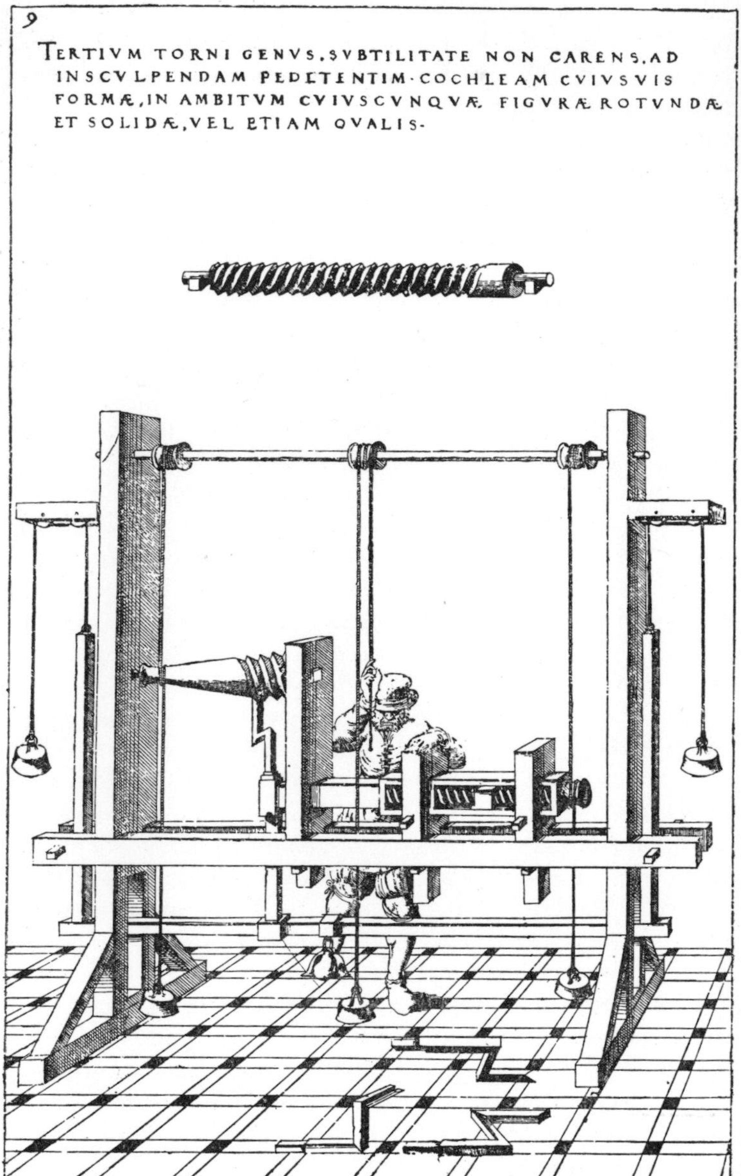

FIG. 30. Screw-cutting lathe. From Jacques Besson's *Theatrum Instrumentorum et Machinarum*, Lyons, 1569. (1st edn. 1568.)

Water clocks, like the clepsydra, measuring time by the amount of water dripping through a small hole, had been used by the ancient Egyptians, and the Greeks had improved them by fitting devices to indicate the hours by a pointer on a scale and to regulate the movement. The water clocks developed by the Arabs and Latin Christians were based on these Greek devices and also on the devices of the automatic puppet theatre, which was popular in the Middle Ages. They were so successful that water clocks remained in use as late as the 18th century. These water clocks were worked by a float suspended in a basin filled and emptied by a regulating mechanism, and the motion of the float was communicated to the indicator, usually some kind of puppet show, by ropes and pulleys. In Islam, they were sometimes very large and were set up where the public could see them; and in Christendom smaller clocks were used in monasteries where they were looked after by a special keeper, one of whose duties was to adjust the clock at night by taking observations of the pole star. One such clock is said to have been made by Gerbert for the monastery at Magdeburg. Other early clocks were worked by a burning candle, and a mid-13th-century work prepared for Alfonso X of Castile describes a clock operated by a falling weight controlled by the resistance created by the passage of mercury through small apertures. In none of these clocks were there any gears.

The essential features of the mechanical clock were a drive by a falling weight which set in motion a train of geared wheels, and an oscillatory escapement mechanism which prevented the weight accelerating as it fell by stopping it at frequent intervals. The earliest illustration of an escapement mechanism appears in the mid-13th century in a device drawn by Villard de Honnecourt for making an angel rotate slowly so that its finger always pointed towards the sun (Plate 6), and it is possible that the first mechanical clocks were made shortly afterwards. There are references to what seem to have been mechanical clocks of some kind in London, Canterbury, Paris and other places during the second half of the 13th century and in Milan, St. Albans, Glastonbury, Avignon, Padua and elsewhere during the first half of the 14th century. Some of these were planetaria, for showing the motions of the heavenly bodies, rather than clocks. Probably the earliest true clocks of which the mechanism is definitely known are the Dover Castle clock, usually dated 1348 but probably later (Plate 7), and Henri de Vick's clock set up in Paris at the Palais Royal, now the Palais de Justice, in 1370. These clocks were regulated by a verge escapement with a foliot balance. The essential components of this mechanism were a crown wheel with saw-like teeth which were engaged alternatively by two small plates or pallets on a rod, so that the wheel was intermittently stopped and released. The foliot was a mechanism for regulating the speed of rotation of the crown or 'escape' wheel, and therefore of the whole train of wheels ending with the axle carrying the hands of the clock. The perfection of this verge escapement and foliot balance marks a limit in clock design on which, in point of accuracy, no real advance was made until the application of the pendulum to clocks in the 17th century, though before that time considerable refinements were made in construction. The early clocks were, in fact, mostly very large and the parts were made by a blacksmith. De Vick's clock was moved by a weight of 500 lbs. which fell 32 feet in 24 hours and had a striking weight of nearly three-quarters of a ton. In the 15th century, clocks became smaller and were used in houses, screws were used to hold the parts together, and the end of the century saw the first 'clock-watches' driven by a spring.

These early clocks were reasonably accurate if set nightly by observing a star, and by 1500 most towns had public clocks on the outside walls of monasteries or cathedrals or on special towers. They either simply struck the hours or also showed them on a circular face marked in divisions of 12 or 24. The effect of placing them in public places was to bring about the complete replacement of the seven variable liturgical hours by the 24 equal hours of the clock. From an early date in Antiquity astronomers had, in fact, divided the day into 24 equal hours, taking the hours of the equinox as standard, and throughout the early Middle Ages this system had existed, particularly in civil life, side by side with the ecclesiastical system. A decisive step was taken in 1370 by Charles V of France when he ordered all churches in Paris to ring the hours and quarters according to time by de Vick's clock, and from that time the equal hours became more common. The division of the hour into 60 minutes and of the minute into 60 seconds also came into general use in the 14th century and was fairly common as early as 1345. The adoption of this system of division completed the first stages in the scientific measurement of time, without which the later refinements of both physics and machinery would scarcely have been possible.

(4) INDUSTRIAL CHEMISTRY

If wood, as Lewis Mumford has vividly pointed out, 'provided the finger exercises for the new industrialism', the development of modern machinery and of precision instruments and scientific apparatus is inconceivable without the artificial products of the chemical industry and above all metals and glass (*cf.* above, pp. 97 *et seq.*).

The metal in the working of which the greatest advances were made during the Middle Ages was iron. Already in Roman times the Gauls and Iberians had become efficient ironsmiths and their knowledge was never lost. By the 13th century iron was being worked in many of the main European fields, in Biscay, Northern France and the Low Countries, the Harz Mountains, Saxony and Bohemia, and in the Forest of Dean, the Weald of Sussex and Kent, Derbyshire and Furness. The striking advances in iron working made during the Middle Ages were the result of using more efficient furnaces which gave higher temperatures for smelting. For this the chief fuel in medieval as in classical times was charcoal. Though 'sea coal' was mentioned by

Nequam, and coal was being mined near Liège and New-castle (whence it was transported to London in flat-bottomed boats) and in Scotland by the end of the 12th century and in most of the major European fields by the end of the 13th century, it was not until the 17th century that a method of using coal for iron working was introduced. This was invented by Dud Dudley about 1620. In the Middle Ages, one of the chief industrial uses of coal was for lime-burning, and already by 1307 the smoke had become such a nuisance in London that attempts were made to prohibit its use there. The improvements made in furnaces in the Middle Ages were due not to better fuel but to the introduction of mechanisms for producing blast air, and the production of charcoal for the ever-increasing needs of metallurgy to supply the demand for swords and armour, nails and horseshoes, ploughs and wheel-rims, bells and cannon remained a serious menace to the forests of Europe till the 18th century. In England it seems to have been the shortage of timber that brought the end of metallurgy in the Weald of Sussex and Kent.

From an early date the draught for furnaces was provided simply by wind tunnels with hand bellows as auxiliaries. This was the method used in the so-called sponge iron process, in which the iron ore was heated with charcoal in small furnaces where the temperature was not high enough to melt the iron but produced a spongy 'bloom' at the bottom of the furnace. By alternate heating and hammer-ing, when the power-driven forge hammer came into play, the bloom was worked into wrought iron rods, which could be rolled and sheared or slit to form plates, or drawn through successively smaller holes in a tempered steel plate to form wire. Steel making was well understood in medieval Christen-dom, though the best steel came from Damascus, where it was made by a process apparently developed originally by the Hindus. Later, excellent steel was made at Toledo.

Improvements in the method of producing blast began with the introduction into the furnace of air under pressure from a head of water, a method that was used in Italy and Spain before the 14th century. Blast was produced also by steam issuing from the long neck of a vessel filled with water and heated, and by bellows operated by horse-driven treadles, but the most outstanding advance was the introduction of bellows driven by water power (Fig. 31). Such blast furnaces made their appearance in the Liège region in 1340 and quickly spread to the Lower Rhine, Sussex and Sweden. These new furnaces became much bigger than the old ones and for the first time it was possible to produce temperatures that would melt the iron, so that it could be obtained directly instead of in the form of a bloom that had to be worked with hammers. Most important of all, the new furnaces made it possible for the first time to produce cast iron on a commercial scale.

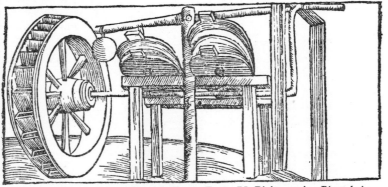

Fig. 31. Water-driven forge bellows. From V. Biringuccio, *Pirotechnia*.

Of the other metals, lead and silver, gold, tin and copper were mined in various parts of medieval Christendom. Cupellation furnaces with water-driven bellows for refining silver from lead appeared in Devon at the end of the 13th century. The lead was oxidized by heating to form litharge, which was skimmed off or absorbed by the porous hearth. Gold was mined in Bohemia, the Carpathians and Carinthia. Tin, of which the Cornish mines were the principal source, was used with copper for making bronze and with copper and calamine (hydrous zinc silicate) for making brass for bells, cannon and monumental and ornamental 'dinanderie', and with lead for making pewter for household ware. Specialised working of metals led to the development of separate guilds of silversmiths and goldsmiths, pewterers, blacksmiths, founders, bladesmiths, spurriers and armourers, and skill in welding, hammering and grinding, chasing and embossing reached a very high level. Specialists also produced needles, scissors, shears, thimbles, forks, files, edged tools for the builder, nails, nuts and bolts and spanners, clocks and locks, and some attempt was made at standardisation. Brass wire was invented in the 11th century and by the 14th century steel wire-drawing was being done by water power. These specialist skills made possible the manufacture of articles of which the value depended on a precise finish. Attention to the finishing processes themselves made it possible to produce such instruments of precision as the astrolabe and the mechanical clock. Recognition of the need to control the content of the alloy used led to the development of assaying, which laid the foundations of quantitative chemistry. Assaying familiarised metallurgists with the use of the balance and led also to the development of other specialised branches of chemistry, of which the production of the mineral acids was one of the most important.

Of the medieval metallurgical processes from which an accurate product was required the founding of bells and guns are perhaps the most interesting. The first European account of bell founding was given early in the 12th century by Theophilus the Priest, and from that time skill in casting bronze and brass developed rapidly, to produce the monumental brasses of the 13th and 14th centuries, and such exquisite products as the southern door of the baptistery of Florence by Andrea Pisano in 1330 and the other even more wonderful doors by Ghiberti about a century later. Large bronze bells began to be made in the 13th century and became numerous in the 14th. The main problem was to produce bells that would ring in tune. The note of a bell depends on the proportions and the amount of metal used, and, though final tuning could be done by grinding down the rim if the note was too flat and by grinding down the inner surface of the sound bow if the note was too sharp, it was necessary for the founder to be able to calculate the exact size and proportions to give something near the right note before he began to cast the bell. For this each founder must have had his own empirical system, for example the system by which bells giving notes with intervals of the tonic, third, fifth and octave were produced by having diameters in the proportions of 30, 24, 20 and 15 and weights in the proportion of 80, 41, 24 and 10 respectively. The scientific temper of the time is shown by the attempt by Walter of Odington, in the late 13th or early 14th century, to devise a rational system according to which each bell would weigh eight-ninths of the bell next above it in weight. In practice this system was distinctly inferior to the empirical systems actually used by bell founders.

The earliest firearms appeared in the West during the first half of the 14th-century but they seem to have been made in China about a century earlier. In both regions considerable progress had previously been made in other forms of pro-jectile-throwing weapons. In the West, by the end of the 12th century, the trebuchet worked with counterweights had begun to drive out the older forms of torsion and tension engines of artillery coming from the Romans or Norsemen; by the early 14th century the crossbow had become a highly effective weapon with sights and a trigger mechanism and the longbow was no less powerful and accurate. The use of gunpowder as a propellant in an effective gun was simply the last of a number of improvements, and firearms did not immediately replace other projectile weapons, though they had become the chief weapon of artillery by the end of the 14th century. Cannon may have been used in the West as early as the siege of Berwick in 1319 and by the English at Crécy in 1346. They were certainly used by the English to capture Calais in 1347 and, according to Froissart, the

English used 400 cannon, probably small mortars, to besiege St. Malo in 1378.

Of the constituents of gunpowder, saltpetre seems to have been known in China before the first century B.C. and knowledge of the explosive properties of a mixture in the right proportions of saltpetre, sulphur and charcoal seems to have been perfected there by about 1000 A.D. In the West, other inflammable mixtures had probably been used in warfare at least since the 7th century A.D., when it is thought that 'Greek fire', probably a mixture of quicklime, naphtha, pitch and sulphur, was used against the Moslem fleet at the siege of Constantinople in 673. Gunpowder itself became known in the West during the second half of the 13th century, perhaps introduced from China through the Mongols.

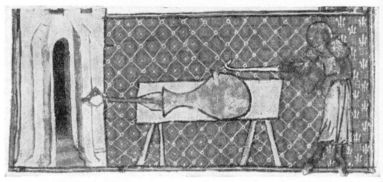

Fig. 32. Knight firing a cannon. From Walter de Milemete's *De Nobilitatibus Sapientiis et Prudentiis Regum*, Christ Church, Oxford, MS. 92.

Roger Bacon referred in his *Opus Majus* and *Opus Tertium* to an explosive powder, and pointed out that its power would be increased by enclosing it in an instrument of solid material. The earliest known Western recipe for gunpowder is in a Latin manuscript of about 1300 of the *Liber Ignium* attributed to a certain Marc the Greek, about whom nothing is known.

Having learnt the explosive and propulsive properties of gunpowder, the West rapidly outstripped China in the manufacture of weapons. The earliest Western cannon were

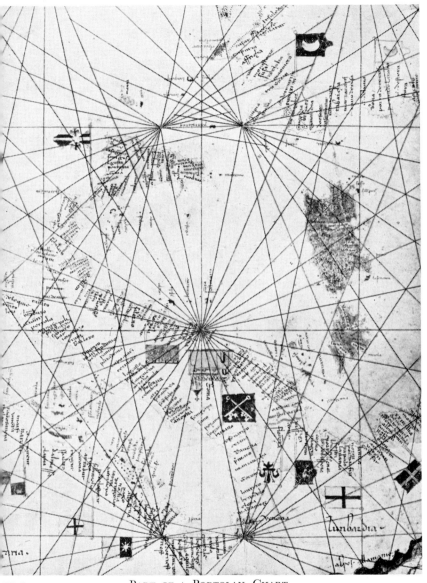

PART OF A PORTOLAN CHART

Showing Italy, Sicily and N. Africa. From British Museum MS. Additional 25691 (*c.* 1327–30; orientated with south at the top, as usual with charts of this period)

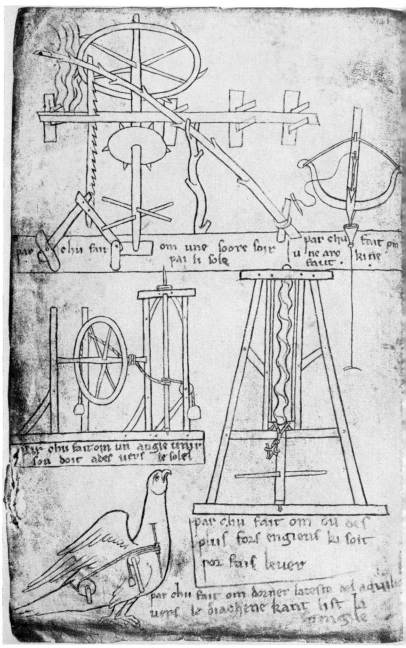

PLATE 6 PAGE FROM THE *ALBUM* OF VILLARD DE HONNECOURT
Showing the escapement mechanism in centre left. Above is a water-
driven saw. From MS. Français 19093 (XIII cent.). In the Bibliothèque
Nationale, Paris

cast in bronze similar to that used for bells, often by the same founder, and the chief centres of manufacture were Flanders, Germany and, to a less extent, England. The earliest known illustration of a cannon in the West is of a small *vaso* or *pot de fer*, as they were called, in a manuscript of a work by Walter de Milemete dedicated to Edward III, in 1327 (Fig. 32). Some early guns were made also of wrought iron strips held together with iron bands, but during the second half of the 14th century they began to be made of cast iron. In the 15th century these cast iron guns reached a considerable size, the two largest known being 'Mad Meg', made in 1430 and now in Ghent, which is 502 centimetres long, has a diameter of 63 centimetres and weighs approximately 340 kilograms, and 'Mons Meg', now in Edinburgh Castle, which is somewhat smaller. These early cannon were all muzzle-loaders firing at first large round stones and later cast-iron balls. Lead shot was used from the 14th century with smaller guns. Breech loading was attempted quite early, but it was impossible to finish the metal surfaces with sufficient precision to produce gas-tight breech locks. A primitive form of rifling was introduced in the bronze guns, and during the 15th century standardisation of guns and shot began to come in, culminating in the standard ordnance propagated by the artillery schools of Burgos and Venice in the early 16th century.

A great advance in gun making was made early in the 16th century by the introduction of a method of boring cast-bronze or iron guns so that they could be given an accurate finish. Machines for boring wood had been known from an early date and, as early as 1496, the German mechanic, Philip Monch, had made an elaborate sketch of a gun borer worked by horse power. Leonardo da Vinci also sketched a boring machine for metal working, and Biringuccio described and illustrated one driven by a waterwheel in his *Pirotechnia* (1540). With the introduction of accurately-bored barrels began a new period in the history of gunnery which lasted until the 19th century.

The experience acquired in the production of metals in the later Middle Ages was transferred to other kinds of mining, and the great demand for minerals generally had some striking economic, political and industrial consequences. By the 14th century, apart from metals and coal, there was mining on a fairly large scale of sulphates in Hungary, rock-salt in Transylvania, calamine and saltpetre in Poland, mercury in Spain and, in the 15th century, of alum in Tuscany and the Papal states. Pumping, ventilation and haulage in ever-deepening seams made mining an expensive business that could be undertaken only by the man with capital, and as early as 1299 Edward I leased silver-lead mines in Devonshire to the Frescobaldi, a family of Florentine merchants and bankers, who in turn financed Edward I and II of England and also Philippe le Bel of France. Perhaps the most striking example of fortune and power acquired from mining is provided by the Fuggers. From small beginnings in the 14th century, the Fuggers had by the 16th century built up such capital from the silver-lead mines of Styria, the Tyrol and Spain that they were in a position to finance the big guns and mercenary troops on the scale required by a European ruler like the Emperor Charles V.

Of the industrial consequences of the growing demand for metals, perhaps the most striking are the improvements in pumps and eventually, at the end of the 17th century, the use of steam power to pump out the subsoil water, the experiments in the use of coal for metallurgy to overcome the increasing shortage of charcoal fuel, and the attempt to find substitutes for metals like tin which, before the exploitation of the mines of the New World and the Far East, was becoming ever scarcer. Of these substitutes the most important for science was glass, which, from the 14th century, was being produced as a substitute for pewter for household ware.

Glass making was well known in the Ancient World, and in various parts of the Roman Empire excellent dishes, bowls, beakers, bottles and other household objects were made from blown glass, and the art of engraving on glass was developed. In the Dark Ages a high technique in glass making was carried on in Byzantium, in various Arabic centres and, more obscurely, also in the West. It was not until the 13th century that glass making began to revive generally in the West, though one of the best accounts of it is to be found in the early 12th-century treatise of Theophilus the Priest. The most famous Western centre was Venice. Though from the 13th century glass making made considerable progress also in Spain, France and England, it was not until the 16th century that glass was made on a large scale outside Italy.

Most medieval glass was blown (Plate 8). The materials, for example sand, carbonate of potash and red lead, were melted together in a furnace and, when the material had cooled enough to become viscous, a blob was picked up on the end of a long rod and rotated, or blown and worked with large tongs, until the required vessel or other object was formed. It might be reheated again to alter the shape. The essentials of the technique were dexterity, speed and the control of the temperature to which the cooling glass was exposed ; on these depended its final strength. For plate glass the sand had to be free from iron oxide, and carbonate of lime, sulphate of soda and some form of carbon were required. The method of making plate glass was to blow a large bubble which was worked into a long, hollow cylinder hanging from the platform on which the blower stood and was eventually slit open and worked flat. This method restricted the size of the sheet.

The chief use of glass in the Middle Ages was for windows and household vessels. Stained-glass windows for churches came in early in the 12th century and painted glass in the 14th. Glass vessels for household purposes were not common before the 16th century, pewter and glazed pottery being the usual materials for hardware, but from the 14th century glass was more commonly used. As early as the 13th century there are references to glass being used for scientific apparatus: Grosseteste and others mentioned optical experiments with a spherical urine flask, and by the early 15th century distilling apparatus was being made of glass. As Mumford has pointed out, the development of chemistry would have been greatly handicapped without glass vessels, which remain neutral in an experiment, are transparent, withstand relatively great heats and are easy to clean and to seal. Optical instruments using lenses and the sciences which, from the early 17th century, developed with them would clearly have been impossible without glass. The Arabs had produced lenses as early as the 11th century, and lenses were discussed by the great Latin optical writers of the 13th century. Though medieval optical glass did not have the excellence of that produced since the 18th century, for which specially pure ingredients are used, it was good enough to make possible the invention of spectacles at the end of the 13th century (see below, pp. 205–6).

In other chemical industries as well as metallurgy and glass making medieval craftsmen acquired a considerable empirical knowledge. Considerable skill in controlling the processes involved was shown in pottery, in tile and brick making, in tanning and soap making, in the processes of malting, yeasting and fermentation involved in brewing, in the fermentation of wine and in the distilling of spirits. Salt making by dissolving the crude material from the mine in water, boiling the brine, and precipitating the crystals in open pans had been known to the Romans and was practised in the Middle Ages at various places, including Droitwich and Nantwich in England. Considerable skill was shown also in the dyeing of wool, silk and linen with vegetable dyes such as woad, madder, weld, lichens and a red dye obtained from 'greyne', an insect resembling cochineal, and in fixing the dye with mordants of which the most usual were alum, potash from wood ashes, tartar deposited by fermenting wine, iron sulphate and 'cineres' (possibly barilla or carbonate of soda). The treatises on the preparation of pigments, glues, siccatives and varnishes written from the eighth to the sixteenth century contained a large variety of recipes

giving practical directions how to prepare chemical substances. At the beginning of the 12th century the treatise by
Theophilus the Priest referred to oil paints, though it was
not before the Van Eycks early in the 15th century that the
siccative properties of oil paints were improved so that they
dried quickly enough for several colours to be put on at the
same time. Medieval painters and illuminators learnt how
to prepare a large variety of colours of vegetable and
mineral origin and new recipes were continually being added,
for example that for 'mosaic gold', a stannic sulphide,
which was discovered about 1300. The ordinary black ink of
medieval manuscripts was usually lampblack mixed with
glue. The practical skill acquired in these industries helped
to lay the foundations of modern chemistry.

(5) MEDICINE

Perhaps of all the practical arts of the Middle Ages, medicine
is the one in which hand and mind, experience and reason,
combined to produce the most striking results. Of the higher
faculties of theology, law and medicine in medieval universities, only in medicine was it possible to have further training
in natural science after the arts degree, and many of the
leaders of science from Grosseteste, in the 13th century, to
William Gilbert, in the 16th, had studied medicine (see above,
pp. 130 *et seq.*; pp. 148 *et seq.*). Medical men like Grosseteste,
Petrus Hispanus and Pietro d'Abano, basing themselves on
the logical writings of Galen, Ali ibn Ridwan and Avicenna,
as well as Aristotle, made some most important contributions
to the logic of induction and experiment which had a
profound effect on science down to the time of Galileo (see
below, pp. 218 *et seq.*). And certainly in practical medicine
the medieval doctors found empirical solutions to some
important problems and established the basic scientific
attitude that characterises modern medical practice.

After the decay of the Roman Empire, medicine in the
West was largely folk-medicine, but some knowledge of

Greek medicine was preserved by writers like Cassiodorus and Isidore of Seville and by the Benedictine monasteries. Latin summaries of parts of Hippocrates, Galen and Dioscorides were known, and something of the gynæcological tradition of the 2nd-century A.D. Soranus survived in books for midwives. A revival of medical learning took place in Carolingian times at Chartres and other schools, in the 10th century the Leech-Books appeared in Anglo-Saxon England and in the 11th the writings of Hildegard of Bingen in Germany. The real revival of Western medicine began in the 11th century when the medical school at Salerno, which had come gradually into existence perhaps a century or two earlier, began its attested activity. Whether it was because of its Greek or Jewish population or because of its contacts with the Arabs in Sicily, certainly before 1050 Gariopontus was quoting freely from Hippocrates, and Petrocellus had written his *Practica;* about the same time Alphanus, Archbishop of Salerno, translated from Greek a physiological work by Nemesius under the title of *Premnon Fisicon;* and before 1087 Constantine the African had translated from Arabic Galen's *Art of Medicine* and *Therapeutics* and various works of Haly Abbas and the Jewish physician, Isaac Isræli. The school of Salerno acquired a considerable reputation, and Sudhoff has suggested that its teachers were practising doctors who taught medicine by dissecting animals. Certainly in the 12th century the *Anatomia Ricardi Anglici* emphasised the need for a knowledge of anatomy and the *Anatomia Porci* attributed to Copho described the public dissection of a pig. At the end of the 12th century Salerno produced the first great Western surgeon, Roger of Salerno, whose work was carried on in the early 13th century by Roland of Parma (Plate 9). About the same time was composed the famous *Regimen Sanitatis Salernitanum,* which remained a classic of medical lore until the 16th century.

In the 12th century, Montpellier also began to rise as a medical centre and, in the 13th century, the university medical schools of Montpellier, Bologna, Padua and Paris gradually superseded Salerno. Medical teaching in these university schools was based on various works by Galen and Hippocrates and by Arab and Jewish doctors, the translation of which into Latin had been chiefly responsible for the revival of Western medicine in the 12th and 13th centuries. Of the Arabic and Jewish works, the most important were Avicenna's encyclopædic *Canon of Medicine*, Isaac Isræli's classic work on fevers and Rhazes' works in which were descriptions of diseases like smallpox and measles. The 10th-century Spanish Moor, Albucasis provided the chief early text-book for surgery, and works by the 9th-century Hunain ibn Ishaq and by Haly Abbas were the chief sources through which Arab ophthalmology became known. Other important works were those by the 7th-century Byzantine, Theophilus on the pulse and the urine, the examination of which was the commonest method of diagnosis in the Middle Ages, and Dioscorides' *De Materia Medica*.

Medical treatment in the Middle Ages, when not confined simply to the Hippocratic method of keeping the patient in bed and letting nature take its course,was based on herbs. In Greek medicine the physiological theory behind the use of herbs was that disease was due to an upset of the balance between the four humours, so that 'cooling' drugs were administered to counteract excessive heat in the patient, 'drying' drugs to counteract excessive moisture, and so on (Fig. 19). The supposed effects of drugs based on this theory were sometimes fanciful, but doctors in the Ancient World from Egyptian times had accumulated an empirical knowledge of the effects of a considerable number of herbal drugs like mint, aniseed, fennel, castor oil, squill, poppy, henbane, mandragora, and also of a few mineral drugs like alum, nitre, hæmatite and copper sulphate. A common fumigant was prepared by burning horns with dung to produce ammonia. To the Greek list the Arabs added some herbs from India like hemp, senna and datura and mineral drugs like camphor, naphtha, borax, antimony, arsenic, sulphur and mercury. The Western doctors made further contributions.

As early as the 12th century, the so-called *Antidotarium Nicolai*, a work on drugs composed at Salerno before 1150, recommended the use of the *spongia soporifera* to induce anæsthesia and Michael Scot, who studied at Salerno, gave the recipe as equal parts of opium, mandragora and henbane pounded and mixed with water. 'When you want to saw or cut a man, dip a rag in this and put it to his nostrils.' Modern experiments suggest that this could not have been a very powerful anæsthetic, and various attempts to improve it were made during the Middle Ages, including, by the 16th century, the use of alcohol fumes. The extraction of the virtues of herbs with alcohol to make what is now known as a tincture was discovered by Arnald of Villanova (*c.* 1235–1311). Minerals like arsenious oxide, antimony and mercury salts were regularly used in drugs by the Bolognese doctors, Hugh (d. 1252–58) and Theodoric Borgognoni (1205–98), and also by Arnald of Villanova and others. Mercury ointments were especially popular as cures for various skin diseases and the salivation they produced was noticed.

A branch of medicine in which the empiricism of the medieval mind showed itself to good effect was observation of the effects of different diseases. A large number of diseases had been recognised and described by Greek and Arabic physicians, and to this body of knowledge additions were made, particularly in the written *consilia* or case-histories that became common from the time of Taddeo Alderotti, of Bologna, in the 13th century. The practice of writing *consilia* was part of the general movement towards strictness in presenting evidence in theology as well as in the profane sciences, and sometimes it led to an emphasis on logical form to the detriment of observation, as when *consilia* were prepared and medical advice given from reports from unseen patients. When used properly and based on individual case-histories, as it was by doctors like Alderotti and Arnald of Villanova in the 13th century, Bernard of Gordon and Gentile da Foligno in the 14th, and Ugo Benzi in the 15th, this practice led to some excellent descriptions of the symptoms and courses of diseases such as bubonic and pneumonic plague, diphtheria, leprosy, phthisis, rabies, diabetes, gout, cancer, epilepsy, a skin disease known as *scabies grossa* or *scabies variola* which some historians have identified with syphilis, affliction with the stone and numerous surgical cases. Many of these *consilia* were printed in the late 15th and 16th centuries. They are the origin of modern case-history books.

The chief limitation of medieval doctors was, in fact, not that they could not recognise diseases but that they could not often cure them. They had very little understanding of either normal or morbid physiology or of the causes of most diseases, and they were sometimes further misled by the habit, coming from Aristotelian philosophy, of regarding each separate symptom and even wounds as manifestations of a separate 'specific form'.

A good idea of the state of medical knowledge in the 14th century can be gathered from the tracts written by physicians at the time of the Black Death. This plague seems to have begun in India about 1332, where an Arab doctor gave an account of it, and to have spread westwards, reaching Constantinople, Naples and Genoa by 1347. It reached a climax in the Mediterranean in 1348, in the North in 1349, and in Russia in 1352. It died down then, but smaller plagues went on recurring in the West at fairly frequent intervals till the end of the 14th century and at less frequent intervals for another three centuries after that. More than twenty tracts written at various places during the years of the Black Death show the characteristics commonly found in late medieval medicine: an orderly approach to the problems of symptoms, progress, causes, transmission, prevention and cure, in which is seen the combination of intense speculation based on causes no longer accepted in the 20th century with some very sound ideas on which effective practical measures were based. The eastern origin of the epidemic was generally recognised and several of the tracts contain full descriptions of the symptoms, for example that written by Gentile da

Foligno at the request of the University of Perugia in 1348 and the *Chirurgia Magna*, written in 1360 by Guy de Chauliac, an eminent product of Montpellier and Bologna and papal physician at Avignon. The symptoms included fever, pain in the side or chest, coughing, short breath and rapid pulse, vomiting of blood, and the appearance of buboes in the groin, under the armpit or behind the ears. Bubonic and pneumonic plague were distinguished. Some tracts gave, as early indications of the onset of the disease, pallor and an expression of anxiety, a bitter taste in the mouth, darkening of ruddy complexions and a prickling of the skin above incipient abesses which gave sharp pains on coughing.

Of the natural causes of the epidemic, considerable attention was devoted to astrological influences, and attempts were made to predict future plagues on the basis of planetary conjunctions. These remote causes were supposed to operate through near causes and in particular to cause the corruption of the air, though other causes of corruption were suggested, such as exhalations from the earthquake of 1347 and the unseasonable and very damp weather. Weather signs as well as astrological signs were watched as indications of the onset of plague, but some writers pointed out the lack of complete correlation of either with epidemics.

About prevention there was considerable uncertainty, most physicians advising flight as the only reliable precaution, and if that was impossible some form of protection against corrupt air such as avoiding damp places, burning aromatic wood in the house, and abstaining from violent exercise which drew air into the body and from hot baths which opened the pores of the skin. Since the corrupt vapours were held to cause plague by acting as a poison in the body one method of prevention was to take various antidotes against poison as, for example, theriac, mithradate, or powdered emerald. Bleeding to reduce the natural heat of the body was also advised. The usual methods of treatment were bleeding to remove the poison, administering purgative drugs, and lancing or cauterising the buboes or the use of a strongly drawing plaster. Attention was given also to maintaining the strength of the heart.

Though the physicians who had to deal with the Black Death were in many ways poorly equipped for the task, their experience made them give serious thought to problems never before discussed. As John of Burgundy put it in a passage translated by A. M. Campbell in her *Black Death and Men of Learning* from his *Treatise on the Epidemic Sickness*, written about 1365:

modern masters everywhere in the world are more skilled in pestilential epidemic diseases than all the doctors of the art of medicine and the authorities from Hippocrates down, however many they are. For no one of them saw so general or lasting an epidemic, nor did they test their efforts by long experiment, but what most of them say and treat about epidemics they have drawn from the sayings of Hippocrates. Wherefore the masters of this time have had greater experience in these diseases than all who have preceded us, and it is truly said that from experience comes knowledge.

The most striking new ideas put forward by the physicians of the Black Death concerned the method of transmission of the epidemic by infection. Of this the Greeks seem to have had little notion, attributing all epidemics to a single general cause, *miasma*. In the Middle Ages, the idea that specific diseases could be caught by infection or contagion was worked out first in connection with leprosy and by the 13th century had been applied to other diseases like erysipelas, smallpox, influenza, diphtheria and typhoid fever. A dancing mania, St. Vitus' Dance, that spread through the Germanies in the late 14th and 15th centuries, was also recognised as contagious. The segregation of lepers was based originally on the ritual of isolation described in the Bible and had been practised in Christendom at least from the 5th century. Leprosy was still a serious menace in the 12th century, when it seems to have increased somewhat and it is said that in France as many as one person in 200 was a leper, but from the end of the 13th century it began to decline. Physicians learnt to recognise the symptoms more accurately; in the mid-13th-century Gilbert the Englishman described the local anæsthesia of the skin which is one of the best diagnostic symptoms, and a century later Guy de Chauliac drew attention to the excessive greasiness of the skin. So successful were the methods of diagnosis and segregation that by the 16th century Europe was almost entirely free from leprosy, and similar preventive measures were taken against other infectious diseases.

Among the tracts written during the Black Death, two by Spanish Moors contained the most remarkable statements about infection. Ibn Khatima of Almeria pointed out that people who came into contact with someone with plague tended to contract the same symptoms as the diseased person, and Ibn al-Khatib of Granada said that infection could take place through clothes and household objects, by ships coming from an infected place, and by people who carried the disease though they were themselves immune. Scarcely less remarkable was the slightly earlier *consilium* on the plague by Gentile da Foligno, who used the words 'seeds (*semina*) of disease' (found also in works by Galen and Haly Abbas) for what would now be called germs, and *reliquæ* for the infectious traces left by patients. Some of the methods of infection suggested by Black Death physicians appear rather strange in the 20th century, for example, one based on the optical theory of the 'multiplication of species' according to which plague could be caught from a glance from the eyes of the patient. When the sick man was in agony the poisonous 'species' was expelled from the brain through the concave optic nerves. But at a time long before the germ theory of disease was properly understood physicians had learned enough about infection to advise governments on the precautions to be taken.

The first commission of public health was organised in 1343 in Venice, and in 1348 Lucca, Florence, Perugia, Pistoia and other towns made laws to prevent infected persons or goods from entering them. The first systematic efforts to isolate plague carriers date from the regulations made by Ragusa in Dalmatia, Avignon and Milan at this time. Ragusa, in 1377, issued a new law ordering the isolation of all travellers from infected regions for 30 days (called the *trentina*) and Marseilles, in 1383, extended this period to 40 days for ships entering the harbour, thus instituting the *quarantine*. Venice opened a quarantine hospital and brought in regulations about the airing of infected houses, washing and sunning of bedding, control of domestic animals, and other hygienic matters. Military hygiene had attracted attention since the early Crusades when losses had been heavy because of ignorance of elementary sanitation, and, in the 13th century, several works had been written on precautions to be taken by soldiers and large bodies of pilgrims. The most outstanding were a work written by Adam of Cremona for the Emperor Frederick II, a short treatise on military hygiene by Arnald of Villanova and the *Régime du Corps* by Aldobrandino of Siena. With the Venetian regulations began the interest of municipalities in hygiene.

A special branch of medicine in which some striking progress was made in the Middle Ages was ophthalmology. Operations like that for cataract had been known since classical times and the Arabs had acquired considerable skill in treating eye complaints, using zinc ointments and performing difficult operations like removing an opaque lens. The most popular Latin work on ophthalmology was written by a 12th-century Jew, Benvenutus Grassus, and based on Eastern sources. In the 13th century Petrus Hispanus described various cataract conditions in great detail and gave an account of the operation with gold needles. The outstanding advance made in the West was the invention of spectacles. That weak sight and particularly the difficulty of reading in the evening was felt as a serious affliction is shown by the number of salves and lotions prescribed for this complaint, but although lenses had been known for some centuries in both Christendom and Islam, it is only at the end of the 13th century that there is evidence of spectacles with convex lenses being used to compensate for long sight. This invention is traditionally associated with the names of two Italian Dominican friars and possibly it had some connection with the Venetian glass industry, though early spectacles were made also of crystal or *beryllus*. Certainly, in 1284, some Venetian bye-laws mentioned *roidi da ogli* and *lapides ad legendum*. The first medical man to refer to spectacles was Bernard of Gordon, in 1303, and references by Guy de Chauliac and others show that by the second half of the 14th century they had become fairly common, though concave lenses for short sight seem to have come in only in the 16th century. From Christendom spectacles spread to the Arabs and China.

In surgery, progress began in the West with Roger of Salerno's *Practica Chirurgica*, written at the end of the 12th century. Roger seems to have been influenced more by Byzantine doctors such as the 6th-century Aëtius and Alexander of Tralles, and the 7th-century Paul of Aegina, than by the Arabs. He shows acute powers of observation and some sound clinical practice. He broke and reset badly-united bones, treated hæmorrhage with styptics and ligatures, had an efficient method of bandaging, and described a remarkable technique for operating for hernia. His early 13th-century follower, Roland of Parma, showed particular skill with head injuries and described trephining and the elevation of depressed fractures. He also recognised the need to keep the hands clean and the patient warm. Both these surgeons were in most of their work 'wound surgeons', and in their treatment of wounds they followed Galen's advice and promoted suppuration by using greasy salves.

This treatment of wounds was opposed in the 13th century by the north Italian surgeons, Hugh and Theodoric Borgognoni, and in the early 14th century by the Frenchman Henry of Mondeville, all of whom had studied at Bologna. They said that it was not only unnecessary but also harmful to generate pus and that the wound should simply be cleaned with wine, the edges brought together with stitches, and then left for nature to heal. Another 13th-century

Italian surgeon, Bruno of Longoburgo, repeated this insistence on keeping wounds dry and clean and spoke of healing 'by first and second intention'. Further advances were made by another Italian, Lanfranchi, who, in his *Chirurgica Magna* of 1296, said that the cut ends of nerves should be stitched together, and by the Fleming, Jan Yperman (d. *c.* 1330), like Mondeville an army surgeon, who described many different cases from personal experience and emphasised the importance of anæsthetics. Mondeville himself invented an instrument for extracting arrows and removed pieces of iron from the flesh by a magnet. Progress in these directions continued throughout the 14th and 15th centuries, but in the mid-14th century Guy de Chauliac unfortunately abandoned the antiseptic treatment of wounds and under the influence of his writings surgeons returned to the salves and suppurations of Galen.

Though in the Middle Ages surgery was concerned mainly with wounds and fractures, it was recognised that surgical treatment was necessary for certain other ailments and in some operations considerable skill was acquired. The operations for the stone and Cæsarian section had been known from classical times and specialised surgical instruments, scalpels, needles and thread, saws, ear syringes, levers, and forceps of all kinds, had been developed by the Arabs. As early as the mid-13th century, Gilbert the Englishman, Chancellor of Montpellier in 1250, recognised the importance of surgical treatment for cancer, and at the end of the 13th century the Italian surgeon, William of Saliceto, described the treatment of hydrocephalic children by removing the fluid through a small hole made in the head with a cautery. Early in the 14th century Mondeville described the healing of wounds in the intestine by the antiseptic method and insisted on the necessity of binding arteries in cases of amputation. Mondino gave excellent descriptions of the operation for hernia both with and without castration, though the difficulty of this is shown by Bernard of Gordon's preference for the truss, of which he gave the first modern description. Gentile da Foligno noted that there was no ancient work on the rupture of the abdominal lining, for which physicians and surgeons had to rely on their own experience. Guy de Chauliac shows himself, in his *Chirurgia Magna* of 1360, also to have been a skilful surgeon and a good observer, and this treatise remained a standard work until the time of Ambrose Paré in the 16th century. He used the *spongia soporifera* and was particularly skilful with hernia and fractures, noting the escape of cerebrospinal fluid in fractures of the skull and the effect of pressure on respiration; he extended fractured limbs with pulleys and weights. A contemporary English surgeon, John Arderne (1307–77), who described the Black Death in England, gave an account of a new syringe and other instruments for use in the cure of fistula; his countryman, John Mirfeld (d. 1407), described a 'tornellus' for reducing certain dislocations. In 15th-century Italy the Brancas used plastic surgery to restore noses, lips and ears, the technique for which was suggested by the Roman doctor Celsus. For the nose, skin was taken in a loop from the upper part of the arm, one end being left attached to the arm until the graft on the nose had become firmly attached. Plastic surgery was practised also by the German army surgeon, Heinrich von Pfolspeundt, who, in 1460, described the gunshot wounds; another German army surgeon, Hans von Gersdorff, in 1517, described some elaborate mechanical apparatus for treating fractures and dislocations.

A special branch of surgery in which progress was made in the Middle Ages was dentistry. The Byzantine and Arabic physicians had recognised caries, treated and filled decayed teeth, and done extractions. The English surgeon, John of Gaddesden (d. 1361), described a new instrument, the pelican, for extracting teeth. Guy de Chauliac prescribed powder made from cuttle-bones and other substances for cleaning the teeth, and described the replacement of lost teeth by pieces of ox bone or by human teeth fastened to the sound teeth with gold wire. Later medieval dental writers

PLATE 7 The Dover Castle Clock (XIV cent.)

PLATE 8

GLASS MAKING

From British Museum MS. Additional 24189 (XV cent.)

described the removal of the decayed parts with a drill or file and the filling of the cavity with gold leaf.

This activity in surgery during the late Middle Ages concentrated attention on the need to study anatomy, and all the great surgeons from the 12th century onwards recognised that good surgery, and even good medicine, was impossible without a knowledge of anatomy (see above, pp. 135–40). For many years the Church had prohibited clerks from shedding blood and therefore from practising surgery; for this reason surgery was never recognised as a subject for study at medieval universities as medicine was. This meant that although some instruction was received in anatomy, the medieval medical student had to get his real knowledge of anatomy, as well as of surgery, as Mondeville advised, by working with a practising surgeon. The result of this exclusion of surgery from the universities, and particularly from the French and English universities, meant that surgery was sometimes relegated as a manual craft to itinerant barbers, who cut for the stone, hernia or cataract and had no training beyond apprenticeship to a barber. Only in Italy was surgery encouraged at the universities; at Bologna in particular *post mortem* examinations were carried out to determine the cause of death and, in the Black Death, to find out something about the effects of this disease. In the 15th century most of the best surgeons were Italians, and it was in Italy that the study of anatomy began to make rapid progress from the end of that century (see below, pp. 368 *et seq.*).

A medieval institution which did much to help not only the care of the sick but also the knowledge obtained from the observation of medical and surgical cases was the hospital. In ancient times Greek doctors had kept patients in their houses and there had been temples of Aesculapius where the sick gathered for treatment, the Romans had built military hospitals, and the Jews had provided houses for the needy. The foundation of large numbers of charitable hospitals for the relief of the poor and treatment of the sick was a product of Christian civilisation. The Emperor Constantine

P

is credited with the first hospital of this kind, and they became very numerous in Byzantium, one particular hospital founded in the 11th century having a total of 50 beds in separate wards for different kinds of patients with two doctors as well as other staff attached to each ward. These Byzantine hospitals were copied by the Arabs, who as early as the 10th century had a hospital in Baghdad with 24 doctors. In the 13th century there was a hospital in Cairo with four wings used respectively for patients with fevers, eye diseases, wounds and diarrhœa and a separate wing for women, with each wing equipped for preparing medicines and supplied with running water from a fountain.

In the West, most monasteries had infirmaries and asylums, and hospitals were founded by special orders of hospitallers like the Order of St. John of Jerusalem and the Brothers of the Holy Ghost. Many of these were leper hospitals, and a great impulse to the founding of hospitals was given by the Crusades, a movement which may have helped to spread this disease. When St. Bartholomew's hospital was founded in London, in 1123, there were already 18 hospitals in England. By 1215, when St. Thomas's was founded, there were about 170. In the 13th century 240 more hospitals were founded, in the 14th century 248, and in the 15th century 91. The same activity occurred in other countries. In 1145 the Brothers of the Holy Ghost founded a hospital at Montpellier which became famous, and from the early 13th century, under the inspiration of Pope Innocent III, Holy Ghost hospitals were founded in almost every town in Christendom. The 13th–century hospitals were usually of one storey and had spacious wards with tiled floors, large windows, the beds in separate cubicles, an ample water supply and arrangements for disposing of sewage. The earlier hospitals were simply for the care of the sick and feeble rather than for treatment, but in the later hospitals different diseases were isolated and specialised therapy introduced. A notable feature of these hospitals was the care of the insane and the sympathetic treatment of psychological disorders. As early as the 7th century Paul of Aegina had discussed at some length the causes and treatment of 'melancholia' and 'mania' and later, in the West, certain hospitals specialised in mental cases, as did the Royal Bethlehem or Bedlam in London at the end of the 13th century. Mental disorders were attributed to three classes of cause: physical as with rabies and alcoholism, mental as with melancholia and aphasia, and spiritual as with demonic possession. Treatment also fell into the same three classes, and in each case the method of trying to cure the patient usually involved some attempt to bring the cause of his suffering into the light of his rational consciousness.

Taken as a whole, medieval medicine is a remarkable product of that empirical intelligence seen in Western technology generally in the Middle Ages. The medical knowledge and treatment, like the other techniques and devices which were introduced, gave Western man power to control nature and to improve the conditions of his own life such as was never possessed in any earlier society. Behind this inventiveness lay, without a doubt, the motive of physical and economic necessity; but, as Lynn White has pointed out in an article contributed to *Speculum* in 1940, 'this "necessity" is inherent in every society, yet has found inventive expression only in the Occident'. Necessity can be a motive only when it is recognised, and among the most important reasons for its recognition in the West must be included the activist tradition of Western theology. By asserting the infinite worth and the responsibility of each person, this theology placed a value upon the care of each immortal soul and therefore upon the charitable relief of physical suffering, and gave dignity to labour and a motive for innovation. The inventiveness that resulted produced the practical skill and flexibility of mind in dealing with technical problems to which modern science is the heir.

V

CRITICISM OF ARISTOTLE
IN THE LATER MIDDLE AGES

(1) THE SCIENTIFIC METHOD

OF THE LATER SCHOLASTICS

THE ACTIVITY OF MIND AND hand that showed itself in
the additions of scientific fact and in the development of
technology made in the 13th and 14th centuries is to be seen
also in the purely theoretical criticisms of Aristotle's theory
of science and fundamental principles that took place at the
same time and were to lead later to the overthrow of his
whole system. Much of this criticism developed from within
the Aristotelian system of scientific thought itself and, indeed,
Aristotle can be seen as a sort of tragic hero striding through
medieval science. From Grosseteste to Galileo he occupied
the centre of the stage, seducing men's minds by the magical
promise of his concepts, exciting their passions and dividing
them, and, in the end, forcing them to turn against him as the
real consequences of his undertaking gradually became clear;
and yet, from the depths of his own system, providing many
of the weapons with which he was attacked.

The most important of these weapons were the result of
the development of ideas on scientific method and, in particular, on induction and experiment and on the role of
mathematics in explaining physical phenomena, for they
gradually led to an entirely different conception of the kind
of question that should be asked in natural science, the kind
of question, in fact, to which the experimental and mathematical methods could give an answer. The field in which
the new kind of question was to produce its greatest effects
from the middle of the 16th century was in dynamics, and it

was precisely Aristotle's ideas on space and motion that came in for the most radical criticism during the later Middle Ages. The effect of this scholastic criticism was to undermine the foundations of his whole system of physics (with the exception of biology) and so to clear the way for the new system constructed by the experimental and mathematical methods. At the end of the medieval period a fresh impetus was given to mathematics by the translation of some previously unknown Greek texts.

The great idea recovered during the 12th century, which made possible the immediate expansion of science from that time, was the idea of rational explanation as in formal or geometrical demonstration; that is, the idea that a particular fact was explained when it could be deduced from a more general principle. This had come through the gradual recovery of Aristotle's logic and of Greek and Arabic mathematics. The idea of geometrical demonstration had, in fact, been the great discovery of the Greeks in the history of science, and it was the basis not only of their considerable contributions to mathematics itself and to physical sciences like astronomy and geometrical optics, but also of much of their biology and medicine. Their bent of mind was to conceive of science, where possible, as a matter of deductions from indemonstrable premises.

In the 12th century, this notion of rational explanation developed first among logicians and philosophers not primarily concerned with natural science at all but engaged in grasping and expounding the principles, first, of the *logica vetus* or 'old logic' based on Boethius and, later in the century, of Aristotle's *Posterior Analytics* and various works of Galen. What these logicians did was to make use of the distinction, ultimately deriving from Aristotle, between experiential knowledge of a fact and rational knowledge of the reason for, or cause of, the fact; they meant by the latter knowledge of some prior and more general principle from which they could deduce the fact. The development of this form of rationalism was, in fact, part of a general intellectual movement in the 12th century, and not only scientific writers such as Adelard of Bath and Hugh of St. Victor, but also theologians such as Anselm, Richard of St. Victor and Abelard tried to arrange their subject-matter according to this mathematical-deductive method. Mathematics was for these 12th-century philosophers the model science and, like good disciples of St. Augustine and Plato, they held that the senses were deceitful and reason alone could give truth.

Though mathematics was regarded in the 12th century as the model science, it was not until the beginning of the 13th century that Western mathematics became worthy of this reputation. The practical mathematics kept alive in Benedictine monasteries during the Dark Ages and taught in the cathedral and monastery schools founded by Charlemagne at the end of the 8th century was very elementary and limited to what was necessary to keep accounts, calculate the date of Easter and measure land for the purposes of surveying. At the end of the 10th century Gerbert had initiated a revival of interest in mathematics, as he did also in logic, by collecting Boethius's treatises on those subjects. Although Boethius's treatise on arithmetic contained an elementary idea of the treatment of theoretical problems based on the properties of numbers, the so-called 'Geometry of Boethius' was, in fact, a later compilation from which most of his own contribution had dropped out. It contained certain of Euclid's axioms, definitions and con- clusions but consisted mainly of a description of the abacus, the device generally used for calculations, and of practical surveying methods and the like. The writings of Cassiodorus and Isidore of Seville, the other sources of the mathematical knowledge of the time, contained nothing fresh (above, pp. 3–5).

Gerbert himself wrote a treatise on the abacus and even improved the current type by introducing apices, and a few other additions were made to practical mathematics during the 11th and 12th centuries, but until the end of the 12th century Western mathematics remained almost entirely a practical science. Eleventh- and 12th-century mathematicians were able to use the conclusions of the Greek geometers for practical purposes, but were unable to demonstrate those conclusions, even though the theorems of the first book of Euclid's *Elements* became known during the 11th century and the whole of that work was translated by Adelard of Bath early in the 12th. Examples of 11th-century geometry are Francon of Liège's attempt to square the circle by cutting up pieces of cardboard, and the correspondence between Raimbaud of Cologne and Radulfus of Liège in which each vainly tried to outdo the other in an unsuccessful attempt to demonstrate that the sum of the angles of a triangle equalled two right angles. Little better work was done till the end of the 12th century.

In arithmetic, the situation was somewhat better owing to the preservation of Boethius's treatise on the subject and, for instance, Francon himself was able to show that it was impossible to express rationally the square root of a number not a perfect square. The marked improvements that took place in Western mathematics early in the 13th century occurred first in the fields of arithmetic and algebra, and this was due largely to the development of this earlier tradition by two scholars of originality. The first was Leonardo Fibonacci of Pisa, who had given the earliest complete Latin account of the Arabic, or Hindu, system of numerals in his *Liber Abaci* in 1202 (see above, p. 34). In later works he made some highly original contributions to theoretical algebra and geometry, his basic knowledge being derived primarily from Arabic sources, but also from Euclid, Archimedes, Hero of Alexandria and the 3rd-century A.D. Diophantus, the greatest of the Greek algebraists. Fibonacci on some occasions replaced numbers by letters in order to generalise his proof. He developed indeterminate analysis and the sequence of numbers such that each is equal to the sum of the two preceding (now called 'Fibonacci sequences'), gave an interpretation of a negative solution as a debt, used algebra to solve geometrical problems (a striking innovation), and gave solutions of various problems involving quartic equations.

The second mathematician of originality in the 13th century was Jordanus Nemorarius, who shows no trace of Arabic influence but developed the Greco-Roman arithmetical tradition of Nicomachus and Boethius, in particular the theory of numbers. Jordanus habitually made use of letters for the sake of generality in arithmetical problems and he developed certain algebraic problems leading to linear and quadratic equations. He was also an original geometer. His treatises contained discussions of old problems, such as the determination of the centre of gravity of a triangle, and also the first general demonstration of the fundamental property of stereographic projection, that circles are projected as circles (*cf.* above, pp. 83–7).

After Jordanus there was a gradual improvement in Western geometry as well as in other parts of mathematics; a number of important original ideas were added. In an edition of Euclid's *Elements*, which he produced in about 1254 and which remained a standard text-book until the 16th century, Campanus of Novara included a study of 'continuous quantities', to which he was led by considering the angle of contingence between a curve and its tangent smaller than any angle between two straight lines. He also proved the irrationality of the 'golden section' and calculated the sum of the angles of a stellated pentagon. In the 14th century the grasp of the principle of geometrical proof made possible the improvements introduced into trigonometry by John Maudith, Richard of Wallingford and Levi ben Gerson (see above, pp. 68–9), and into the theory of proportions by Thomas Bradwardine and his followers in Merton College, Oxford, and by Albert of Saxony and others in Paris and Vienna. This work on proportions, like the striking work of Nicole Oresme on the use of co-ordinates and the use of graphs to represent the growth of a function, was developed chiefly in connection with certain physical problems; it will be considered on a later page. Of considerable importance also were the improvements introduced into the methods of calculation in the Hindu system of numerals during the 13th and 14th centuries. The methods of multiplying and dividing used by the Hindus and Moslems had been very uncertain. The modern method of multiplication was introduced from Florence, and the modern technique of division was also invented during the later Middle Ages. This made division into an ordinary matter for the counting house, whereas it had formerly been a formidably difficult operation even for skilled mathematicians. The Italians also invented the system of double-entry book keeping, and the commercial nature of their interests is shown by their arithmetic books in which problems are concerned with such practical questions as partnership, exchange, simple and compound interest, and discount.

The recovery of the idea of a demonstrative science in which a fact was explained when it could be deduced from a prior and more general principle, and the great improvements in mathematical technique that took place in Western Christendom during the 13th century, were the chief intellectual achievements that made 13th-century science possible at all. The new methods also raised important methodological problems that had never been adequately considered by either the Greeks or the Arabs: the problems how, in natural science, to arrive at the prior principles or the general theory from which the demonstration of the particular fact was to proceed; and how, among several possible theories, to distinguish between the false and the true, the defective and the complete. The development of the inductive side of natural science, and, in fact, the thorough-going conception of natural science as a matter of experiment as well as of mathematics, may well be considered the chief advance made by the medieval Latin Christians over the Greeks and Arabs.

Among ancient Greek writers known in the early 13th century, only Aristotle and certain medical writers, in particular Galen, had seriously discussed the inductive side of science, and Aristotle himself was, of course, a doctor. Certain of Aristotle's followers in the Lyceum and in Alexandria, in particular Theophrastus and Strato, had had a very clear understanding of some of the general principles of the experimental method, and experiment seems to have been practised fairly generally by members of the medical school at Alexandria. But the writings of these authors were practically unknown in the Middle Ages. Even in their own time their methods did not have the transforming effect on Greek science which the medieval methods were to have in the modern world.

Among the Arabs, experiments had been carried out by a number of scientific writers, by Alkindi and Alhazen in optics and by Rhazes, Avicenna and others in alchemy; and certain Arab medical men, especially Ali ibn Ridwan and Avicenna, had made contributions to the theory of induction. But for one reason or another Arabic science failed to become thoroughly experimental in outlook, though it was certainly the example of Arab work that stimulated some of the experiments made by Christian writers, for instance Roger Bacon and Theodoric of Freiberg and possibly Petrus Peregrinus, discussed on earlier pages.

The experimental science that was to reach maturity only in the early 17th century developed in a tradition that was different from either the Greek or the Arabic. It owes its origin to the marriage of the manual habits of technics with the rational habits of logic and mathematics that took place in 13th-century Christendom. It was nursed in 13th- and 14th-century Oxford, Paris and Germany; it grew up in 15th- and 16th-century Italy; it burst from the constraining hands of its late scholastic guardians in the 17th century and conquered all Europe. Examples of the use of the experimental method which illustrate its development are described elsewhere in this book; in this section a brief account will be given of the theory of experimental science that was developed in the 13th and 14th centuries, particularly in Oxford, to which was due the beginnings of the conscious.

understanding of the nature of the enterprise in which the new science was engaged.

Among the first to understand and use the new theory of experimental science was Robert Grosseteste, who was the real founder of the tradition of scientific thought in medieval Oxford and, in some ways, of the modern English intellectual tradition. Grosseteste united in his own work the experimental and the rational traditions of the 12th century and he set forth a systematic theory of experimental science. He seems to have studied medicine as well as mathematics and philosophy, so he was well equipped. He based his theory of science in the first place on Aristotle's distinction between knowledge of a fact and knowledge of the reason for the fact. His theory had three essentially different aspects which, in fact, characterise all the discussions of methodology down to the 17th century and indeed down to the present day: the inductive, the experimental, and the mathematical.

The problem of induction, Grosseteste held, was to discover the cause from knowledge of the effect. Knowledge of particular physical facts, he said, following Aristotle, was had through the senses, and what the senses perceived were composite objects. Induction involved the breaking up of these objects into the principles or elements that produced them or caused their behaviour, and he conceived of induction as an upward process of abstraction going from what Aristotle had said was 'more knowable to us', that is, the composite objects perceived through the senses, to abstract principles prior in the order of nature but at first less knowable to us. We must proceed inductively from effects to causes before we can proceed deductively from cause to effect. What had to be done in trying to explain a particular set of observed facts was, therefore, to arrive at a statement or definition of the principle or 'substantial form' that caused them.

To arrive at such a definition Grosseteste described, first, a dual process which he called 'resolution and composition'.

These names came from Galen and other late Greek writers. The central principle of his method Grosseteste derived, in fact, from Aristotle, but he developed it more fully than Aristotle had done. By resolution he showed how to arrive at what he called the nominal definition. He began by collecting instances of the phenomenon under examination and noting the attributes all had in common, till he arrived at the 'common formula' which stated the empirical connection observed, a causal connection being suspected when attributes were found frequently associated together. Then, by the opposite process of composition, by rearranging the propositions so that the more particular were seen to follow deductively from the more general, he showed that the relation of general to particular was one of cause and effect. That is, he arranged the propositions in causal order. He illustrated his method by showing how to arrive at the common principle causing animals to have horns which, he said in his commentary on the *Posterior Analytics*, book 3, chapter 4, 'is due to the lack of teeth in the upper mandible in those animals to which nature does not give other means of preservation in place of horns', as she does to the deer with its rapid flight and to the camel with its large body. In horned animals the earthy matter that would have gone to form the upper teeth went instead to form the horns. He added: 'Not having teeth in both jaws is also the cause of having several stomachs', a correlation which he traced to the poor mastication of food by animals with only one row of teeth.

Besides this orderly process by which the causal principle was reached by resolution and composition Grosseteste also envisaged the possibility, as Aristotle had, of a theory or principle explaining repeatedly observed facts being reached by a sudden leap of intuition or scientific imagination. In either case, the further problem then presented itself, namely, how to distinguish between false and true theories. This introduced the use of specially arranged experiments or, where it was not possible to interfere with natural conditions, for example in the study of comets or heavenly bodies, the making of observations that would give the answer to specific questions.

Grosseteste held that it was never possible in natural science to arrive at a complete definition or an absolutely certain knowledge of the cause or form from which effects followed, as it was, for example, with the abstract subjects of geometry like triangles. A triangle could be completely defined by certain of its attributes, for instance by defining it as a figure bounded by three straight lines; from this definition all its other properties could be analytically deduced, so that cause and effect were reciprocal. This was not possible with material subjects because the same effect might follow from more than one cause and it was never possible to know all the possibilities. By making deductions from the various theories advanced and by eliminating theories whose consequences were contradicted by experience, it was possible, Grosseteste held, to approach closer to a true knowledge of the causal principles or forms really responsible for events in the world of our observation.

As he said in his commentary on the *Posterior Analytics*, book 1, chapter 14:

'This therefore is the way by which the abstracted universal is reached from singulars through the help of the senses . . . For when the senses several times observe two singular occurrences, of which one is the cause of the other or is related to it in some other way, and they do not see the connection between them, as, for example, when someone frequently notices that the eating of scammony happens to be accompanied by the discharge of red bile, and does not see that it is the scammony that attracts and withdraws the red bile; then, from the constant observation of these two observable things, he begins to form a third unobservable thing, namely, that scammony is the *cause* that withdraws red bile. And from this perception repeated again and again and stored in the memory, and from the sensory knowledge from which the perception is built up, the functioning of the reasoning begins. The functioning reason therefore begins to wonder and to consider whether things really are as the sensible recollection says, and these two lead the reason to the experiment, namely, that he should adminster scammony after all other causes purging red bile have been isolated and excluded. When he has administered scammony many times with the sure exclusion of all other things that withdraw red bile, then there is formed in the reason this universal, namely, that all scammony of its nature withdraws red bile, and this is the way in which it comes from sensation to a universal experimental principle.'

His method of elimination or falsification Grosseteste based on two assumptions about the nature of reality. The first was the principle of the uniformity of nature, meaning that forms are always uniform in the effects they produce. 'Things of the same nature are productive of the same operations according to their nature', he said in his tract *De Generatione Stellarum* (published by Baur in his edition of Grosseteste's philosophical works). Aristotle had stated the same principle. Grosseteste's second assumption was the principle of economy, which he generalised from various statements of Aristotle. This principle Grosseteste used both as describing an objective characteristic of nature and as a pragmatic principle. 'Nature operates in the shortest way possible' he said in his *De Lineis, Angulis et Figuris,* and he used this as an argument to support the law of reflection of light and his own theory of refraction. He said also, in his commentary on the *Posterior Analytics,* book 1, chapter 17:

that demonstration is better, other circumstances being equal, which necessitates the answering of a smaller number of questions for a perfect demonstration, or requires a smaller number of suppositions and premises from which the demonstration proceeds . . . because it gives us knowledge more quickly.

Grosseteste used his method of falsification consciously in several of his scientific opuscula where it was appropriate, for instance in his studies on the nature of the stars, on comets, on the sphere, on heat, and on the rainbow. A good example is in the tract *De Cometis* in which he considered in turn four different theories put forward by earlier writers to account for the appearance of comets. The first was that put forward by observers who thought that comets were produced by the reflection of the sun's rays falling on a heavenly body. This hypothesis was falsified, he said, by two considerations: first, in terms of another physical theory, because the reflected rays would not be visible unless they were associated with a transparent medium of a terrestrial and not a celestial nature; and secondly, because it was observed that

the tail of the comet is not always extended in the opposite direction to the sun, whereas all reflected rays would go in the opposite direction to the incident rays at equal angles.

He considered the other hypotheses in the same way in terms of 'reason and experience', rejecting those contrary either to what he regarded as an established theory verified by experience or to the facts of experience, till he came to his final definition which he held survived these tests, that 'a comet is sublimated fire assimilated to the nature of one of the seven planets'. This theory he then used to explain various further phenomena, including the astrological influence of comets.

Of even greater interest is the method Grosseteste used in his attempt to explain the shape of the rainbow (see above, p. 74), when he seized upon simpler phenomena which could be investigated experimentally, the reflection and refraction of light, and tried to deduce the appearance of the rainbow from the results of a study of these. Grosseteste's own work on the rainbow is somewhat elementary, but the experimental investigation of the subject which Theodoric of Freiberg undertook is truly remarkable both for its precision and for the conscious understanding he shows of the possibilities of the experimental method (see above, pp. 78 *et seq.*). The same characteristics are to be found in the work of other experimental scientists who came after Grosseteste, for instance in that of Albertus Magnus, Roger Bacon, Petrus Peregrinus, Witelo and Themon Judæi. Even though the same scientists sometimes showed a strange indifference to precise measurements, and sometimes even described purely imaginary experiments copied from earlier writers, or 'thought experiments', in support of statements, it was they who introduced into European science the experimental method that was to be used by Galileo and William Harvey.

Different from, though in many cases (as indeed in the case of Galileo himself) scarcely to be separated from, the experimental method and the making of special observations to verify or falsify theories, was the use of mathematics in natural science. Grosseteste himself, because of his 'cosmology of light' (see above, pp. 51, 71 *et seq.*), said in his little work, *De Natura Locorum*, that from the 'rules and principles and fundamentals . . . given by the power of geometry, the careful observer of natural things can give the cause of all natural effects'. And elaborating this idea in his *De Lineis* he said:

The usefulness of considering lines, angles and figures is the greatest because it is impossible to understand natural philosophy without these . . . For all causes of natural effects have to be expressed by means of lines, angles and figures, for otherwise it would be impossible to have knowledge of the reason for those effects.

Grosseteste, in fact, regarded the physical sciences as being subordinate to the mathematical sciences in the sense that mathematics could provide the reason for observed physical facts, though, at the same time, he maintained the Aristotelian distinction between the mathematical and the physical propositions in a given theory, and asserted the necessity of both for a complete explanation. Essentially the same attitude was taken by the majority of scientists throughout the Middle Ages, and, indeed, in a different form by most writers in the 17th century. Mathematics could describe what happened, could correlate the concomitant variations in the observed events, but it could not say anything about the efficient and other causes *producing* the movement because it was, in fact, explicitly an abstraction from such causes (see above, p. 51). This is the attitude seen in both optics and astronomy in the 13th century (see above, pp. 72, 56 *et seq.*).

As time went on, the retention of causal, ' physical ' explanations, which usually meant explanations taken from Aristotle's qualitative physics, became more and more of an embarrassment. The great advantage of mathematical

theories was just that they could be used to correlate concomitant variations in a series of observations made with
measuring instruments so that the truth or falsehood of these
theories, and the precise occasions where they failed, could
easily be determined experimentally. It was just this consideration which brought about the triumph of Ptolemaic
over the Aristotelian astronomy at the end of the 13th century
(see above, p. 62). In contrast with this clearly understood
role of mathematics in a scientific investigation, it was
difficult to see what to do with a theory of 'physical' causes,
however necessary they might seem to be theoretically for a
complete explanation of the observed occurrences. Moreover, many aspects of Aristotle's physical philosophy were a
positive hindrance to the use of mathematics. From the
beginning of the 14th century attempts were made to
circumvent these difficulties by devising new systems of
physics, partly under the influence of a revived Neoplatonism
and partly under the influence of the nominalism revived by
William of Ockham.

Improvements were made in the theory of induction by
several writers after Grosseteste and the enormous and
sustained interest taken in this purely theoretical and logical
question is a good indication of the intellectual climate in
which natural science was conducted before the middle of
the 17th century. Perhaps it does something to explain why
the brilliant beginnings of experimental science seen in the
13th and early 14th centuries did not at once go on to bring
about what, in fact, only happened in the 17th century.
For some four centuries from the beginning of the 13th century, the question guiding scientific inquiry was to discover
the real, the enduring, the intelligible behind the changing
world of sensible experience, whether this reality was
something qualitative, as it was conceived of at the beginning of that period, or something mathematical, as Galileo
and Kepler were to conceive of it at the end. Some aspects of
this reality might be revealed by physics or natural science,
others by mathematics, others again by metaphysics; yet

though these different aspects were all aspects of a single reality, they could not all be investigated in the same way or known with the same certainty. For this reason it was essential to be clear as to the methods of investigation and explanation legitimate in each case, and what each could reveal of the underlying reality. In most scientific writings down to the time of Galileo a discussion of methodology is carried on *pari passu* with the account of a concrete investigation, and this was a necessary part of the endeavour of which modern science is the result. But from the beginning of the 14th century to the beginning of the 16th there was a tendency for the best minds to become increasingly interested in problems of pure logic divorced from experimental practice, just as in another field they became more interested in making purely theoretical, though also necessary, criticisms of Aristotle's physics without bothering to make observations (see below, pp. 235 *et seq.*).

Perhaps the first writer after Grosseteste seriously to discuss the problem of induction was Albertus Magnus. He had a good grasp of the general principles as they were then understood, but of greater interest is the work done by Roger Bacon. In chapter 2 of the sixth part of his *Opus Majus*, 'On Experimental Science', Bacon said:

This experimental science has three great prerogatives with respect to the other sciences. The first is that it investigates by experiment the noble conclusions of all the sciences. For the other sciences know how to discover their principles by experiments, but their conclusions are reached by arguments based on the discovered principles. But if they must have particular and complete experience of their conclusions, then it is necessary that they have it by the aid of this noble science. It is true, indeed, that mathematics has universal experiences concerning its conclusions in figuring and numbering, which are applied likewise to all sciences and to this experimental science, because no science can be known without mathematics. But if we turn our attention to the experiences which are particular and complete and certified wholly in their own discipline, it is necessary to go by way of the considerations of this science which is called experimental.

The first prerogative of Roger Bacon's experimental science was thus to confirm the conclusions of mathematical reasoning; the second was to add to deductive science knowledge at which it could not itself arrive, as, for instance, in alchemy; and the third was to discover departments of knowledge still unborn. His experimental science was, he admitted, as much a separate applied science, in which results of the natural and speculative sciences were put to the test of practical utility, as an inductive method. His attempt to discover the cause of the rainbow (see above, pp. 76 *et seq.*), with which he illustrated the first prerogative of experimental science, shows that he had grasped the essential principles of induction by which the investigator passed from observed effects to the discovery of the cause and isolated the true cause by eliminating theories contradicted by facts.

For some three centuries after the middle of the 13th century a most interesting series of discussions of induction was made by members of the various medical schools, and in this the tendency towards pure logic becomes very marked. Galen himself had recognised the need for some method of discovering the causes which explained the observed effects, when he drew a distinction between the 'method of experience' and the 'rational method'. He referred to effects or symptoms as 'signs', and he said that the 'method of experience' was to go inductively from these signs to the causes which produced them, and that this method necessarily preceded the 'rational method' which demonstrated syllogistically[1] from causes to effects. Galen's ideas had

---

(1) The syllogism is a form of reasoning in which, from two given propositions, the premisses, with a common or middle term, is deduced a third proposition, the conclusion, in which the non-common terms are united. For example, from the major premiss, 'whatever has an opaque body interposed between it and its source of light loses its light', and the minor premiss, 'the moon has an opaque body interposed between it and its source of light', the conclusion follows, 'therefore the moon loses its light', that is, suffers an eclipse. In this way an eclipse of the moon is explained as an instance of a more general principle.

been developed by Avicenna in his *Canon of Medicine* and this work contained an interesting discussion of the conditions which must be observed in inducing the properties of medicines from their effects. The subject was taken up in the 13th century by the Portuguese doctor, Petrus Hispanus, who died in 1277 as Pope John XXI, in his *Commentaries on Isaac*, a work on diets and medicines. First, he said, the medicine administered should be free from all foreign substances. Secondly, the patient taking it should have the disease for which it was especially intended. Thirdly, it should be given alone without admixture of other medicine. Fourthly, it should be of the opposite degree to the disease.[1] Fifthly, the test should be made not once only but many times. Sixthly, the experiments should be with the proper body, on the body of a man and not of an ass. On the fifth of these conditions a contemporary, John of St. Amand, repeated the warning that a medicine which had had a heating effect on five men would not necessarily always have a heating effect, for the men in question might all have been of a cold and temperate constitution, whereas a man of hot nature would not find the medicine heating.

From the beginning of the 14th century the subject of induction was taken up in the medical school of Padua where, owing to the influence of the Averroïsts who had come to dominate the university, the philosophical climate was thoroughly Aristotelian. From the time of Pietro d'Abano in his famous *Conciliator* in 1310, down to Zabarella in the early 16th century, these medical logicians developed the methods of 'resolution and composition' into a theory of experimental science very different from the method simply of observing ordinary, everyday occurrences with which Aristotle and some of the earlier scholastics had been content to verify their scientific theories. Starting from observations, the complex fact was 'resolved' into its component parts:

(1) *I.e.*, if the disease causes an excess of one quality such as heat the medicine should cause a decrease in that quality, that is, have a cooling effect (*cf.* above, pp. 131 *et seq.*)

the fever into its causes, since any fever comes either from the heating of the humour or of the spirits or of the members; and again the heating of the humour is either of the blood or of the phlegm, etc.; until you arrive at the specific and distinct cause and knowledge of that fever,

as Jacopo da Forli (d. 1413) said in his commentary *Super Tegni Galeni*, comm. text 1. A hypothesis was then excogitated from which the observations could again be deduced, and these deduced consequences suggested an experiment by which the hypothesis could be verified. This method was followed by doctors of the period in the autopsies performed to discover the origin of a disease or the causes of death, and in the clinical study of medical and surgical cases recorded in their *consilia*. It has been shown that Galileo himself derived much of the logical structure of his science from his Paduan predecessors, whose technical terms he used (see below, pp. 291 *et seq.*), though he did not go so far as to accept the conclusion of a late member of this school, Agostino Nifo (1506), who said that since the hypotheses of natural science rested simply on the facts they served to explain, therefore all natural science was merely conjectural and hypothetical.

Of even greater importance for the whole of natural science were the discussions of induction made by two Franciscan friars of Oxford living at the end of the 13th and the beginning of the 14th centuries. With them, and particularly with the second of them, began the most radical attack on Aristotle's system from a theoretical point of view. Both were preoccupied with the natural grounds of certainty in knowledge and the first, John Duns Scotus (*c.* 1266–1308), may be considered as summing up the tradition of Oxford thought on 'theory of science' which began with Grosseteste, before that tradition was projected violently in new directions by his successor, William of Ockham (*c.* 1300–49).

The principal contribution made by Scotus to the problem of induction was the very clear distinction he drew between causal laws and empirical generalisations. Scotus said that the certainty of the causal laws discovered in investigating the physical world was guaranteed by the principle of the uniformity of nature, which he regarded as a self-evident assumption of inductive science. Even though it was possible to have experience of only a sample of the correlated events under investigation, the certainty of the causal connection underlying the observed correlation was known to the investigator, he said (in his *Oxford Commentary*, book 1, distinction 3, question 4, article 2), 'by the following proposition reposing in the soul: *Whatever occurs as in a great many cases from some cause which is not free* [*i.e.*, not free-will] *is the natural effect of that cause*'. The most satisfactory scientific knowledge was that in which the cause was known, as, for instance, in the case of an eclipse of the moon deducible from the proposition: 'an opaque object interposed between a luminous object and an illuminated object impedes the transmission of light to such an illuminated object'. Even when the cause was not known and 'one must stop at some truth which holds as in many cases, of which the extreme terms [of the proposition] are frequently experienced united, as, for example, that a herb of such and such a species is hot'; even, that is, when it was impossible to get beyond an empirical generalisation; the certainty that there was a causal connection was guaranteed by the uniformity of nature.

William of Ockham, on the other hand, was sceptical about the possibility of ever knowing particular causal connections or ever being able to define particular substances, though he did not deny the existence of causes or of substance as the identity persisting through change. He believed, in fact, that empirically established connections had a universal validity by reason of the uniformity of nature, which he held, like Scotus, to be a self-evident assumption of inductive science. His importance in the history of science comes partly from some improvements he introduced into the theory of induction, but much more from the attack he made on contemporary physics and metaphysics as a result of the methodological principles which he adopted.

His treatment of induction Ockham based on two principles. First, he held that the only certain knowledge about the world of experience was what he called 'intuitive knowledge' gained by the perception of individual things through the senses. Thus, as he said in the *Summa Totius Logicæ*, part 3, 2, chapter 10, 'when some sensible thing has been apprehended by the senses . . . the intellect also can apprehend it', and only propositions about individual things so apprehended were included in what he called 'real science'. All the rest, all the theories constructed to explain the observed facts, comprised 'rational science', in which names stood merely for concepts and not for anything real.

Ockham's second principle was that of economy, the so-called 'Ockham's razor'. This had already been stated by Grosseteste, and Duns Scotus and some other Oxford Franciscans had said that it was 'futile to work with more entities when it was possible to work with fewer'. Ockham expressed this principle in various ways throughout his works, a common form being one that was used in his *Quodlibeta Septem*, quodlibet 5, question 5: 'A plurality must not be asserted without necessity'. The well-known phrase *Entia non sunt multiplicanda præter necessitatem* was introduced only in the 17th century by a certain John Ponce of Cork, who was a follower of Duns Scotus.

The improvements Ockham made in the logic of induction were based principally on his recognition of the fact that 'the same species of effect can exist through many different causes', as he said in the same chapter of the *Summa Totius Logicæ* as quoted from above. He also said in his *Super Libros Quatuor Sententiarum*, book 1, distinction 45, question 1, D:

This is sufficient for something being the immediate cause, namely, that when it is present the effect follows and when not present, all other conditions being the same, the effect does not follow.

This amounts to what J. S. Mill was to call the Method of

Agreement and Difference. Since the same effect might have different causes, it was necessary to eliminate rival hypotheses. 'So', he said in the same work, prologue, question 2, G:

let this be posited as a first principle: all herbs of such and such species cure a fevered person. This cannot be demonstrated by syllogism from a better-known proposition, but it is known by intuitive knowledge and perhaps of many instances. For since he observed that after eating such herbs the fevered person was cured and he removed all other causes of his recovery, he knew evidently that this herb was the cause of recovery, and then he has experimental knowledge of a particular connection.

At the end of the passage already quoted from book 1 of this work Ockham added: 'All causes properly so-called are immediate causes'. He denied that it could be proved either from first principles or from experience that any given effect had a final cause. 'The special characteristic of a final cause', he said in his *Quodlibeta Septem*, quodlibet 4, question 1, 'is that it is able to cause when it does not exist'; 'from which it follows that this movement towards an end is not real but metaphorical' (he concluded in his *Super Quatuor Libros Sententiarum*, book 2, question 3, G). Only immediate or proximate causes were real, and the 'total cause' of an event was the aggregate of all the antecedents which sufficed to bring about the event.

The effect of Ockham's attack on contemporary physics and metaphysics was to destroy belief in most of the principles on which the 13th-century system of physics was based. In particular, he attacked the Aristotelian categories of 'relation' and 'substance' and the notion of causation. He held that relations, such as that of one thing being above another in space, had no objective reality apart from the individual perceptible things between which the relation was found. Relations, according to him, were simply concepts formed by the mind. This view was incompatible with the Aristotelian idea of the cosmos as having an objective principle of order according to which its constituent substances were arranged, and it opened the way for the notion that all motion was relative in an indifferent geometrical space without qualitative differences.

In discussing 'substance', Ockham said that experience was had only of attributes and that it could not be demonstrated that any given observed attributes were caused by a particular 'substantial form'. He held that the regular sequences of events were simply sequences of fact, and that the primary function of science was to establish these sequences by observation. It was impossible to be certain about any particular causal connections, for experience gave evident knowledge only of individual objects or events and never of the relation between them as cause and effect. For example, the presence of fire and the sensation of burning were found associated together, but it could not be demonstrated that there was any causal connection between them. It could not be proved that any particular man was a man and not a corpse manipulated by an angel. In the natural course of things a sensation was had only from an existing object, but God could give us a sensation without an object. This attack on causation was to lead Ockham to make revolutionary statements on the subject of motion (see below, pp. 248–9).

An even greater degree of philosophical empiricism, and one not to be attained again until the writings of David Hume in the 18th century, was reached by a French contemporary of Ockham, Nicholas of Autrecourt (d. after 1350). He doubted the possibility of knowing the existence of substance or causal relations at all. As with Ockham, from a limitation of evidential certitude to what was known through 'intuitive experience' and logically necessary implications, he concluded, as J. R. Weinberg translates him in his book, *Nicolaus of Autrecourt* (1948, p. 31): 'from the fact that one thing is known to exist, it cannot be evidently inferred that another thing exists', or does not exist; from which it followed that from a knowledge of attributes it was impossible to infer the existence of substances. And, he said (p. 69) :

concerning things known by experience in the manner in which it is said to be known that the magnet attracts iron or that rhubarb cures cholera, we have only a conjecturative habit but not certitude. When it is said that we have certitude concerning such things in virtue of a proposition reposing in the soul that *that which occurs as in many cases from an unfree course is the natural effect of it*, I ask what you call a natural cause, *i.e.*, do you say that that which produced in the past as in many cases and up to the present will produce in the future if it remains and is applied? Then the minor [premiss] is not known, for allowing that something was produced as in many cases, it is nevertheless not known that it ought to be thus produced in the future.

And so, he said, in a passage published by Hastings Rashdall in the *Proceedings of the Aristotelian Society*, N.S. vol. 7:

Whatever conditions we take which may be the cause of any effect, we do not evidently know that, when conditions are posited, the effect posited will follow.

The effect on philosophy in general of this search for evident knowledge was to divert interest within the discussions of the schools away from the traditional problems of metaphysics to the world of experience. Ockhamite nominalism or, as it may more properly be called, conceptualism, went to show that in the natural world all was contingent and therefore that observations were necessary to discover anything about it.

The relation of faith to reason remained a central problem in medieval speculation, and a diversity of attitudes was taken to it by Augustinians, Thomists, Averroïsts and Ockhamites. 'The spirit and the enterprise' of early medieval philosophy was, as R. McKeon put it in his *Selections from Medieval Philosophers* (vol. 2, pp. ix-x), 'of faith engaged in understanding itself'. Between Augustine and Aquinas philosophy had passed from the consideration of truth as a reflection of God to truth in the relation of things to each other and to man, leaving their relation to God for theology. Ockham himself firmly divorced theology from philosophy, the former deriving its knowledge from revelation and the latter from sensory experience, from which alone it took its origin. And whereas the Averroïsts were driven to assent to the possibility of 'double truth' (see above, p. 43), the Ockhamites, for instance Nicholas of Autrecourt, sought a solution to the problem in their doctrine of 'probabilism'. By this they meant that natural philosophy could offer a probable but not a necessary system of explanations, and that where this probable system contradicted the necessary propositions of revelation, it was wrong. In his own attempt to reach the most probable system of physics Nicholas made a thorough-going attack on the Aristotelian system and arrived at the conclusion that the most probable system was one based on atomism. After this time, no further attempts were made to construct systems rationally synthesising the contents of both faith and reason. Instead, there began a period of increasing reliance on the literal word of the Bible instead of the teaching of a Divinely instituted Church, a period of speculative mysticism seen in Eckhart (c. 1260–1327) and Henry Suso (c. 1295–1365), and of empiricism and scepticism seen in Nicholas of Cusa (1401–64) and Montaigne (1533–92). Nicholas of Cusa, for example, held that though it was possible to approach closer and closer to truth, it was never possible to grasp it finally, just as it was possible to draw figures approximating more and more closely to a perfect circle, yet no figure we drew would be so perfect that a more perfect circle could not be drawn. Montaigne was even more sceptical. Indeed, since the 14th century the stream of sceptical empiricism has flowed strongly in European philosophy, and it has done its work of directing attention to the conditions of human knowledge which has produced some of the most important clarifications of scientific methodology.

(2) MATTER AND SPACE IN LATE MEDIEVAL PHYSICS

The most radical attacks made in the 14th century on Aristotle's whole system of physics concerned his doctrines about matter and space, and about motion. Aristotle had denied the possibility of atoms, void, infinity and plural worlds, but when his strict determinism had been condemned by the theologians in 1277 this opened the way to speculation on these subjects. With the assertion of God's omnipotence, philosophers argued that God could create a body moving in empty space or an infinite universe and proceeded to work out what the consequences would be if He did. This seems a strange way to approach science, but there is no doubt that it was science they were approaching. They discussed the possibility of plural worlds, the two infinities and centre of gravity; and they discussed also the acceleration of freely falling bodies, the flight of projectiles, and the possibility of the earth's having motion. Not only did the criticisms of Aristotle remove many of the metaphysical and 'physical' restrictions his system had placed on the use of mathematics, but also many of the new concepts reached were either incorporated directly into 17th-century mechanics or were the germs of theories to be expressed in the new language created by mathematical and experimental techniques.

The form of atomism found in Plato's *Timæus* and Lucretius' *De Rerum Natura*, and in the works of several other ancient Greek writers[1], had been developed by some 13th-

(1) The development of the atomic theory in the Ancient World after the time of Plato and Aristotle (for development down to Plato see note on p. 14) was largely the work of Epicurus (340–270 B.C.), Strato of Lampsacus (*fl.c.* 288 B.C.), Philo of Byzantium (2nd century B.C.), and Hero of Alexandria (1st century B.C.). The theory of Epicurus was expounded by Lucretius (*c.* 95–55 B.C.) in his poem, *De Rerum Natura*. Epicurus made two changes in Democritus's theory. He held, first, that the atoms fell perpendicularly in empty space owing to their weight and secondly, that interactions between them which resulted in the formation of bodies took place as a result of 'swerves' which occurred by chance and led to collisions. He assumed a limited number of shapes but an infinite number of atoms of each shape. Different kinds of atoms had different weights, but all fell with the same velocity. Epicurus also stated a principle which had been held by certain previous atomists, namely, that all bodies of any weight

century philosophers. Grosseteste, for example, had said that
the finite space of the world was produced by the infinite
'multiplication' of points of light, and he also regarded heat
as due to a scattering of molecular parts consequent on
movement. Even Roger Bacon, though he followed Aristotle
and tried to show that atomism led to consequences which
contradicted the teachings of mathematics, for instance
the incommensurability of the diagonal and side of a square
(see above, p. 14, note), agreed with Grosseteste in regarding
heat as a form of violent motion. Towards the end of the 13th
century several writers adopted atomist propositions, though
these were refuted by Scotus while discussing the question
whether angels could move from place to place with continuous movement. Similar propositions were refuted again
early in the 14th century by Thomas Bradwardine (*c.* 1290–
1349). The propositions refuted were that continuous matter
consisted either of *indivisibilia,* that is, discontinuous atoms
separated from each other, or of *minima,* that is, atoms joined
to each other continuously, or of an infinite number of
actually existing points.

At the turn of the 13th century, a complete form of
atomism was put forward by Giles of Rome (1247–1316)
who derived the basis of it from Avicebron's theory of matter
as extension successively specified by a hierarchy of forms

---

whatever would fall in a void with the same velocity. Differences in
velocity of given bodies in a given medium, *e.g.,* air, were due to
differences in the proportion of resistance to weight. On collision,
atoms became interlocked by little branches or antlers; only the
atoms of the soul were spherical. To meet Aristotle's objection based
on the change of properties in compounds, he assumed that a 'compound body' formed by the association of atoms could acquire new
powers not possessed by individual atoms. The infinite number of
atoms produced an infinite number of universes in infinite space. It
seems that Strato's treatise *On the Void* was the basis of the introduction to Hero's *Pneumatica.* Strato combined atomist with Aristotelian
conceptions and took an empirical view of the existence of void,
which he used to explain the differences in density between different
bodies. In this he was followed by Philo in his *De Ingeniis Spiritualibus*
(which was not widely known in the Middle Ages) and by Hero, who

(see above, p. 50). Giles held that magnitude might be consideredin three ways: as a mathematical abstraction, and as realised in an unspecified and in a specified material substance. An abstract cubic foot and a cubic foot of unspecified matter were then potentially divisible to infinity, but in the division of a cubic foot of water a point was reached at which it ceased to be water and became something else. The geometrical arguments against the existence of natural *minima* were therefore irrelevant. Nicholas of Autrecourt was led, by the impossibility of demonstrating that there was in a piece of bread anything beyond its sensible accidents, to abandon altogether the explanation of phenomena in terms of substantial forms and to adopt a completely Epicurean physics. He came to the probable

---

denied the existence of a continuous extended vacuum but made use of interstitial vacua between the particles of bodies to explain the compressibility of air, the diffusion of wine into water, and similar phenomena. These writers also carried out experiments to demonstrate the impossibility of an extended void. Aristotle had proved that air had body by showing that a vessel must be emptied of air before it could be filled with water. Philo and Hero both performed the experiment, also described by Simplicius, showing that in a water clock or clepsydra, water could not *leave* a vessel unless there was a means for air to enter it. Philo also described two other experiments proving the same conclusion. He fixed a tube to a globe containing air and dipped the end of the tube under water, and showed that when the globe was heated air was expelled and when it cooled the contracting air drew water up the tube after it. The air and water remained in contact, preventing a vacuum. He also showed that when a candle was burnt in a vessel inverted over water, the water rose as the air was used up. Apart from these and some other Alexandrian writers, such as the doctor Erasistratus and members of the Methodical sect, atomism was not favourably regarded in Antiquity. It was opposed by the Stoics, although they believed in the possibility of void within the universe and in an infinite void beyond its boundaries; and it was opposed also by a number of other writers such as Cicero, Seneca, Galen and St. Augustine. But atomism was briefly discussed by Isidore of Seville, Bede, William of Conches and several Arab and Jewish writers such as Rhazes (d. *c.* 924) and Maimonides (1135–1204).

conclusion that a material *continuum* was composed of minimal, infra-sensible indivisible points and time of discrete instants, and he asserted that all change in natural things was due to local motion, that is to the aggregation and dispersal of particles. He also believed that light was a movement of particles with a finite velocity. He was obliged, to retract some of his theses. These discussions survived in nominalist teaching in the 15th and 16th centuries, in writings of Nicholas of Cusa and Giordano Bruno (1548–1600), and eventually led to the atomic theory being used to explain chemical phenomena in the 17th century.

Concerning the problem of void, which arose partly out of the discussion of whether there were plural worlds—for if there were what lay between them?—such writers at the end of the 13th and beginning of the 14th century as Richard of Middleton (*fl.c.* 1294) and Walter Burley (d. after 1337) went so far as to say that it was a contradiction of God's infinite power to say that He could not maintain an actual void. Nicholas of Autrecourt went further and affirmed the probable existence of a vacuum: 'There is something in which no body exists, but in which some body can exist', he said in a passage translated by J. R. Weinberg in his *Nicolaus of Autrecourt*, p. 161. Most writers accepted Aristotle's arguments and rejected an actually existing void (see above, p. 48), though they might accept Roger Bacon's description of void as a mathematical abstraction. 'In a vacuum nature does not exist', he said in the *Opus Majus*, part 5, part 1, distinction 9, chapter 2.

For vacuum rightly conceived of is merely a mathematical quantity extended in the three dimensions, existing *per se* without heat and cold, soft and hard, rare and dense, and without any natural quality, merely occupying space, as the philosophers maintained before Aristotle, not only within the heavens, but beyond.

Some of the physical arguments against the existence of

void were taken from such ancient Greeks as Hero and Philo, whose experiments with the candle and the water clock or clepsydra were known to several writers, in particular Albertus Magnus, Pierre d'Auvergne (d. 1304), Jean Buridan (d. after 1358) and Marsilius of Inghen (d. 1396). Some of these writers also mentioned another experiment in which water was shown to mount in a J-tube when air was sucked out of the long arm with the short arm under water. Another experiment was made with a water clock, with which it was shown that water would not run out of the holes in the bottom when the hole at the top was closed with the finger. This was contrary to the natural motion of water downwards and Albertus Magnus explained this as due to the impossibility of void, which meant that water could not run out unless air could enter and maintain contact with it. Roger Bacon was not satisfied with such a negative explanation. He held that the final cause of the phenomenon was the order of nature, which did not admit void, but the efficient cause was a positive 'force of universal nature', an adaptation of the 'common corporeity' of Avicebron (see above, p. 50), which pressed on the water and held it up. This was similar to the explanation already given by Adelard of Bath. Giles of Rome later substituted another positive force, *tractatus a vacuo* or suction by a vacuum, a universal attraction which kept bodies in contact and prevented discontinuity. The same force, he held, caused the magnet to attract iron. Another 14th-century writer, John of Dumbleton (*fl.c.* 1331–49), said that to maintain contact celestial bodies would, if necessary, abandon their natural circular motions as particular bodies and follow their universal nature or 'corporeity', even though this involved an unnatural rectilinear movement. In the 15th and 16th centuries, Roger Bacon's full theory was forgotten in Paris and condensed into the 'nature abhors a vacuum' that provoked the sarcasms of Torricelli and Pascal.

The possibility of both infinite addition and division of magnitude led to interesting discussions on the logical basis of mathematics. It was asserted by Richard of Middleton and later by Ockham that no limit could be assigned to the size of the universe and that it was potentially infinite (see above, p. 50). It was not actually infinite, for no sensible body could be actually infinite. Richard of Middleton tried to show also that this last conclusion was incompatible with Aristotle's doctrine of the eternity of the universe, which Albertus Magnus and Thomas Aquinas had said could be neither proved nor disproved by reason but must be denied from revelation. Richard said that as indestructible human souls were continually being generated, if universe had existed from eternity there would now be an infinite multitude of such beings. An actually infinite multitude could not exist, therefore the universe had not existed from eternity. The whole discussion led to an examination of the meaning of infinity. The development of the geometrical paradoxes that would arise from the categorical assertion of an actually existing infinity, such as in Albert of Saxony's discussion of whether there could be an infinite spiral line on a finite body, led Gregory of Rimini (1344) to try to give precise signification to the words 'whole', 'part', 'greater', 'less'. He pointed out that they had a different meaning when referring to finite and infinite magnitudes, and that 'infinity' had a different signification according to whether it was taken in a distributive or collective sense. This problem was discussed in the *Centiloquium Theologicum* attributed to Ockham. Conclusion 17, C shows that the author had achieved a logical subtlety which was to be recovered only in the 19th and 20th centuries in the mathematical logic of Cantor, Dedekind and Russell.

There is no objection to the part being equal to its whole, or not being less, because this is found, not so much extensively but intensively, wherever the remaining part is infinite intensively; . . . in the whole universe there are no more parts than in one bean, because in a bean there is an infinite number of parts.

These discussions of infinity and other problems, such as

the maximum resistance a force could, and the minimum it could not overcome, laid the logical basis of the infinitesimal calculus. Medieval mathematics was limited in range and it was only when humanists had drawn attention to Greek mathematics, and especially to Archimedes, that the mathematical developments which actually took place in the 17th century became a possibility.

Associated with the problem of infinite magnitude was that of plural worlds. It was asserted in 1277 by the Archbishops of Paris and Canterbury that the existence of several universes did not involve a contradiction, and the problem was usually discussed in connection with gravity and the natural place of the elements. The 6th-century A.D. Greek philosopher Simplicius, known in the 13th century in William of Moerbeke's translation, had interpreted Aristotle's statements about gravity as meaning that the intensity of the tendency of bodies towards their natural place varied with distance from that place. Several 13th-century writers, for instance Thomas Aquinas, accepted this theory. They regarded gravity as an *external* force of attraction analogous to magnetism and held that the weight of heavy bodies therefore varied with distance from the centre of the universe. Averroës had maintained that Aristotle had regarded gravity as the *intrinsic* tendency of a body to move to its natural place in the universe and such writers as Albertus Magnus agreed with this interpretation, which indeed seems to be what Aristotle meant. These writers rejected the idea that gravity was a kind of attraction at a distance exerted by the natural place or the centre of the universe or a body (the earth) already there. They held that in any movement the mover must accompany the moving body and they regarded gravity as an intrinsic property causing movement. In the 14th century Ockham altogether denied the premises of this argument (see below, pp. 248–50), but most of the greatest doctors of the 14th century, such as Jean de Jandun and Albert of Saxony, took the Averroïst view.

The question then arose, what was the natural place of an element, for example earth, at which it came to rest? In discussing this problem Albert of Saxony (*c.* 1316–90) distinguished between the centre of volume and the centre of gravity. The weight of each piece of matter was concentrated at its centre of gravity and earth was in its natural place when its centre of gravity was at the centre of the universe. The natural place of water was in a sphere round the earth so that it exerted no pressure on the surface of the earth which it covered.

Albert of Saxony refuted the Simplician theory of attraction at a distance, but in the course of so doing he gave an elaborate account of it, and this led to its being used to support the belief in plural worlds which reappeared with the revival of Platonism in the 15th century.

Heraclides of Pontus and the Pythagoreans maintain that each of the stars constitutes a world, that it consists of an earth surrounded by air and that the whole is swimming in illimitable ether,

the 5th-century A.D. Greek writer Joannes Stobæus had said in his *Eclogarum Physicorum*, chapter 24. The theory of gravity derived from the *Timæus* was that the natural movement of a body was to rejoin the element to which it belonged, in whichever world it was, while violent movement had the opposite effect (see above, p. 16). The Aristotelian objection that if there were plural worlds there would be no natural place thus lost its point. Matter would simply tend to move towards the world nearest it. This theory was mentioned by Jean Buridan (d. after 1358), and it was adopted by Nicole Oresme and later by the leading 15th-century Platonist, Nicholas of Cusa, who said that gravitation was a local phenomenon and each star a centre of attraction capable of keeping together its parts. Nicholas of Cusa also believed that each star had its inhabitants, as the earth did. Albert of Saxony had retained the essential structure of the Aristotelian universe; Ockham, though he held, like Avicebron, that the matter of elementary and celestial bodies was the same, said that only God could corrupt the celestial substance. Nicholas of Cusa said that there was absolutely no distinction between celestial and sublunary matter and that since the universe, while not actually infinite, had no boundaries, neither the earth nor any other body could be its centre. It had no centre. Each star, of which our earth was one, consisted of the four elements arranged concentrically round a central earth and each was separately suspended in illimitable space by the exact balance of its light and heavy elements.

(3) DYNAMICS—TERRESTRIAL AND CELESTIAL

Aristotle's dynamics involved several propositions all of which came to be criticised in the later Middle Ages. In the first place Aristotle considered that local motion, like any other kind of change, was caused when a potentiality in any object to move was made actual by contact with a motive force (see above, pp. 82 *et seq.*). That is, an arrow had always had a potentiality for flight and when the arrow was expelled from the bowstring this potentiality became actual. For Aristotle, if movement were to continue, the 'moving force' had to remain in contact with the object moved, as, for example, he supposed the Intelligences to move the heavenly bodies. Aristotle held further that the velocity of a moving body was directly proportional to the motive power and inversely proportional to the resistance of the medium in which movement took place. This gave the law, velocity (v) $\propto \dfrac{\text{motive power (p)}}{\text{resistance (r)}}$. Any increase in velocity in a given medium could therefore be produced only by an increase in motive power. He believed that in a void, if it could exist, bodies would fall with an infinite velocity. He thought that in a given medium bodies of various materials but of the same shape and size fell with velocities proportional to their various weights. He had seen that bodies falling vertically in air accelerated steadily and he thought that this was because the body moved more quickly as it got nearer to its natural place in the universe. The problem of how a projectile continued to move after it had left the bow or hand he explained by supposing that the bowstring or hand communicated a certain quality or 'power of being a movent', as he said in the *Physics* (p. 267a 4), to the air in contact with it, that this transmitted the impulse to the next layer of air and so on, thus keeping the arrow in motion until the power gradually decayed. If there could be a void a projectile would thus be unable to move in it.

Parts of Aristotle's dynamics had already been criticised in the Ancient World by members of other schools of thought. The Greek atomists had considered it an axiom that all bodies of whatever weight would fall in a void with the same velocity, and that differences in the velocity of given bodies in a given medium, for instance air, were due to differences in the proportion of resistance to weight (see above, p. 236, note). The Alexandrian mechanicians and the Stoics had also admitted the possibility of void, but Philo had said that differences in velocity of fall were due to different 'weight-forces' corresponding to different 'masses', and from this Hero drew the corollary that if two bodies of a given weight were fused, the speed of fall of the united body would be greater than that of each singly. The Christian scholar, John Philoponus of Alexandria, writing in the 6th century A.D., had also rejected both Aristotle's and the atomists' laws regarding falling bodies and maintained that in a void a body would fall with a finite velocity characteristic of its gravity, while in air this finite velocity was decreased in proportion to the resistance of the medium. The rotation of celestial spheres provided an example of a finite velocity that took place in the absence of resistance. Philoponus also pointed out that the velocities of bodies falling in air were not simply proportional to their weights, for when a heavy and a less heavy body were dropped from the same height the difference between their times of fall was much smaller than that between their weights. Philoponus did accept

Aristotle's theory for explaining the continuous acceleration of falling bodies, though this was not accepted by other late Greek physicists. Some of these put forward an adaptation of the Platonic conception of *antiperistasis*, according to which the falling body forced down the air which then drew the body after it and so on, natural gravity both receiving continuously increasing assistance from the traction of the air and continuously causing an increase in that assistance. As to the continued motion of projectiles, Philoponus pointed out the absurdity of supposing that the air could keep a projectile in motion, and put forward the original idea that the instrument of projection imparted motive power not to the air but to the projectile itself; the air, he said, hindered rather than assisted its subsequent motion. Philoponus' arguments were quoted, although without mention of his name, by Simplicius and through his works they became known in the 13th century. Simplicius himself had explained the continued acceleration of falling bodies by means of his theory of gravity. He held that the continually increasing motive power which, on Aristotelian principles, would be necessary to cause such acceleration was due to the increasing weight of the body as it approached the centre of the universe. The continued movement of projectiles he explained by the *antiperistasis* theory, holding that the projectile at the moment of discharge compressed the air in front of it which then circulated to the rear of the projectile and pushed it and so on in a vortex.

In the 13th and 14th centuries several writers accepted the view that the air was the cause both of the acceleration of freely falling bodies and of a supposed initial acceleration and the observed continued motion of projectiles. This was the theory adopted in the *De Ratione Ponderis* by the unknown author of the school of Jordanus Nemorarius (above, pp. 86–7). Thomas Aquinas accepted it to explain the movement of projectiles and so did Walter Burley; in part the theory was still accepted in the 16th century even by such physicists as Leonardo da Vinci, Cardano and Tartaglia.

During the 13th and 14th centuries criticisms were made both of these explanations of projectiles and falling bodies and of Aristotle's law of motion itself. New explanations were put forward. Roger Bacon said that in a heavy body each particle naturally tended to fall by the shortest route to the centre of the universe, but that each was displaced from this straight path by the particles lateral to it. The resulting mutual interference by the different particles acted as an internal resistance which would make movement in a void, where there was no external resistance, take time and not be instantaneous as had been argued by Aristotle.

Aristotle's whole conception that velocity was proportional to motive power divided by resistance was called in question in the 14th century by Thomas Bradwardine and by a certain Magister Claius. Aristotle himself had made some reservations about this law of motion for he had realised that, as in the case of a man trying to move a heavy weight, the motive power might not overcome the resistance at all, so that there might be no movement. This conclusion was inconsistent with the law $v \propto p/r$, for according to this law velocity would always have a finite value. Averroës had tried to overcome this difficulty by saying that velocity followed the *excess* of power over resistance, and some 13th-century Latin writers supposed movement to arise only when p/r was greater than 1. Thomas Bradwardine, in his *Tractatus Proportionum* (1328), limited comparisons of the proportion of power to resistance to cases when this was so. He tried, in what seems to be one of the earliest attempts to use algebraic functions to describe motion, to show how the dependent variable v was related to the two independent variables p and r. This he did by giving an interpretation of Aristotle's law based on the theorem given in Campanus of Novara's commentary on Euclid's fifth book, in which it was proved that if $a/c = b/c$, then $a/c = (a/b)^2$. Bradwardine argued that Aristotle's law meant that if a given ratio p/r produced a velocity v, then the ratio that would double this velocity was not $2^p/_r$ but $(^p/_r)^2$, and the ratio that would halve it was $\sqrt{^p/_r}$. The exponential function by which he related these variables may be written, in modern terminology, $v = \log\ (^p/_r)$. This was the form in which Aristotle's law of motion was almost universally accepted in the 14th and 15th centuries, though at the end of the 14th century Magister Claius revived another modification of it which had been popular in the 13th century and was to be taught to Galileo in the 16th. This modification came from Philoponus, who had maintained that velocity was proportional only to motive power and that resistance merely reduced it from a finite value. Thus, according to Claius, heavy bodies would fall in a void faster than light bodies but none would have an infinite velocity.

As to the nature and physical cause of motion, at least three different views were hotly argued in the 14th century, the first two of which began from the standpoint that motion was a process by which potentiality was made actual. The first view was that usually associated with Duns Scotus, namely, the theory that motion was a 'fluent form' or *forma fluens*. According to this theory, motion was an incessant flow in which it was impossible to divide or isolate a state, and a moving body was successively determined by a form distinct at once from the moving body itself and from the place or space through which it moved. This theory was held by Jean Buridan and Albert of Saxony. The second view was that motion was a 'flux of form' or *fluxus formæ*, according to which motion was a continuous series of distinguishable states. One form of this theory was held by Gregory of Rimini, who identified motion with the space acquired during the movement, and said that during motion the moving body acquired from instant to instant a series of distinct attributes of place. The third view of motion was that of William of Ockham.

When Ockham came to consider these problems he rejected altogether Aristotle's basic principle that local motion was a realised potentiality. He defined motion as the successive existence, without intermediate rest, of a continuous identity existing in different places, and for him movement itself was a concept having no reality apart from the moving bodies that could be perceived. It was unnecessary to postulate any inhering form to cause the movement, any real entity distinct from the moving body, any flux or flow. All that need be said was that from instant to instant a moving body had a different spatial relationship with some other body. 'I say therefore', he said in his *Super Quatuor Libros Sententiarum*, book 2, question 26, M,

that the moving thing in such a motion (*i.e.*, projectile motion), after the separation of the moving body from the prime projector, is the very thing moved according to itself and not by any separate power, for this moving thing and the motion cannot be distinguished.

Ockham was here approaching the concept of inertia[1], which was to revolutionise physics in the 17th century. His ideas were taken over by Nicholas of Autrecourt who said, as Weinberg has put it (p. 168):

'*x* is moved' means '*x* is at *a* at time *t*, *x* is separated from point *b* at time *t*, *x* is at *b* at time t_1, and separated from *a*'.

This fitted in with Nicholas' theory of the atomic nature of a *continuum* and of time. This Ockhamite concept of motion is particularly suggestive of 17th-century ideas when it was held in conjunction with the concept of infinite space, an idea which led to the 'geometrisation of space' in the 17th century. This conjunction was made by a late 14th-century writer, Marsilius of Inghen, though he did not himself

(1) According to the theory of inertia a body will remain in a state of rest or of motion with uniform velocity in a straight line unless acted on by a force. This conception was the basis of Newton's mechanics. For Newton uniform rectilinear motion was a condition or state of the body equivalent to rest and no force was required to maintain such a state. The theory of inertia was thus directly contrary to Aristotle's theory according to which motion was not a state but a process and a moving body would cease to move unless continually acted on by a moving force.

accept Ockham's concept of motion. Another important 14th-century writer, Nicole Oresme (d. 1382), put forward the idea that absolute motion could be defined only with reference to an immovable infinite space, placed beyond the fixed stars and identified with the infinity of God, but he adhered to the theory of *forma fluens* to explain motion. Ockham's ideas did not in fact bring about a revolution in dynamics in the 14th century. He simply put forward his theory of motion after a philosophical criticism of the basic idea of Aristotle's mechanics, namely, that motion was a process by which potentiality was made actual, and did not develop it in detail. He was not generally followed by his contemporaries.

A theory of motion put forward by Jean Buridan to explain the continued movement of projectiles and the acceleration of freely-falling bodies did place 14th-century dynamics on an entirely new footing and did eventually give rise to the 17th-century theory of inertia. This was the theory of *impetus*. The propelling action of the air Buridan rejected as absurd; the explanation of the acceleration of falling bodies by attraction to the natural place he rejected because he maintained that the mover must accompany the body moved. Following Philoponus, he said that in the case of projectiles the motive power was impressed on the projectile itself. A 13th-century version of Philoponus' theory had asserted that this *virtus impressa*, as it was then called, would, owing to its 'violent' and unnatural character, undergo of its own accord a gradual decay, so that a projectile fired horizontally would gradually turn downwards. Buridan's strategic move was to substitute for the self-corrupting *virtus impressa* a persistent *impetus* given to the body by the agent that set it in motion, a motive power which would maintain the body at uniform velocity indefinitely if it were not for the action of external forces. In projectiles this *impetus* was gradually reduced by air resistance and natural gravity downwards; in falling bodies it was gradually increased by natural gravity acting as an accelerating force adding successive increments of *impetus*, or 'accidental gravity', to that already acquired. Thus, while Buridan preserved Aristotle's principle that motion was a process maintained by a motive power (*impetus*) which must accompany a moving body to keep it moving, he succeeded in combining this with the idea that force was something which *altered* motion and did not merely maintain it. This is the definition of force on which Newton was to build his mechanics. *Impetus* in Buridan's dynamics was, in fact, analogous to *momentum* in Newton's, and his measure of *impetus* by the quantity of matter in a body multiplied by its velocity was similar to Newton's definition of momentum as the product of mass multiplied by velocity. The chief difference between the two was that Buridan said that, in the absence of external forces, *impetus* would persist indefinitely as well in a circle as in a straight line, whereas Newton's momentum would persist only in a straight line and would require a force to bend it in a circle.

Buridan said, in book 8, question 12 of his *Quæstiones Octavi Libri Physicorum:*

a mover in moving a body impresses on it a certain *impetus*, a certain power capable of moving this body in the direction in which the mover set it going, whether upwards, downwards, sideways or in a circle. By the same amount that the mover moves the same body swiftly, by that amount is more powerful the *impetus* that is impressed on it. It is by this *impetus* that the stone is moved after the thrower ceases to move it; but because of the resistance of the air and also because of the gravity of the stone, which inclines it to move in a direction opposite to that towards which the *impetus* tends to move it, this *impetus* is continually weakened. Therefore the movement of the stone will become continually slower, and at length this *impetus* is so diminished or destroyed that the gravity of the stone prevails over it and moves the stone down towards its natural place.

One can, I think, accept this explanation because the other explanations do not appear to be true whereas all the phenomena accord with this one.

For if it is asked why I can throw a stone farther than a

feather and a piece of iron or lead suited to the hand farther than a piece of wood of the same size, I say that the cause of this is that the reception of all forms and natural dispositions is in matter and by reason of matter. Hence, the greater quantity of matter a body contains the more *impetus* it can receive and the greater the intensity with which it can receive it. Now in a dense, heavy body there is, other things being equal, more *materia prima* than in a rare, light body.[1] Therefore a dense, heavy body receives more of this *impetus* and receives it with more intensity [than a rare, light body]. In the same way a certain quantity of iron can receive more heat than an equal quantity of wood or water. A feather receives so feeble an *impetus* that it is soon destroyed by the resistance of the air and, similarly, if one projects with equal velocity a light piece of wood and a heavy piece of iron of the same size and shape, the piece of iron will go farther because the *impetus* impressed on it is more intense, and this does not decay as fast as the weaker *impetus*. It is for the same cause that it is more difficult to stop a big mill wheel, moved rapidly, than a smaller wheel: there is in the big wheel, other things being equal, more *impetus* than in the small. In virtue of the same cause you can throw farther a stone of one pound or half a pound than the thousandth part of this stone: in this thousandth part the *impetus* is so small that it is all soon overcome by the resistance of the air.

This seems to me to be also the cause on account of which the natural fall of heavy bodies goes on continually accelerating. At the beginning of this fall, gravity alone moved the body: it fell then more slowly; but in moving this gravity impressed on the heavy body an *impetus*, which *impetus* indeed moves the body at the same time as gravity. The movement therefore becomes more rapid, and by the amount that it is made more rapid, so the more

(¹) Buridan's *materia prima* was, like that in the *Timæus*, already extended with dimensions. Quantity of matter was then proportional to volume and density. Duhem (*Etudes sur Léonard de Vinci*, 3e série, 1913, pp. 46–9) suggests that he approached the notion of density through that of specific weight, to which it was proportional. The Greek pseudo-Archimedean *Liber Archimedis de ponderibus* defined specific weight and showed how to compare the specific weights of different bodies by the hydrostatic balance or aerometer. This was well known in the 13th and 14th centuries.

intense the *impetus* becomes. It is thus evident that the movement will go on accelerating continually.

Anyone who wants to jump far draws back a long way so that he can run faster and so acquire an *impetus* which, during the jump, carries him a long distance. Moreover, while he runs and jumps he does not feel that the air moves him but he feels the air in front of him resist with force.

One does not find in the Bible that there are Intelligences charged to communicate to the celestial spheres their proper motions; it is permissible then to show that it is not necessary to suppose the existence of such Intelligences. One could say, in fact, that God, when he created the Universe, set each of the celestial spheres in motion as it pleased him, impressing on each of them an *impetus* which has moved it ever since. God has therefore no longer to move these spheres, except in exerting a general influence similar to that by which he gives his concurrence to all phenomena. Thus he could rest on the seventh day from the work he had achieved, confiding to created things their mutual causes and effects. These *impetūs* which God impressed on the celestial bodies have not been reduced or destroyed by the passage of time, because there was not, in celestial bodies, any inclination towards other movements, and there was no resistance which could corrupt and restrain these *impetūs*. All this I do not give as certain; I would merely ask theologians to teach me how all these things could come about . . .[1]

He went on, in his *Quæstiones in Libros Metaphysicæ*, book 12, question 9:

Many posit that the projectile, after leaving the projector, is moved by an *impetus* given by the projector, and that it is moved as long as the *impetus* remains stronger than the resistance. The *impetus* would last indefinitely if it were not diminished by a resisting contrary, or by an inclination to a contrary motion; and in celestial motion there is no resisting contrary . . .

Terrestrial and celestial movements were thus included by Buridan in one system of mechanics. In this he was followed by Albert of Saxony and Nicole Oresme, and the theory of

(1) Translated from the Latin published by Anneliese Maier, *Zwei Grundprobleme der Scholastischen Naturphilosophie*, Rome, 1951, pp. 211–2.

impetus came to have wide acceptance in 14th-, 15th- and 16th-century France, England, Germany and Italy, though it was vigorously opposed by Ockham. In the 14th century Buridan himself explained the bouncing of a tennis ball by saying that the initial *impetus* compressed the ball by violence when it struck the ground, and when it sprang back this imparted a new *impetus* which caused the ball to bounce up. He gave a similar explanation for the vibration of plucked strings and the oscillation of a pendulum.

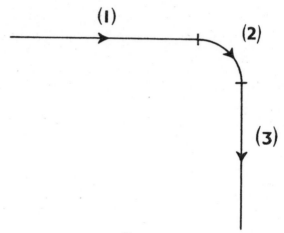

FIG. 33.

Albert of Saxony used Buridan's theory in his explanation of the trajectory of a projectile by compound *impetus*, an idea which itself went back to the 2nd-century B.C. Greek astronomer, Hipparchus, whose account was preserved in Simplicius' commentary on *De Cælo*. According to Aristotelian principles an elementary body could have only one simple motion at any time, for a substance could not have two contradictory attributes simultaneously since, if it had two, one would destroy the other. Albert of Saxony held that the trajectory of a projectile was divided into three periods: (1) an initial period of purely violent motion during which the impressed *impetus* annihilated natural gravity; (2) an intermediate period of compound *impetus* during which movement was both violent and natural; and (3) a final . period of purely natural movement vertically downwards after natural gravity and air resistance had overcome the impressed *impetus* (Fig. 33). He considered air resistance as having a definite frictional value even when the projectile was at rest. In a horizontally fired projectile, motion during the first period was in a horizontal straight line until it suddenly curved during the second period to fall vertically in the third. When fired vertically upwards the projectile came to rest during the second period (or *quies media*) and then descended when natural gravity overcame air resistance. This theory was accepted by Blasius of Parma (d. 1416), Nicholas of Cusa, Leonardo da Vinci and other followers of Albert of Saxony until it was modified in accordance with mathematical principles, first by Tartaglia in the 16th century and finally by Galileo in the 17th.

Nicole Oresme made use of Buridan's theory of *impetus* in his French commentary on Aristotle's *De Cælo*, *Le Livre du Ciel et du Monde*, written in 1377, when he was expounding the orthodox astronomical system. He compared the celestial machine to a clock set going by the Creator and then left to itself. He said, in book 2, chapter 2 :

et excepté la violence, c'est aucunement semblable quant un homme a fait un horloge, et il le lesse aler et estre meü par soy. Ainsi lessa Dieu les cielz estre meüz continuelment selon les proporcions que les vertus motivez ont aux resistences et selon l'ordrenance establie.

Oresme followed Buridan also in attributing the permanence of the *impetus* of the spheres to the absence of any resistance in that region, though other 14th-century writers, for example, Albert of Saxony, explained it as due simply to their incorruptible substance.

In another part of *Le Livre du Ciel et du Monde* Oresme postulated the rotation of the earth at the centre of an otherwise motionless universe, and here he made use of

Buridan's theory of *impetus* as well as the Pythagorean theory of gravity to overcome the traditional objections to the earth's movement. The possibility that the earth might be in motion had been discussed and rejected in the 13th century by two Persian astronomers, al-Katibi and al-Shirazi, though no connection has been established between them and Oresme. It had been asserted in 1277 that the centre of the universe could, without absurdity, be said to move. Oresme said that the centre of the universe had nothing to do with gravity, which was simply the tendency of heavier bodies to go to the centre of spherical masses of matter. He also denied the Aristotelian principle, used later by Tycho Brahe against Copernicus, that an elementary body could have only one simple movement which, for earth, was rectilinearly downwards. Elementary bodies, he said, could have dual movements. The natural and therefore perpetual movement of earth was rotation, and he attributed to the earth a natural and therefore permanent *impetus* causing its rotation. Oresme took from Witelo's *Perspectiva* the principle that to be perceptible to man motion must be observed in relation to two or more points, and he pointed out that although the sun, moon and stars appeared to rise and set daily, it was impossible to tell whether the earth or the heavens was in motion or at rest. All that could be observed was their relative motion. The arguments with which he then met Aristotelian and Ptolemaic 'physical' objections to the earth's rotation were similar to those used later by Copernicus and Bruno. One of the most important of these objections was the argument from detached bodies, that is, that if the earth were rotating on its axis any body thrown above its surface would be left behind to the west, birds, when they flew into the air, would be unable to return to their nests, and there would be a continuous strong east wind. To this Oresme replied that there would be neither a strong east wind nor would a stone or arrow sent upwards be left behind to the west, because air and water were included in the earth's rotation. So an arrow fired vertically upwards would have two movements, one vertically from the bow and another in a circle from being on the globe. The actual path of the arrow would be the resultant of the composition of these two movements, and just as to a person on a moving ship any movement rectilinear with reference to the parts of the ship appeared rectilinear, so to a person on earth the arrow would appear to fall vertically to the point from which it was fired. It was more reasonable, he said, to suppose that it was the earth which rotated and not the sky, for the latter would have to do so at an enormous speed. Then, he went on in book 2, chapter 25:

Since all the effects which we see can be made and all appearances saved by a small operation, that is the daily rotation of the earth, which is very small compared with that of the sky, without the multiplication of operations which are so diverse and out-rageously large, it follows that [if the latter existed] God and nature would have made and ordered them for nothing, and that is not fitting, as the saying goes.

Oresme's theory also did away with the need for the 9th sphere. He said it was not against scripture because this was meant merely to conform 'to the manner of common human speech'. He concluded somewhat abruptly:

Considering everything that has been said, one can then conclude that the earth is moved and the sky not, and there is no evidence to the contrary.

Albert of Saxony had said in his *Quæstiones in Libros de Cælo et Mundo*, book 2, question 26:

we cannot in any manner, by the movement of the earth and the repose of the sky, save the conjunctions and oppositions of the planets, any more than the eclipses of the sun and moon.

Buridan also had rejected the theory of the earth's motion. These phenomena could not, in fact, have been saved by the single diurnal movement of the earth discussed by Oresme. Neither he nor Nicholas of Cusa (1401–64), who in the next century threw out the suggestion that in every twenty-four hours the 8th sphere revolved twice about its poles while the earth revolved once, offered any mathematical system in place of Ptolemy's. And so astronomers, while not unaware of its defects, naturally retained Ptolemy's well-developed hypothesis until a better was forthcoming. Oresme's treatise was never printed and it is not known whether Copernicus ever saw it. The question of plural worlds on which, for instance, Leonardo da Vinci sided with Nicholas of Cusa against Albert of Saxony, continued to excite passionate debates at the end of the 15th century and long afterwards, and these authors were read in northern Italy when Copernicus was at Bologna and Padua. Cusa had given Buridan's theory a Platonic twist by attributing the permanence of celestial rotation to the perfect spherical form of the spheres; the circular movement of a sphere on its centre would continue indefinitely, he said in his *De Ludo Globi*, and as the movement given to the ball in a game of billiards would continue indefinitely if the ball were a perfect sphere, so God had only to give the celestial sphere its original *impetus* and it has continued to rotate ever since and kept the other spheres in motion. This explanation was adopted by Copernicus. And when Copernicus eventually offered a mathematical alternative to Ptolemy and had to consider gravitation and the other physical problems involved, his work was a direct development of that of his predecessors.

(4) MATHEMATICAL PHYSICS

IN THE LATER MIDDLE AGES

One of the most important changes facilitating the increasing use of mathematics in physics was that introduced by the theory that all real differences could be reduced to differences in the category of quantity; that, for example, the intensity of a quality, such as heat, could be measured in exactly the same way as could the magnitude of a quantity. This change was what chiefly distinguished the mathematical physics of the 17th century from the qualitative physics of

Aristotle. It was begun by the scholastics of the later Middle Ages.

For Aristotle, quantity and quality belonged to absolutely different categories. A change in quantity, for instance growth, was brought about by the addition of either continuous (length) or discontinuous (number) homogeneous parts. The larger contained the smaller actually and really and there was no change of species. Although a quality, for instance heat, might exist in different degrees of intensity, a change of quality was not brought about by the addition or subtraction of parts. If one hot body was added to another the whole did not become hotter. A change of intensity in a quality therefore involved the loss of one attribute, that is, one species of heat, and the acquisition of another.

Those who, in the 14th century, took the opposite side to Aristotle in this discussion of the relation of quality to quantity, or, as it was called, the 'intension and remission of forms', maintained that when two hot bodies were brought into contact, not only the heats but also the bodies were added together. If it were possible to abstract the heat from one body and add it alone to another body, the latter would become hotter. In the same way if it were possible to abstract the gravity from one body and add it to the mass of another body, the latter would become heavier. It was thus asserted, and supported by the authority of Scotus and Ockham, that the intensity of a quality such as heat was susceptible to measurement in numerical degrees, in the same way as the magnitude of a quantity.

Aristotle had analysed physical phenomena into irreducibly different species, but for mathematics one quantity is the same as another. Mathematical physics reduces differences of species to minute geometrical structure and movement. The origin of this idea is to be found in Pythagoras and Plato and it was developed by Augustinian-Platonists like Grosseteste, Roger Bacon and Theodoric of Freiberg. Galen also had suggested representing heat and cold in degrees and this became a commonplace among medieval doctors. In the 14th century these ideas led to the first systematic attempt to express qualities in terms of measurements. At the same time motion, where the statically conceived Greek geometry had been impotent, was first treated mathematically, thus leading to the foundation of the science of kinematics.

It was asserted that it was possible to treat degrees of intensity arithmetically and to speak of the speed with which intensity or *intensio*, for instance heat or velocity, increased or decreased in relation to *extensio*, for instance quantity of matter or time. A change was said to be 'uniform' when, in uniform local motion, equal distances were covered in equal successive intervals of time, and 'difform' when, in accelerated or retarded motion, unequal distances were covered in equal intervals of time. Such a 'difform' change was said to be 'uniformly difform' when the acceleration or retardation was uniform; otherwise it was 'difformly difform'.

These conceptions were combined with graphical methods. The Greeks and Arabs had sometimes used algebra in connection with geometry, and the graphical representation of the degrees of *intensio* of a quality against *extensio* by means of rectilinear co-ordinates had become fairly common in both Oxford and Paris by the early years of the 14th century. It was used, for example, by Albert of Saxony and Marsilius of Inghen. The most striking advances were made by Oresme, who was an original mathematician: he had conceived the notion of fractional powers, afterwards developed by Stevin, and given rules for operating them. Oresme represented *extensio* by a horizontal straight line (*longitudo*) and made the height (*altitudo vel latitudo*) of perpendiculars proportional to *intensio*. His object was to represent the 'quantity of a quality' by means of a geometrical figure of an equivalent shape and area. He held that properties of the representing figure could represent properties intrinsic to the quality itself, though only when these remained invariable characteristics of the figure during all geometrical transformations. He even suggested the extension of these methods to figures in three dimensions. Thus Oresme's *longitudo* was not strictly equivalent to the abscissa of Cartesian analytical geometry; he was not interested in plotting the positions of points in relation to the rectilinear co-ordinates, but in the figure itself. There is in his work no systematic association of an algebraic relationship with a graphical representation, in which an equation in two variables is shown to determine a specific curve formed by simultaneous variable values of *longitudo* and *latitudo*, and *vice versa*. Nevertheless, his work was a step towards the invention of analytical geometry and towards the introduction into geometry of the idea of motion which Greek geometry had lacked. He used his method to represent linear change in velocity correctly.

According to the definitions given above, the velocity of a body moving with uniform acceleration, which William of Heytesbury (*fl.c.* 1330–71) defined as 'the velocity of a velocity', would be uniformly difform with respect to time. It was proved at Oxford sometime before 1335 that the space traversed in a given time by a body moving with uniformly accelerated velocity was equal to the product of the total time of moving multiplied by the mean of the initial and final velocities. An arithmetical proof of this was given by the Mertonians, John of Dumbleton, William of Heytesbury and Richard Swineshead (*fl.c.* 1348), who was called *Calculator*. Oresme, in his *De Configurationibus Intensionum*, part 3, chapter 7, afterwards gave the following geometrical proof of this rule, which may be called the Mertonian Rule. He said:

Any uniformly difform quality has the same quantity as if it uniformly informed the same subject according to the degree of the mid-point. By 'according to the degree of the mid-point' I understand: if the quality be linear. If it were superficial it would be necessary to say: 'according to the degree of the middle line' . . .
We will demonstrate this proposition for a linear quality.
Let there be a quality which can be represented by a triangle,

ABC (Fig. 34). It is a uniformly difform, quality which, at point B, terminates at zero. Let D be the mid-point of the line representing the subject; the degree of intensity that affects this point is represented by the line DE. The quality that will have everywhere the degree thus designated can then be represented by the quadrangle AFGB . . . But by the 26th proposition of Euclid Book I, the two triangles EFC and EGB are equal. The triangle, which represents the uniformly difform quality and the quadrangle AFGB, which represents the uniform quality, according to the degree of the mid-point, are then equal; the two qualities which can be represented, the one by the triangle and the other by the quadrangle, are then also equal to one another, and it is that which was proposed for demonstration.

The reasoning is exactly the same for a uniformly difform quality which terminates in a certain degree . . .

On the subject of velocity, one can say exactly the same thing as for a linear quality, only, instead of saying: 'mid-point', it would be necessary to say: 'middle instant of the time of duration of the velocity'.

It is then evident that any uniformly difform quality or velocity whatever is equalled by a uniform quality or velocity.

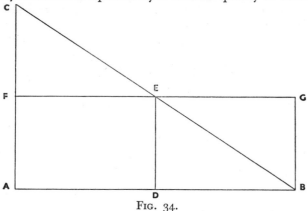

FIG. 34.

Though Albert of Saxony had given a plausible demonstration that a freely falling body moved with uniformly accelerated velocity, it was apparently not until the 16th century that the Mertonian Rule was used to calculate the space fallen in a given time. This was done first in 1572 by the

Spanish scholastic Dominico Soto who, resolving Albert of Saxony's hesitations as to whether velocity should be taken as proportional to space or time, chose the latter and brought together the two fundamental kinematical laws of falling bodies[1] 60 years before their expression by Galileo, who supported them by fresh arguments. Galileo himself used Oresme's proof.

Thus the 14th-century attempt to express the quantitative equivalent of qualitative differences led to genuine discoveries concerning both mathematics and physical fact. The latter were extended by the encouragement given to physical measurement, although here ideas were ahead of practical possibilities determined by the scope and accuracy of the available instruments. For example, Ockham said that time could be considered objectively only in the sense that by enumerating the successive positions of a body moving with uniform motion, this motion could be used to measure the duration of the motion or rest of other things. The sun's motion could be used to measure terrestrial movements, but the ultimate reference of all movement was the sphere of the fixed stars, which was the fastest and most uniform motion there was. Other writers elaborated systems for measuring time in fractions (*minutæ*) and the division of the hour into minutes and seconds was in use early in the 14th century. Although mechanical clocks had come in during the 13th century, they were too inaccurate for measuring small intervals of time, and the water-clock and sand-glass continued to be used. The accurate measurement of very short intervals was not, in fact, possible before the invention of the pendulum clock by Huygens in 1657.

The idea of representing heat and cold in numerical degrees was also familiar to physicians. As a zero point Galen

(1) These are that when a heavy body falls freely it moves with uniformly accelerated motion and that velocity increases in direct proportion to time. A third aspect of falling bodies, that the acceleration is the same for all bodies of any substance, was first fully appreciated only by Galileo.

had suggested a 'neutral heat' which was neither hot nor cold. Since the only means of determining the degree of heat was by direct sense-perception and a person of hotter temperature would perceive this 'neutral temperature' as cold, and *vice versa*, he had suggested, as a standard neutral degree of heat, a mixture of equal quantities of what he regarded as the hottest (boiling water) and coldest (ice) possible substances. From these ideas Arab and Latin physicians developed the idea of scales of degrees, a popular scale being one ranging from 0 to 4 degrees of heat or of cold. Drugs also were supposed to have something analogous to a heating or cooling effect and were given their place on a scale. Natural philosophers adopted a scale of 8 degrees for each of the four primary qualities. Though in these attempts to estimate degrees of heat, it was known that heat caused expansion, the only thermometer was still the senses.

Besides the water clock and sand-glass, the mechanical clock, the astronomical instruments already described, and such 'mathematical instruments' as the straight-edge, square, compass and dividers, the only other scientific measuring instruments available in the 14th and 15th centuries were, in fact, the rules, measures, balances and weights for employing the standards of length, capacity and weight recognised in trade. Balances of both the equal-arm and steel-yard type date from Antiquity and were used by alchemists and by assayors in metallurgy.

Further attempts to make use of measurement and experiment in science were made during the 15th century, when the scientific leadership of Europe passed from the Anglo-French universities to Germany and Italy. Attempts had been made in the 14th century to express the relationship between the elements graphically on a chart and to state the proportions of the elements and the degrees of the primary qualities for each of the metals, spirits (quicksilver, sulphur, arsenic, sal ammoniac), etc. In the fourth book of his *Idiota*, entitled *De Staticis Experimentis*, Nicholas of Cusa suggested that such problems should be solved by weighing. His conclusions imply the idea of the conservation of matter.

Idiot . . . For weighing a piece of Wood, and then burning it thoroughly, and then weighing the ashes, it is knowne how much water there was in the wood, for there is nothing that hath a heavie weight but water and earth. It is knowne moreover by the divers weight of wood in aire, water and oyle, how much the water that is in the wood, is heavier or lighter than clean spring water, and so how much aire there is in it. So by the diversity of the weight of ashes, how much fire there is in them : and of the Elements may bee gotten by a nearer conjecture, though precision be always inattingible. And as I have said, of Wood, so may be done with Herbs, flesh and other things.

Orator. There is a saying, that no pure element is to be given, how is this to be prov'd by the Ballance?

Idiot. If a man should put a hundred weight of earth into a great earthen pot, and then should take some Herbs, and Seeds, and weigh them, and then plant or sow them in that pot, and then should let them grow there so long, untill hee had successively by little and little, gottenan hundred weight of them, he would finde the earth but very little diminished, when he came to weigh it againe: by which he might gather that all the aforesaid herbs, had their weight from the water. Therefore the waters being ingrossed (or impregnated) in the earth, attracted a terrestreity, and by the opperation of the Sunne, upon the Herb were condensed (or were condensed into an Herb). If those Herbs bee then burn't to ashes, mayst thou not guesse by the diversity of the weights of all, how much earth thou foundest more than the hundred weight, and then conclude that the water brought all that? For the Elements are convertible one into another by parts, as wee finde by a glass put into the snow, where wee shall see the aire condensed into water, and flowing in the glass.

The *Statick Experiments* contained several other suggested applications of the balance. One of these, the comparison of the weights of herbs with those of blood or urine, was directed towards understanding the action of medicines. This was investigated in a different way in the *Liber Distillandi* published by Hieronymus Brunschwig in Strassburg in 1500, in which it was recognised that the action of drugs depended on pure principles, 'spirits' or 'quintessences' which could be extracted by steam distillation and other chemical methods. Cusa also suggested that the time a given weight of water took to run through a given hole might be used as the standard of comparison for pulse rates. The purity of samples of gold and other metals, he said, could be discovered by determining their specific weights, using Archimedes' principle. The balance might be used also to measure the 'virtue' of a lodestone attracting a piece of iron and, in the form of a hygrometer consisting of a piece of wool balancing a weight, to determine the 'weight' of the air. The same device was described by Leon Battista Alberti (1404–72) and by Leonardo da Vinci (1452–1519). The air might also be 'weighed', Cusa said, by determining the effect of air resistance on falling weights while time was measured by the weight of water running through a small hole.

Whether might not a man, by letting a stone fall from a high tower, and letting water run out of a narrow hole, into a Bason in the meane time; and then weighing the water that is runne out, and doing the same with a piece of wood of equall bignesse, by the diversity of the weights of the water, wood, and stone, attain to know the weight of the aire?

Cusa's suggestions were sometimes a little vague and it is rather tantalising that the last experiment should have been described without reference to the dynamics of falling bodies. This problem was taken up, suggestively but inadequately, by the Italian doctor Giovanni Marliani (d. 1483). Marliani, whose discussion of the intensity of heat in the human body involved some observations on heat regulation, developed Bradwardine's modification of Aristotle's law of motion. In criticising the Aristotelian law Marliani made experiments based on dynamical deductions from the statics of Jordanus Nemorarius, which had been kept alive at Oxford, and had been made known to the Italians by the *Tractatus de Ponderibus* of Blasius of Parma (d. 1416). Marliani showed in his

De Proportione Motuum in Velocitate that the period of a pendulum decreased with decreasing length and that the rate at which balls rolled down inclined planes increased with the angle of inclination. But he did not determine the precise quantitative relations involved.

Better work was done in astronomy by Georg Puerbach (1423–61) and Johannes Müller or Regiomontanus (1436–76). Puerbach, who held a professorship at Vienna, assisted in a revision of the *Alfonsine Tables*, and perceiving, as some 14th-century writers had done, the advantage of using sines instead of chords, he computed a table of sines for every 10′. Regiomontanus, who knew the work of Levi ben Gerson (see above, p. 68), wrote a systematic treatise on trigonometry which was to have a great influence, computed a table of sines for every minute and a table of tangents for every degree, and completed a text-book begun by Puerbach and based on Greek sources, the *Epitome in Ptolemæi Almagestum*, which was printed at Venice in 1496. Regiomontanus' pupil, Bernard Walther (1430–1504), with whom he collaborated in the observatory built at Nuremberg, was the first to employ for purposes of scientific measurement a clock driven by a hanging weight. In this the hour wheel was fitted with 56 teeth so that each tooth represented a fraction more than a minute.

The mathematical physics of the 14th and 15th centuries developed without a break into that of the 16th and 17th centuries, but in comparison with the latter the former was limited in both experimental and mathematical technique. The failure to put into general practice the experimental method so brilliantly initiated in the 13th century and the excessive passion for logic, which affected science as a whole, meant that the factual basis of the theoretical discussions was sometimes very slight. The mathematical expression of qualitative intensity in the 'art of latitudes', as it was called, thus gave rise to the same naïve excesses as the analogous attempts, to which this was the father, at omnicompetent mechanism in the 17th and 18th centuries. For instance,

Oresme extended the *impetus* theory to psychology. One of his followers, Henry of Hesse (1325–97), while doubting whether the proportions and intensions of the elements in a given substance were knowable in detail, seriously considered the possibility of the generation of a plant or animal from the corpse of another species, for example of a fox from a dead dog. For although the number of permutations and combinations was enormous, during the corruption of a corpse the primary qualities might be altered to the proportions in which they occurred in some other living thing. Swineshead had discussed latitudes of moral virtue. Gentile da Foligno (d. 1348) applied the method to Galen's physiology and this was elaborated in the 15th century by Jacopo da Forli and others who treated health as a quality like heat and expressed it in numerical degrees. Such elaborately subtle and entirely sterile misapplications of a method called down the ridicule of humanists like Luis Vives (1492–1540) and Pico della Mirandola (1463–94), and made Erasmus (1467–1536) groan when he remembered the lectures he had had to endure at the university. The same geometrical ideal was expressed again in 1540 by Rheticus when he said that medicine could achieve the perfection to which Copernicus had brought astronomy, and again by Descartes.

*   *   *   *

Many scholars now agree that 15th-century humanism, which arose in Italy and spread northwards, was an interruption in the development of science. The so-called 'revival of letters' deflected interest from matter to literary style and, in turning back to Classical Antiquity, its devotees affected to ignore the scientific progress of the previous three centuries. The same absurd conceit that led the humanists to abuse and misrepresent their immediate predecessors for using Latin constructions unknown to Cicero and to put out the propaganda which, in varying degrees, has captivated historical opinion until quite recently, also allowed them to borrow from the scholastics without acknowledgment. This habit affected almost all the great scientists of the 16th and 17th centuries, whether Catholic or Protestant, and it has required the labours of a Duhem or a Maier to show that their statements on matters of history cannot be accepted at their face value.

This literary movement performed some important services for science. Ultimately perhaps the greatest of these was the simplification and clarification of language, although this occurred mainly in the 17th century when it applied particularly to French; the most immediate service was to supply the means of developing mathematical technique. The development and physical application of the many problems discussed in Oxford, Paris, Heidelberg or Padua in terms of logic and simple geometry were sharply limited by lack of mathematics. It was unusual for medieval university students to progress beyond the first book of Euclid, and although the Hindu system was known, Roman numerals continued in use, although not among mathematicians, into the 17th century. Competent mathematicians, such as Fibonacci, Jordanus Nemorarius, Bradwardine, Oresme, Richard of Wallingford and Regiomontanus were, of course, better equipped and made original contributions to geo-metry, algebra and trigonometry, but there was no con-tinuous mathematical tradition comparable with that in logic. The new translations by the humanists, presented to the public through the newly-invented printing press, placed the wealth of Greek mathematics within easy grasp. Some of these Greek authors, such as Euclid and Ptolemy, had been studied in the preceding centuries; others, such as Apollonius and Diophantus, were available in earlier translations but not generally studied; while others, in particular Archi-medes, had been almost or entirely unknown. The scholastic idea of expressing quality as quantity and change in terms of mathematics, when united with the practice of the scholastic theory of induction and experimental method, could then be developed into the mathematical physics and infinitesimal calculus of Galileo, Descartes and Newton and through them into the application of the principle of measurement to all science, physical and biological.

Not only mathematics and physical science, but also biology benefited from the translations published by the humanists. The humanist press made readily available the works of biological authors which had been either, like Celsus (*fl.* 14–37 A.D.), previously unknown or, like Theophrastus, known only through secondary sources, and new translations of Aristotle and Galen. The new texts acted as a stimulus to the study of biology in what was at first a very curious way, for not the least important motive was the desire of humanist scholars, with their excessive adulation of Antiquity, to identify animals, plants and minerals mentioned by classical authors. The limitations of this motive were eventually made evident by the very biological studies which it inspired, for these revealed the limitations of classical knowledge, and this was shown still further by the new fauna and flora discovered as a result of geographical exploration, by the increasing practical knowledge of anatomy being acquired by the surgeons, and by the brilliant advances in biological illustration stimulated by naturalistic art. This original humanist motive does draw attention to a feature of 16th- and early 17th-century science in nearly all its branches which historians of science of an earlier generation than the present would have been inclined to associate rather with the preceding centuries; for it was just this extravagant reverence for the ancients, just this devotion to the texts of Aristotle or Galen, which provoked the sarcastic hostility of the contemporary scientists who were trying to use their eyes to look at the world in a new way. And the beginning of this new science dates from the 13th century.

In concluding this chapter, the principal original contributions made during the Middle Ages to the development of natural science in Europe may be summarised as follows:

1. In the field of scientific method, the recovery of the idea of rational explanation and in particular of the use of

mathematics raised the problem of how to construct and to verify or falsify theories, and this problem was solved by the scholastic theory of induction and experimental method. Examples of this are seen in optics and magnetics in the 13th and 14th centuries.

2. Another important contribution to scientific method was the extension of mathematics to the whole of physical science, at least in principle, Aristotle having restricted the use of mathematics in his theory of the subordination of one science to another by sharply distinguishing the explicative roles of mathematics and 'physics'. The effect of this change was not so much to destroy this distinction in principle as to change the kind of question scientists asked. They began, in fact, to show less interest in the 'physical' or metaphysical question of cause and to ask the kind of question that could be answered by a mathematical theory within reach of experimental verification. Examples of this method are seen in statics, optics and astronomy in the 13th and 14th centuries.

3. Besides these ideas on method, though often closely connected with them, a radically new approach to the question of space and motion began at the end of the 13th century. Greek mathematicians had constructed a mathematics of rest, and important advances in statics had been made during the 13th century; the 14th century saw the first attempts to construct a mathematics of change and motion. Of the various elements contributing to this new dynamics, the ideas that space might be infinite and void, and the universe without a centre, destroyed Aristotle's cosmos with its qualitatively different directions and led to the idea of relative motion. Concerning motion, the chief new idea was that of *impetus*, and the most significant characteristics of this concept are that the quantity of *impetus* was proportional to the quantity of *materia prima* in the body and the velocity imparted to it, and that the *impetus* imparted would persist indefinitely were it not for air resistance and the action of gravity. *Impetus* was still a 'physical' cause in the

Aristotelian sense and, in considering motion as a state requiring no continuous efficient causation, Ockham came closer to the 17th-century idea of inertial motion. The theory of *impetus* was used to explain many different phenomena, for instance the motion of projectiles and falling bodies, bouncing balls, pendulums and the rotation of the heavens or of the earth. The possibility of the last was suggested by the concept of relative motion, and objections to it from the argument from detached bodies were met by the idea of 'compound *impetus*' advanced by Oresme. The kinematic study of accelerated motion began also in the 14th century, and the solution of one particular problem, that of a body moving with uniform acceleration, was to be applied later to falling bodies. Discussions of the nature of a continuum and of maxima and minima began also in the 14th century.

4. In the field of technology, the Middle Ages saw the most rapid progress since prehistoric times. Beginning with new methods of exploiting animal-, water- and wind-power, new machines were developed for a variety of purposes, often requiring considerable precision. Some technical inventions, for instance the mechanical clock and magnifying lenses, were to be used as scientific instruments. Measuring instruments such as the astrolabe and quadrant were greatly improved as a result of the demand for accurate measurement. In chemistry, the balance came into general use. Empirical advances were made and the experimental habit led to the development of special apparatus.

5. In the biological sciences, some considerable technical advances were made. Important works were written on medicine and surgery, on the symptoms of diseases, and descriptions were given of the flora and fauna of different regions. A beginning was made with classification, and the possibility of having accurate illustrations was introduced by naturalistic art. Perhaps the most important medieval contribution to theoretical biology was the elaboration of the idea of a scale of animate nature.

6. Concerning the question of the purpose and nature of science, two medieval contributions may be singled out. The first is the idea, first explicitly expressed in the 13th century, that the purpose of science was to gain power over nature useful to man. The second is the idea insisted on by the theologians, that neither God's action nor man's speculation could be constrained within any particular system of scientific or philosophical thought. Whatever may have been its effects in other branches of thought, the effect of this idea on natural science was to bring out the relativity of all scientific theories and the fact that they might be replaced by others more successful in fulfilling the requirements of the rational and experimental methods.

Thus the experimental and mathematical methods were a growth, developing within the medieval system of scientific thought, which was to destroy from within and eventually to burst out from Aristotelian cosmology and physics. Though resistance to the destruction of the old system became strong among certain of the late scholastics, and especially among those whose humanism had given them too great a devotion to the ancient texts and those by whom the old system had been too closely linked with theological doctrines, it was the growth of these 13th- and 14th-century experimental and mathematical methods that brought about the movement which by the 17th century had become so striking as to be called the Scientific Revolution.

VI

THE REVOLUTION IN SCIENTIFIC THOUGHT IN THE 16TH AND 17TH CENTURIES

(I) THE APPLICATION OF THE MATHEMATICAL METHOD TO MECHANICS

How THE SCIENTIFIC REVOLUTION of the 16th and 17th centuries came about is easier to understand than the reason why it should have taken place at all. As far as the internal history of science is concerned it came about by men asking questions within the range of an experimental answer, by limiting their inquiries to physical rather than metaphysical problems, concentrating their attention on accurate observation of the kinds of things there are in the natural world and the correlation of the behaviour of one with another rather than on their intrinsic natures, on proximate causes rather than substantial forms, and in particular on those aspects of the physical world which could be expressed in terms of mathematics. Those characteristics which could be weighed and measured could be compared, could be expressed as a length or number and thus represented in a ready-made system of geometry, arithmetic or algebra in which consequences could be deduced revealing new relations between events which could then be verified by observation. The other aspects of matter were ignored.

The systematic use of the experimental method by which phenomena could be studied under simplified and controlled conditions, and of mathematical abstraction which made possible new classifications of experience and the discovery of new causal laws, enormously speeded up the tempo of scientific progress. One outstanding fact about the scientific revolution is that its initial and in a sense most important stages were carried through before the invention of the new measuring instruments, the telescope and microscope, thermometer and accurate clock, which were later to become indispensable for getting the accurate and satisfactory answers to the questions which were to come to the forefront of science. In its initial stages, in fact, the scientific revolution came about rather by a systematic change in intellectual outlook, in the type of question asked, than by an increase in technical equipment. Why such a revolution in methods of thought should have taken place is obscure. It was not simply a continuation of the increasing attention to observation and to the experimental and mathematical methods that had been going on since the 13th century, because the change took on an altogether new speed and a quality that made it dominate European thinking. It is not an adequate explanation to say that the new approach was simply the result of the work done on inductive logic and mathematical philosophy by the scholastic philosophers down to the 16th century or the result of the revival of Platonism in the 15th century. It cannot be attributed simply to the effect of the rediscovery of some hitherto unknown Greek scientific texts, such as the work of Archimedes, though these certainly stimulated mathematical thought.

Various aspects of the social and economic conditions of the 16th and 17th centuries certainly provided motives and opportunities that might stimulate science. At the beginning of the 16th century some outstanding scholars showed a renewed interest in the study of the technical processes of manufacture, and this helped to unite the mind of the philosopher with the manual skill of the craftsman. Luis Vives wrote in 1531 in his *De Tradendis Disciplinis* advocating the serious study of the arts of cooking, building, navigation, agriculture and clothmaking, and specifically urged that scholars should not look down on manual workers or be ashamed of asking them to explain the mysteries of their crafts. Rabelais, writing two years later, suggested that a proper branch of study for a young prince was to learn how the objects he used in ordinary life were made. Rabelais described how Gargantua and his tutor visited goldsmiths and jewellers, watchmakers, alchemists, coiners and many other craftsmen. In 1568 a Latin reader published in Frankfort for the use of school children seems to have been inspired by the same respect for skilled craftsmanship, for it took the form of a series of Latin verses each describing the work of a different craftsman, for example a printer, a papermaker, a pewterer or a turner. A marked advance was made during the 16th century also in the publication of treatises written by the educated on various technical processes. Of these, *De Re Metallica* (1556) by Georg Bauer (or Agricola) on mining and metallurgy and the treatises by Besson, Biringuccio, Ramelli and the early 17th-century Zonca are the most outstanding examples (*cf.* above, pp. 144–6). This interest in the technical achievements of the various crafts was expressed most clearly by Francis Bacon (1561–1626), first in 1605 in *The Advancement of Learning* and later more fully in the *Novum Organum*. Bacon was of the opinion that technics or, as he called it, the mechanical arts, had flourished just because they were firmly founded on fact and modified in the light of experience. Scientific thought, on the other hand, had failed to advance just because it was divorced from nature and kept remote from practical experiment. In his view the learning of the schoolmen had been 'cobwebs of learning . . . of no substance or profit' and the new humanistic learning must be directed to the benefit of man. In the 16th century several mathematicians such as Thomas Hood (*fl.* 1582–98) and Simon Stevin (1548–1620) were definitely employed by governments to solve problems of navigation or fortification. In the latter part of the 17th century the Royal Society interested itself in the technical processes of various trades in the hope that the information collected would not only provide a solid foundation for the speculations of scholars, but also would be of practical value to mechanics and artificers themselves. Several treatises were collected on special subjects: Evelyn wrote a *Discourse of Forest-Trees and the Propagation of Timber*, Petty on dyeing, and Boyle a general essay entitled *That the Goods of Mankind may be much increased by the Naturalist's Insight into Trades*. The English History of Trades did not get written, but the idea was attractive and almost a century later twenty volumes on arts and crafts were published by the Paris Academy of Sciences.

There are also, certainly, examples of this new interest of the learned in technical questions leading scientists to make contributions to fundamental problems. The attempt to calculate the angle at which a gun must be fired to give the maximum range led Tartaglia (*c.* 1500–57) to criticise the whole Aristotelian conception of motion and attempt new mathematical formulations, though the problem was solved only by Galileo. The experience of engineers who built water pumps is said to have influenced Galileo and Torricelli in their experiments with barometers, and the rumour that some Dutch lens-grinders had invented a telescope is said to have stimulated Galileo to study the laws of refraction with the object of constructing one himself. The need for an accurate clock for determining longitude, which became increasingly pressing with the extension of ocean voyages, both Galileo and Huygens had in mind when they did their fundamental work on the pendulum.

The existence of motives and opportunities, even when they brought fundamental scientific problems into prominence, does not explain the intellectual revolution which made it possible for scientists to solve these problems, and the history of the interaction between motives, opportunities, skills and intellectual changes that brought about the Scientific Revolution has, in fact, yet to be written.

The internal revolution in scientific thought that took place during the 16th and 17th centuries had, then, two essential aspects, the experimental and the mathematical, and it was precisely those branches of science which were most amenable to measurement that showed the most spectacular developments. In Antiquity mathematics had been used most successfully in astronomy, optics and statics and to these the medieval schoolmen added dynamics. These were also the branches of science which showed the greatest advances in the 16th and 17th centuries and, in particular, it was the successful application of mathematics to mechanics that changed men's whole conception of Nature and brought about the destruction of the whole Aristotelian system of cosmology.

One of the first to try to express nature in terms of the new mathematics was Leonardo da Vinci (1452–1519). Leonardo received his early education in the Platonic city of Florence and later worked in Milan and the other northern Italian towns where the scientific ideal was Aristotelian. Nearly all his physical conceptions were derived from scholastic writers, such as Jordanus Nemorarius, Albert of Saxony and Marliani, but he was able to develop their mechanical ideas through his new knowledge of Greek mathematicians like Archimedes, to whose *On Plane Equilibriums* he had access in manuscript.

Among ancient mathematicians Archimedes had been the most successful in combining mathematics with experimental inquiry; because of this he became the ideal of the 16th century. His method was to select definite and limited problems. He then formulated hypotheses which he either regarded, in the Euclidean manner, as self-evident axioms or could verify by simple experiments. The consequences of these he then deduced and experimentally verified. Thus, in the work just mentioned, he began with the two axioms that equal weights suspended at equal distances are in equilibrium, and that equal weights suspended at unequal distances are not in equilibrium but that which hangs at the greater distance descends. These axioms contained the principle of the lever, or, what is equivalent, of the centre of gravity, and from them Archimedes deduced numerous consequences.

Leonardo's mechanics, like those of his predecessors, was based on Aristotle's axiom that motive power is proportional to the weight of the body moved and the velocity impressed on it. Jordanus Nemorarius and his school had developed this axiom to express the principle of virtual velocity or work, and applied it, with the notion of the statical moment, to the lever and the inclined plane. Leonardo used the conclusions of this school and made various advances on them. He recognised that the effective (or potential) arm of a balance was the line which, passing through the fulcrum, was at right angles to the perpendicular passing through the suspended weight. He recognised that a sphere on an inclined plane moved until it reached a point where its centre of gravity was vertically above its point of contact, though he rejected Jordanus' correct treatment of motion down an inclined plane for an incorrect solution given by Pappus. He did recognise that the velocity of a ball rolling down an inclined plane was uniformly accelerated and showed that the velocity of a falling body increased by the same amount for a given vertical fall whether it descended vertically or down an incline. He also recognised that only the vertical component need be considered in estimating motive power and that the principle of work was incompatible with perpetual motion: he said that if a wheel were moved for a time by a given quantity of water and if this water were neither added to nor allowed a greater fall, then its function was finished. The principle of work, with that of the lever, he used also to develop the theory of pulleys and other mechanical appliances. In hydrostatics he recognised the fundamental principles that liquids transmit pressure and that the work done by the mover equals that done by the resistance. In hydrodynamics he developed the principle which the school of Jordanus had derived from Strato, that with a given fall the smaller the section the greater the velocity of a flowing liquid.

Leonardo's dynamics was based on the theory of *impetus*, which, he held, carried the moving body in a straight line.

But he adhered (like Cardano, Tartaglia and other later 16th-century Italian mechanicians) to the Aristotelian view that the supposed acceleration of a projectile after leaving the projector was due to the air. He accepted also Albert of Saxony's division of the trajectory of a projectile into three periods, but he recognised that the actual motion of a body might be the resultant of two or more different forces or velocities. He applied the principle of compound *impetus*, together with that of centre of gravity which he derived from Albert of Saxony and developed for solid figures, to a number of problems including percussion and the flight of birds.

In addition to his studies in mechanics Leonardo also used Greek geometry in an attempt to improve the theory of lenses and the eye which he derived from an edition of Pecham's *Perspectiva Communis*, printed in 1482. He made certain advances but suffered, like his predecessors, from the belief that the visual function resided in the lens instead of the retina and from the inability to understand that an inverted image on the latter was compatible with seeing the world in the way we do. His devotion to the Archimedean ideal of measurement is shown by the scientific instruments which he tried to improve or devise, such as the clock, a hygrometer similar to Cusa's to measure moisture in the atmosphere, a hodometer similar to Hero's to measure distance travelled, and an anemometer to measure the force of the wind. Though he wrote no book and his illegible mirror-written notes covered with sketches were not deciphered and published until much later, many of them not until the 19th century, his work was not lost to his immediate posterity. His manuscripts were copied in the 16th century and his mechanical ideas were pillaged by Hieronymo Cardano (1501–76) and passed to Stevin and through Bernardino Baldi to Galileo, Roberval and Descartes. The Spaniard Juan Batiste Villalpando (1552–1608) made use of his ideas on the centre of gravity and from him they went through the widely-read mathematical commentator, Marin Mersenne, to the 17th century.

The natural philosophers who succeeded Leonardo developed still further the powerful mathematical technique which was becoming possible with the recovery and printing of some hitherto unknown or little studied Greek texts. The earliest printed Latin edition of Euclid appeared at Venice in 1482 and Latin editions of Archimedes, Apollonius and Diophantus were made by Francesco Maurolyco (1494–1575) and of Euclid, Apollonius, Pappus, Hero, Archimedes and Aristarchus by Federigo Commandino (1509–75).

The first advances in mathematical technique were in algebra. The first comprehensive printed *Algebra*, that of Luca Pacioli (1494), contained the problem of cubic equations (those involving cubes of numbers, *e.g.*, x^3), which were first solved by Tartaglia (whose real name was Nicolo Fontana of Brescia). His work was pirated by Hieronymo Cardano, who anticipated him in publication (1545). Cardano's former servant and pupil, Lodovico Ferrari (1522–65), first solved quartic equations (involving x^4). Limitations in the general theory of numbers prevented the understanding of quintics (involving x^5) until the 19th century, but François Viète (1540–1603) gave a method of obtaining numerical values of the roots of polynomials and introduced the principle of reduction. The theory of equations was also developed by the English mathematician, Thomas Harriot (1560–1621). To the earlier algebraists negative roots had seemed unintelligible. These were first understood by Albert Girard (1595–1632), who also extended the idea of number to include 'imaginary' quantities like $\sqrt{-1}$, which had no place in the ordinary numerical scale extending from zero to infinity in both the negative and positive directions. At the same time improvements were made in algebraic symbolism. Viète used letters for unknowns and constants as an essential part of algebra. Stevin invented the present mode of designating powers and introduced fractional indices. His symbolism was later generalised by Descartes in the form x^3, $x^{\frac{1}{2}}$, etc. Other symbols such as $+$, $-$, $=$, $>$, $<$, $\sqrt{\,}$, etc., to represent operations which had previously been written out in words, had been gradually introduced from the end of the 15th century, so that by the first decades of the 17th century algebra and arithmetic had been standardised into something like their present form.

About the same time two important advances were also made in geometry. The first was the introduction of analytical geometry, the second the emergence of infinitesimal calculus. A step towards analytical geometry had been made by Nicole Oresme and there are reasons for believing that Descartes, who was not in the habit of mentioning those to whom he was indebted, knew his work. The man to whom Descartes was probably most indebted here was Pierre de Fermat (1601–65), who fully grasped the equivalence of different algebraic expressions and geometrical figures traced by loci moving with reference to co-ordinates. If his predecessors invented the method, it was Descartes who, in his *Géométrie* (1637), first developed its full power. He rejected the dimensional limitation on algebra and by letting, for instance, squares or cubes of terms (x^2, y^3) represent lines, he was able to put geometrical problems into algebraic form and to use algebra to solve them. Problems of motion thus received fruitful development when a curve could be represented as an equation. Descartes also showed that the entire conic sections of Apollonius were contained in a single equation of the second degree.

Descartes' analytical geometry depended on the assumption that a length was equivalent to a number; this no Greek would have accepted. The second mathematical advance made during the early years of the 17th century depended on a similar pragmatic illogicality. To compare rectilinear and curvilinear figures, Archimedes had used the 'method of exhaustions'. In this the area of a curvilinear figure could be determined from that of inscribed and circumscribed rectilinear figures by making them approach the curve by increasing the number of their sides. When determining elliptical areas Kepler had introduced the idea of the infinitely small into geometry and Francesco Bonaventura Cavalieri (1598–1647) made use of this idea to develop Archimedes' method into the 'method of indivisibles'. This depended on considering lines as composed of an infinite number of points, surfaces of lines and volumes of surfaces. The relative magnitudes of two surfaces or solids could then be found simply by summation of series for points or lines. In contrast with Descartes' analytical geometry, which was not generally used in physics until the end of the 17th century, the 'method of indivisibles' arose directly out of physical problems. It was later developed by Newton and Leibniz into the infinitesimal calculus.

Aristotle had maintained, as against the Pythagorean theory of Plato, that mathematics, though useful in defining the relations between certain events, could not express the 'essential nature' of physical things and processes, for it was an abstraction excluding from consideration irreducible qualitative differences which, nevertheless, existed. According to Aristotle, the study of physical bodies and events was the proper object not of mathematics but of physics and, in studying them, he arrived at such essential distinctions not only as those between irreducibly different qualities perceived through the senses but also, in the consideration of observed motions, as those between natural and violent movements, gravity and levity and terrestrial and celestial substance. This point of view had been shared by Euclid and was accepted by Tartaglia in his commentary on the *Elements*. Tartaglia said that the subject-matter of physics, which was gained through sensory experience, was distinct from the subject-matter of geometrical demonstration. A physical speck, for instance, was divisible to infinity, but a geometrical point, being without dimensions, was by definition indivisible. The subject-matter of geometry, he said, was continuous quantity, point, line, volume, and its definitions were purely operational. Geometry was not concerned with what exists; it could deal with physical properties like weight or time only when these had been translated into

FIG. 35. The mathematical disciplines and philosophy. The student is met by Euclid at the outer gate. Inside he finds Tartaglia surrounded by the mathematical disciplines: Arithmetic, Music, Geometry, Astronomy, Astrology, etc. A cannon is firing, showing the trajectory

lengths by measuring instruments. Since its principles were known by abstraction from material things, the conclusions it demonstrated were applicable to them. Thus physics might use mathematics, but was left with an independent non-mathematical field of its own.

With the increasing success of mathematics in solving concrete physical problems during the 16th century, the area of this purely physical preserve was reduced. The practical geometers of the 16th century developed the idea of using measurements, for which instruments of increasing accuracy were required, to determine whether what held true in mathematical demonstrations also held true in physical things. For instance, Tartaglia accepted the Aristotelian principle, which had led to the three-fold division of the trajectory of a projectile (*cf.* Fig. 33), that an elementary body could have only a single movement at any time (since if it had two one would eliminate the other). When he came to make a mathematical study of the flight of a projectile, he realised that when fired out of the vertical it began its descent under the action of gravity *immediately* after leaving the gun (*cf.* Fig. 35). He had to maintain, therefore, that natural gravity was not entirely eliminated by *impetus*. Cardano (who also developed Leonardo's ideas on the balance and virtual velocities) went a step further. He drew a distinction in mechanics between mathematical relations and moving powers or principles, the proper subject of 'metaphysics', and accepted the old forms of such powers. He objected altogether to the arbitrary separation of mathematical subject-matter into irreducibly different classes, such as in the different periods in the trajectory of a projectile. Viète took the same view.

The old problem of projectiles had, in fact, gained a new

---

of the projectile. At the far gate stand Aristotle and Plato, to welcome the student into the presence of Philosophy. Plato holds a scroll with the inscription 'No-one inexpert in geometry may enter here'. From Tartaglia's *La Nuova Scientia*, Venice, 1537.

importance in the 16th century when improved types of bronze cannon with accurately bored barrels began to replace the 14th- and 15th-century cast-iron monsters, and when a more powerful kind of gunpowder was produced in Germany. At the same time improvements were made in small-arms, particularly in methods of firing, and from the end of the 15th century the old method of touching off the powder by applying a burning match to the touch hole was replaced by a number of improved devices. First came the match-lock which enabled the burning match to be brought down by pressing a trigger. This was applied to the arquebus, the common infantryman's weapon after the battle of Pavia, in 1525. Then came the wheel-lock using pyrites instead of a burning match, though this was too dangerous to be much used. Finally, by 1635, came a device using flint which became the flint-lock used by the soldiers of Marlborough and Wellington. Problems of theoretical ballistics did not arise in the use of small arms, but with the heavy guns, as the range increased with more powerful gunpowder, problems of sighting became serious. Tartaglia devoted much time to these problems and the invention of the gunner's quadrant has been attributed to him. Later, Galileo, Newton and Euler made further contributions, though it was not until the second half of the 19th century that accurate ballistic tables were constructed on the basis of experiments.

Another 16th-century mathematician and physicist who made a critical scrutiny of Aristotelian theories and exposed some of their contradictions, even as a system of physics, was Giovanni Battista Benedetti (1530–90). He had read Philoponus' criticism of Aristotle's ideas on falling bodies (see above, p. 245). He imagined a group of bodies of the same material and weight falling beside each other first separately and then connected, and he concluded that their being in connection could not alter their velocity. A body the size of the whole group would, therefore, fall with the same velocity as each of its components. He therefore concluded that all bodies of the same material (or 'nature'), whatever their size, would fall with the same velocity, though he made the mistake of believing that the velocities of bodies of the same volume but different material would be proportional to their weights. Inspired by Archimedes, he thought of weight as proportional to the relative density in a given medium[1]. He then used the same argument as Philoponus to prove that velocity would not be infinite in a void (see above, pp. 245, 248). Benedetti also held that in a projectile natural gravity was not entirely eliminated by the *impetus* of flight, and he followed Leonardo in maintaining that *impetus* engendered movement only in a straight line, from which it might be deflected by a force, such as the 'centripetal' force exerted by a string which prevented a stone swung in a circle flying off at a tangent.

Sixteenth-century physicists increasingly turned from Aristotle's qualitative 'physical' explanations to the mathematical formulations of Archimedes and to the experimental method and, although their enunciations were not always rigorous, their instincts were usually sound. Like Archimedes, they tried to conceive of a clear hypothesis and put it to the test of experience. Thus, beginning with the assumption that perpetual motion was impossible, Simon Stevin (1548–1620) was led to a clear appreciation of the basic principles of both hydrostatics and statics. In the former science he concluded (1586) that any given mass of water was in equilibrium in all its parts, for if it were not it would be in continuous movement, and he then used this theory to show that the pressure of a liquid on the base of the containing vessel depended only on depth and was independent of shape and volume. Equipotential points were those on the same horizontal surface.

With the same assumption of the impossibility of perpetual motion he showed also why a loop of cord, on which weights

(1) Archimedes' principle asserts that when a body floats its weight is equal to the weight of the liquid displaced and when it sinks its weight decreases by that amount.

were attached at equal distances apart, would not move when hung over a triangular prism (Fig. 36). He showed that as long as the bottom of the prism was horizontal no movement occurred in the upper section of the cord when the suspended section was removed, and from this he arrived at the conclusion that weights on inclined planes were in equilibrium when proportional to the lengths of their supporting planes cut by the horizontal. The same conclusion had, in fact, been reached in the 13th century in

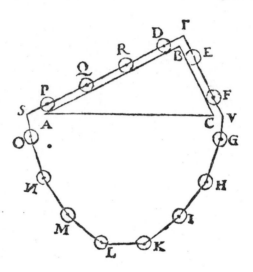

Fig. 36. Stevin's demonstration of the equilibrium of the inclined plane. From *Beghinselen des Waterwichts*, Leyden, 1586.

De Ratione Ponderis, of which Tartaglia had published an edition in 1565 (see above, pp. 86–7). This conclusion implied the idea of the triangle or parallelogram of forces, which Stevin applied to more complicated machines.

An important statical principle arising out of this work of Stevin, though the germ of it came from Albert of Saxony, was enunciated by Galileo Galilei (1564–1642). This was that a set of connected bodies, such as those on Stevin's inclined plane, could not set themselves in motion unless this resulted in the approach of their common centre of gravity towards the centre of the earth. The work done was then equal to the product of the weight moved multiplied by the vertical distance. The correct mathematical formulation of this principle was made by Galileo's pupil, Torricelli.

Stevin himself performed the experiment often attributed to Galileo of dropping simultaneously two leaden balls, one ten times heavier than the other, from a height on to a sounding-board. They struck the ground at the same instant and he asserted that the same held for bodies of equal size but different weight, that is of different material. Similar experiments had, in fact, been mentioned in the writings of critics of Aristotle since Philoponus, though the result was not always the same because of the appreciable effect of air resistance on the lighter bodies. Stevin and his predecessors recognised that their observations were incompatible with the Aristotelian law of motion, according to which velocity should be directly proportional to the moving cause, with falling bodies their weight, and inversely proportional to air resistance. Stevin did not develop the dynamical consequences of his observations.

It was, in fact, Galileo who was chiefly responsible for carrying the experimental and mathematical methods into the whole field of physics and for bringing about the intellectual revolution by which first, dynamics and then, all science were established in the direction from which there was no return. The revolution in dynamics in the 17th century was brought about by the substitution of the concept of inertia, that is, that uniform motion in a straight line is simply a state of a body and is equivalent to rest, for the Aristotelian conception of motion as a process of becoming which required for its maintenance continuous efficient causation. This Aristotelian conception of motion was based on the general principle that every effect requires a cause, and on such simple observations as that bodies do stop and come to rest if nothing continues to push them. The problem of the persistence of motion was brought to the fore because it was this Aristoteian conception which lay behind some of the most important objections to Copernicus' theory of the earth's rotation, for instance that based on the argument from detached bodies (see above, p. 256, below, p. 312), and the question of the truth of the Copernican theory was perhaps the chief scientific problem of the 16th and early 17th centuries. To prove this theory was the great passion of Galileo's scientific life. To do so Galileo tried to ignore the naïve inductions from common-sense experience, which were the basis of Aristotle's physics, and to look at things in a new way.

Galileo's new way of looking at the facts of experience represented a change of emphasis which was all important, though each of its two main characteristics had antecedents in an earlier tradition; the proof of it was that it bore fruit in the rapid solution of many different scientific problems. First, he put aside all discussion of the 'essential natures' that had been the subject-matter of Aristotelian physics and concentrated on describing what he observed, that is, on the phenomena. This is seen in his *Dialogues Concerning the Two Principal Systems of the World* (1632) when, during the Second Day, Salviati, representing Galileo himself, replies as follows to the assertion made by Simplicio, the Aristotelian, that everyone knows that what causes bodies to fall downwards is gravity:

you are out, *Simplicius*, you should say, that everyone knowes, that it is called Gravity: but I do not question you about the name, but the essence of the thing, of which essence you know not a tittle more than you know the essence of the mover of the stars in gyration: unlesse it be the name that hath been put to this, and made familiar, and domestical, by the many experiences which we see thereof every hour in the day: but not as if we really understand any more, what principle or vertue that is which moveth a stone downwards, than we know who moveth it up-wards, when it is separated from the projicient, or who moveth the Moon round, except (as I have said) onely the name, which more particularly and properly we have assigned to the motion of descent, namely, Gravity; whereas for the cause of circular motion, in more general terms, we assign the *Vertue impressed*, and call the same an *Intelligence*, either assisting, or informing; and to infinite other motions we ascribe Nature for their cause.

This attitude to such so-called causes Galileo learnt from the nominalism which had penetrated the Averroïst schools of northern Italy during the 15th century. Such words as 'gravity', he held, were simply names for certain observed regularities, and the first business of science was not to seek unfindable 'essences' but to establish these regularities, to discover proximate causes, that is, those antecedent events which, when other conditions were the same, always and alone produced the given effect. 'I say, therefore', says Salviati, during the Fourth Day of the *Two Principal Systems*,

that if it be true, that of one effect there is but one sole primary cause, and that between cause and effect, there is a firm and constant connection; it is necessary that whensoever there is seen a firm and constant alteration in the effect, there be a firm and constant alteration in the cause.

This theory Galileo wittily illustrated in his *Il Saggiatore*, question 45:

If Sarsi wishes me to believe, on the word of Suidas, that the Babylonians cooked eggs by whirling them swiftly in a sling, I will believe it; but I shall say that the cause of such an effect is very remote from that to which they attribute it, and to discover the true cause I shall argue as follows: If an effect, which has succeeded with others at another time, does not take place with us, it necessarily follows that in our experiment there is something lacking which was the cause of the success of the former attempt; and, if we lack but one thing, that one thing is alone the true cause; now, we have no lack of eggs, nor of slings, nor of stout fellows to whirl them, and yet they will not cook, and indeed, if they be hot they will cool the more quickly; and, since nothing is wanting to us save to be Babylonians, it follows that the fact of being Babylonians and not the attrition of the air is the cause of the eggs becoming hard-boiled, which is what I wish to prove.

In its business of discovering proximate causes, Galileo held, science began with observations and observations had the last word, and from the logic of science of the later Middle Ages he learnt how to arrive at general theories by induction from experience, to vary the conditions and isolate causes (as in the previous quotation), and to verify or falsify theories by experiment. 'I do believe for certain', says Salviati, during the First Day of the *Two Principal Systems*,

that he [Aristotle] first procured by the help of the senses, such experiments and observations as he could, to assure him as much as it was possible of the conclusion, and that he afterwards sought out the means how to demonstrate it: For this is the normal course in demonstrative Sciences, and the reason thereof is, because when the conclusion is true, by the help of the resolutive Method, one may hit upon some proposition before demonstrated, or come to some principle known *per se*; but if the conclusion be false, a man may proceed *in infinitum*, and never meet with any truth already known; but very oft he shall meet with some impossibility or manifest absurdity. Nor need you question but that *Pythagoras* a long time before he found the demonstration for which he offered the Hecatomb, had been certain, that the square of the side subtending the right angle in a rectangle triangle, was equal to the square of the other two sides: and the certainty of the conclusion conduced not a little to the investigating of the demonstration, understanding me always to mean in demonstrative Sciences. But what ever was the method of Aristotle, and whether his arguing *a priori* preceded sense *a posteriori*, or the contrary; it sufficeth that the same Aristotle preferreth (as hath been oft said) sensible experiments before all discourses.

And he went on, during the Second Day:

I know very well, that one sole experiment, or concludent demonstration, produced on the contrary part, sufficeth to batter to the ground . . . a thousand . . . probable Arguments[1].

(1) Galileo seems to have thought that science advanced through a series of alternatives each decided by a crucial experiment. He also seems to have believed in a 1 : 1 relationship between cause and effect instead of the cause being *all* the antecedents necessary to produce the effect as Ockham and the 14th-century 'terminists' had held.

Though, in this side of his scientific method, Galileo was, in fact, not at all original in principle and though, to verify or falsify hypotheses, he sometimes also retained such old practices as using 'thought experiments', often with the same common-sense examples as those quoted by such scholastic writers as Roger Bacon or Jean Buridan, and never performed, he made the great advance of combining the scholastic logic of science systematically with mathematics and with accurate, systematic measurement so as to express the regularities observed in phenomena in quantitative terms.

This was the means by which he combined his experimental method with the second main characteristic of his new approach to science, which was to try to express the observed regularities in terms of a mathematical abstraction, of concepts of which no exemplaries need actually be observed but from which the observations could be deduced. This was an important change because, though such abstractions were certainly used in some late scholastic sciences like optics and astronomy, good examples being the eccentrics and epicycles postulated to 'save the appearances' and, in a somewhat different sense, the intangible 'substantial form' regarded simply as a theory, most pre-Galilean science was in practice constricted by the dominance of naïve and direct generalisations from common-sense experience. Galileo's use of mathematical abstractions enabled him firmly to establish the technique, already introduced by some 13th- and 14th-century experimenters, of investigating a phenomenon by specially arranged experiments, in which irrelevant conditions were excluded so that the phenomenon could be studied in its simplest quantitative relations with other phenomena. Only after these relations had been established and expressed in a mathematical formula did he re-introduce the excluded factors, or carry his theory into regions not readily amenable to experimentation.

In Galileo's eyes, one of the principal assets of the Copernican system was that Copernicus had escaped the naïve empiricism of Aristotle and Ptolemy and taken a more sophisticated attitude to theories used to 'save the appearances'. 'Nor can I sufficiently admire the eminencie of those men's wits,' says Salviati, during the Third Day of the *Two Principal Systems*,

that have received and held it [the Copernican system] to be true, and with the sprightliness of their judgements offered such violence to their own sences, as that they have been able to prefer that which their reason dictated to them, to that which sensible experiences represented most manifestly to the contrary . . . I cannot find any bounds for my admiration, how that reason was able in *Aristarchus* and *Copernicus*, to commit such a rape upon their Sences, as in despight thereof, to make herself mistress of their credulity.

Galileo believed the mathematical theories from which he deduced the observations to represent the enduring reality, the substance, underlying phenomena. Nature was mathematical. This view he owed partly to the Platonism which had been popular in Italy, particularly in Florence, since the 15th century. One essential element of this Pythagorean Platonism which had been made increasingly plausible by the success of the mathematical method in 16th-century physics, was the idea that the behaviour of things was entirely the product of their geometrical structure. During the Second Day of the *Two Principal Systems*, Salviati replies to Simplicio's assertion that he agreed with Aristotle's judgment that Plato had doted too much upon geometry—

for that in conclusion these Mathematical subtilties *Salviatus* are true in abstract, but applied to sensible and Physical matter, they hold not good—

by saying that the conclusions of mathematics are exactly the same in the abstract and the concrete.

And it would be a new thing that the computations and rates made in abstract numbers, should not afterwards answer to the Coines of Gold and Silver, and to the merchandizes in concrete.

In the same way,

the *Geometrical Philosopher* would observe in concrete the effects demonstrated in abstract.

The faith that inspired nearly all science until the end of the 17th century was that it discovered a real intelligible structure in objective Nature, an *ens reale* and not merely an *ens rationis*. Kepler believed himself to be discovering a mathematical order which provided the intelligible structure of the real world; Galileo said, during the First Day of the *Two Principal Systems*, that of mathematical propositions human understanding was 'as absolutely certain . . . as Nature herself'. In fact, though Galileo rejected the kind of 'essential natures' the Aristotelians had been seeking, he simply brought in another kind by the back door. He asserted that since mathematical physics could not deal with the non-mathematical, what was not mathematical was subjective (see below, pp. 392–3). As he affirmed in *Il Saggiatore*, question 6:

Philosophy is written in that vast book which stands forever open before our eyes, I mean the universe; but it cannot be read until we have learnt the language and become familiar with the characters in which it is written. It is written in mathematical language, and the letters are triangles, circles and other geometrical figures, without which means it is humanly impossible to comprehend a single word.

Galileo's Platonism was of the same kind as that which had led to Archimedes being known in the 16th century as the 'Platonic philosopher', and with Galileo mathematical abstractions got their validity as statements about Nature by being solutions of particular physical problems. By using this method of abstracting from immediate and direct experience, and by correlating observed events by means of mathematical relations which could not themselves be observed, he was led to experiments of which he could not have thought in terms of the old common-sense empiricism. A good example of his method is his work on the pendulum.

By abstracting from the inessentials of the situation, 'the opposition of the air, and line, or other accidents' he was able to demonstrate the law of the pendulum, that the period of oscillation is independent of the arc of swing and simply proportional to the square-root of the length. This having been proved, he could then reintroduce the previously excluded factors. He showed, for instance, that the reason why a real pendulum, of which the thread was not weightless, came to rest, was not simply because of air resistance, but because each particle of the thread acted as a small pendulum. Since they were at different distances from the point of suspension, they had different frequencies and therefore inhibited each other.

Another good example of his method is his study of freely-falling bodies, one of the foundations of 17th-century mechanics. Disregarding Aristotle's conception of motion as a process requiring a continuous cause, and the Aristotelian categories of movement based on purely 'physical' principles still accepted by such writers as Cardano or Kepler, he looked for a definition which would enable him to measure motion. He said, during the First Day of the *Two Principal Systems:*

We will . . . call that equal velocity, when the spaces passed have the same proportion, as the times wherein they are passed.

In this he followed such 14th-century physicists as Heytesbury and Swineshead, whose works had been printed at the end of the 15th century and taught to Galileo during his youth at Pisa. He tried to arrange things so that he could study the problem under simple and controlled experimental conditions, for example in balls rolling down an inclined plane. He made a few preliminary observations, and analysed the mathematical relations obtaining between two factors only, space and time, excluding all the others. Then he tried to invent what he called a 'hypothetical assumption', which was a mathematical hypothesis from which he could deduce consequences that could be tested experimentally; and since, as Salviati said during the Second Day of the *Two Principal Systems*, 'Nature . . . doth not that by many things, which may be done by few', he adopted the simplest possible hypothesis. During the Third Day of the *Dialogues Concerning Two New Sciences* (1638) he gave the definition of uniformly accelerated motion as a motion which, 'when starting from rest, acquires during equal time-intervals equal increments of velocity'. This, he said, he adopted for one reason, because Nature employs 'only those means which are most common, simple and easy'. His experimental verification consisted of a series of measurements showing the concomitant variations in space travelled and time passed. If the consequences of his hypothesis were verified, he regarded this hypothesis as a true account of the natural order. If they were not, he tried again, until he reached a hypothesis which was verified; and then the particular instance, for example the observed facts about falling bodies, was explained by being shown to be the consequences of a general law. The object of science for Galileo was to explain the particular facts of observation by showing them to be consequences of such general laws, and to build up a whole system of such laws in which the more particular were consequences of the more general.

Galileo's approach to physical problems is clearly seen in the *Two New Sciences*, in his deduction of the kinematical laws of freely falling bodies, when Salviati turns away from the suggestion that certain physical causes might account for the facts and concentrates on the kinematical aspect of the problem.

The present does not seem to be the proper time to investigate the cause of the acceleration of natural motion concerning which various opinions have been expressed by various philosophers, some explaining it by attraction to the centre, others by repulsion between the very small parts of the body, while still others attribute it to a certain stress in the surrounding medium which closes in behind the falling body and drives it from one of its positions to another. Now, all these fantasies, and others too, ought to be examined; but it is not really worth while. At present it is the purpose of our Author merely to investigate and to demonstrate some of the properties of accelerated motion (whatever the cause of this acceleration may be)—meaning thereby a motion, such that the momentum of its velocity goes on increasing after departure from rest in simple proportionality to time, which is the same as saying that in equal time-intervals the body receives equal increments of velocity; and if we find that the properties [of accelerated motion] which will be demonstrated later are realised in freely falling and accelerated bodies, we may conclude that the assumed definition includes such a motion of heavy bodies and that their speed goes on increasing as the time and the duration of the motion.

Galileo proved by Oresme's method (Fig. 34), that the distance travelled by a body whose velocity increased uniformly in proportion to time was proportional to the square of the time. He verified this with balls rolling down an inclined plane. This experiment he possibly carried out as early as 1604, though it was not published until 1638. In the absence of an accurate clock, he defined equal intervals of time as those during which equal weights of water issued from a small hole in a bucket; a very large amount of water was used relative to the amount issuing through the hole, so that the decrease in head was unimportant. His hypothesis proved correct, and he tried to show that no other was compatible with his observations.

Another aspect of freely-falling bodies, that all bodies of any substance fall with the same acceleration, Galileo arrived at by the same method of abstraction. In an early work, *De Motu* (*c.* 1590), Galileo mentioned an experiment of dropping blocks of wood and lead from a height and said that the lead left the wood behind. There is no conclusive evidence that he ever performed such an experiment from the leaning tower of Pisa; but when two other Italian scientists, Giorgio Coresio and Vincenzo Renieri, did this, in 1612 and 1641 respectively, the heavier weight always reached the ground first, thus proving that Aristotle was right. Galileo in his maturity was not upset by this. He made an abstraction from air resistance, which he said retarded the lighter body more than the heavier, and considered motion without it in a vacuum. Velocity, according to Aristotle, should then have been infinite; but, during the Second Day of the *Two Principal Systems*, Salviati asks

whether there be not in the moveable, besides the natural inclination to the contrary term, another intrinsick and natural quality, which maketh it averse to motion?

This internal resistance to motion is what Newton later called 'mass'. It was implied by Galileo's supposition that in a vacuum all bodies would fall with the same acceleration, differences in weight being exactly counterbalanced by equal differences in mass (above, p. 83, note).

Using this concept of mass, or quantity of matter, Galileo took up the problem of the persistence of motion; his work on this problem made the concept of inertia inevitable. From the observation that on a balance a large weight placed a short distance from the fulcrum would oscillate in

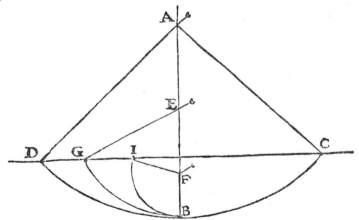

FIG. 37. Galileo's demonstration of inertia with the pendulum. From *Discorsi e Dimostratione Mathematiche intorno à due nuove Scienze*, Bologna, 1655 (1st edn. Leyden, 1538), Third Day.

equilibrium with a small weight placed a proportionately longer distance from the fulcrum, he derived the idea that what persists in motion is the product of quantity of matter multiplied by velocity. This product he called *impeto*, or *momento*, which was not a cause of motion like Buridan's *impetus*, but an effect and measure of it. The problem of the persistence of motion was therefore the problem of the persistence of momentum. Previous discussions of this problem had been based on the Aristotelian conception of motion as a process, but Galileo ignored this. He assumed, in the *Two New Sciences*, Third Day, that the momentum of a given body falling down an inclined plane was proportional only to the vertical distance, and independent of the inclination; from this he concluded that a body falling down one plane would acquire momentum that would carry it up another to the same height. The swinging bob of a pendulum was equivalent to such a body, and he showed that if released at C (Fig. 37) it would ascend to the same horizontal line DC, whether it went by the arc BD or, when the string was caught by the nails E or F, by the steeper arcs BG or BI. This result he developed as follows:

Furthermore we may remark that any velocity once imparted to a moving body will be rigidly maintained as long as the external causes of acceleration or retardation are removed, a condition which is found only on horizontal planes; for in the case of planes which slope downwards there is already present a cause of acceleration, while on planes sloping upwards there is retardation; from this it follows that motion along a horizontal plane is perpetual; for, if the velocity be uniform, it cannot be diminished or slackened, much less destroyed. Further, although any velocity which a body may have acquired through natural fall is permanently maintained so far as its own nature is concerned, yet it must be remembered that if, after descent along a plane inclined downwards, the body is deflected to a plane inclined upward, there is already existing in this latter plane a cause of retardation; for in any plane this same body is subject to a natural acceleration downwards. Accordingly we have here the superposition of two different states, namely, the velocity acquired during the preceding fall which, if acting alone, would carry the body at a uniform rate to infinity, and the velocity which results from a natural acceleration downwards common to all bodies.

As he had already argued in the *Two Principal Systems*, perpetual motion was the limiting case, reached in an ideal world without friction, as the acceleration and retardation given respectively by downwards and upwards sloping planes each gradually tended to zero with the approach of the planes to the horizontal. The *impeto*, or momentum, impressed on a body by its movement then persisted indefinitely. Thus motion was no longer conceived of as a process requiring a cause commensurate with the effect but, as Ockham had said, was simply a state of the moving body persisting unchanged unless acted on by a force. Force could therefore be defined as that which produced, not velocity, but a *change* of velocity from a state either of rest or of uniform motion. Further, when a body was acted on by two forces, each was independent of the other. Galileo assumed for practical purposes that the uniform motion preserved in the absence of an external force would be rectilinear, and this enabled him to calculate correctly the trajectory of a projectile. In the *Two New Sciences*, Third Day, he showed that the path of a projectile, which moved with a constant horizontal velocity received from the gun and a constant acceleration vertically downwards, was a parabola, and that the range on a horizontal plane was greatest when the angle of elevation was 45 degrees.

Galileo certainly arrived by implication at the conception of inertial motion, which was the illumination of mind which made it possible for Newton to complete the terrestrial and celestial mechanics of the 17th century; but Galileo himself did not explicitly state the concept of inertia. He was investigating the geometrical properties of bodies in the real world, and in the real world it was an empirical observation that bodies fell downwards towards the centre of the earth. Thus, adapting the Pythagorean theory, he regarded gravity as the natural tendency of bodies to proceed to the centre of the collection of matter in which they found themselves, and weight as an innate physical property possessed by bodies; this was the source of movement or *impeto*. Apart from mass, weight was the one 'natural' property he left to bodies, and 'natural gravity' the only force he considered. In the real world, therefore, the 'plane' along which movement would continue indefinitely was a spherical surface with its centre at the centre of the earth. As he said in the *Two Principal Systems*, Second Day:

A superficies, which should be neither declining nor ascending, ought in all its parts to be equally distant from the centre . . . A ship which moveth in a calm at sea, is one of those moveables, which run along one of those superficies that are neither declining nor ascending, and therefore disposed, in case all obstacles external and accidental were removed, to move with the impulse once imparted incessantly and uniformly.

And, in the First Day, he said:

methinks it may rationally be concluded, that for maintenance of perfect order amongst the parts of the World, it is necessary to say, that moveables are moved onely circularly; and if there be any that move not circularly, these of necessity are immoveable: there being nothing but rest and circular motion apt to the conservation of order.

This conception of motion enabled Galileo to say that the circular motion of the heavenly bodies, once acquired, would be retained. Moreover, he said that it was impossible to prove whether the space of the real universe was finite or infinite. His universe thus contained bodies with independent physical properties, which affected their movements in real space. The same line of thought can be seen in the remark in the *Two Principal Systems* that a cannon ball without weight would continue horizontally in a straight line, but that in the real world, where bodies had weight, the movement which bodies conserved was in a circle. For practical purposes of calculation he assumed, as in his work on the trajectory of a projectile, that it was rectilinear motion that was conserved. But his conception of motion enabled him to say that in the heavenly bodies circular motion would be conserved. He did not have to explain their movements by gravitational attraction.

The intellectual revolution which had cost the 'Tuscan artist' such an anguish of effort, and yet left him still just short of reducing physics completely to mathematics, made it possible for his followers to take the geometrisation of the real world as evident. Cavalieri got rid of gravity as an innate physical property, and said that like any other force it was due to external action. Evangelista Torricelli (1608–47) regarded gravity as a dimension of bodies similar to their geometrical dimensions. Giordano Bruno (1548–1600), continuing the scholastic discussion of plural worlds and the infinity of space, had realised that Copernicus, in making it plausible to take any point as the centre of the universe, had abolished absolute motions (see below, pp. 309 *et seq.*). He had popularised the idea that space was actually infinite and therefore without favoured natural directions. The French mathematician, Pierre Gassendi (1592–1655), whose predecessors in the 16th century had, unlike the Italians, sometimes tended to identify the continuous quantity of geometry with physical extension, identified the space of the real world with the abstract, homogeneous, infinite space of Euclidean geometry. He had learnt from Democritus and Epicurus to conceive of space as a void, and from Kepler to regard gravity as an external force (see below, pp. 321 *et seq.*). He therefore concluded, in his *De Motu Impresso a Motore Translato* published in 1642, that since a body moving by itself in a void would be unaffected by gravity, and since such a space was indifferent to the bodies in it, as Aristotle's space and its remnants in Galileo were not, the body would continue in a straight line for ever. Gassendi thus first published the explicit statement that the movement which a body tended to conserve indefinitely was rectilinear, and that a change in either velocity or direction required the operation of an external force. He also first consciously eliminated the notion of *impetus* as the cause of motion. With the complete geometrisation of physics, the principle of inertial motion thus became self-evident.

Gassendi had been anticipated in the expression of this

principle, though not in its publication, by René Descartes (1596–1650) in his book *Le Monde*, begun some time before 1633. Descartes had intended this work to be a system of celestial mechanics based on the Copernican theory, but, discouraged by the condemnation of Galileo in 1633 for the similar excursion made in the *Two Principal Systems*, which carried him into Biblical criticism (see below, pp. 324 *et seq.*), he dropped the project, and the incompleted work was not published until 1664, when its author was already dead. The mechanical ideas contained in *Le Monde* he again resumed in the *Principia Philosophiæ* (1644). Carrying to an extreme, which Galileo had been unable to realise, the notion that the mathematical was the only objective aspect of nature, he said that matter must be understood simply as extension (see below, pp. 393–4). In creating the universe of infinite extension God also gave it motion. All sciences were thus reduced to measurement and mathematics[1], and all change to local motion. Motion, being something real, could neither increase nor decrease in total amount, but could only be transferred from one body to another. The universe therefore continued to run as a machine, and each body persisted in a state of motion in a straight line, the geometrically simplest form in which God set it going, unless acted on by an external force. Only a void was indifferent to the bodies in it and, since Descartes accepted the Aristotelian principle that extension, like other attributes, could exist only by inhering in some substance, he held that space could not be a void, which was nothing, but must be *plenum*. Only a *tendency* to continuous velocity in a straight line would

[1] He 'neither admits nor hopes for any principles in physics other than those which are in geometry or in abstract mathematics, because thus all the phenomena of nature are explained, and sure demonstrations of them can be given', *Princ. Philos.*, II, 64. When mathematics was used to express physical events the necessary requirement was that 'all the things which follow from them agree with experience', *Princ. Philos.*, III, 46. Descartes' position in the Augustine-Platonist tradition was thus similar to that of Grosseteste or Roger Bacon.

therefore be possible in the real world. For Descartes the real world was simply geometry realised; movement he conceived of simply as a geometrical translation, with time as a geometrical dimension like space. The movement that was always in a straight line was motion at an instant.

This theory left Descartes with the problem of the curvilinear motion of the planets. Having rejected action at a distance and all causes of deflection from inertial motion except mechanical contact, he could not accept a theory of gravitational attraction. He therefore tried to explain the facts by vortices in the *plenum*. He considered the original extension to have consisted of blocks of matter, each of which revolved rapidly about its centre. The consequent attrition then produced three kinds of secondary matter, characterised by luminosity (sun and stars), transparency (inter-planetary space, *i.e.*, æther) and opacity (earth). The particles of these matters were not atomic but divisible to infinity, and their geometrical shapes accounted for their various properties. They were all in contact, so that motion could occur only by each successively replacing the next and thus producing a vortex, in which motion was transmitted by mechanical pressure. Such vortices carried the heavenly bodies round and were also the means of propagation of such influences as light and magnetism. The *plenum*, or æther, which owed some of its characteristics to Gilbert and Kepler, was thus loaded with the physical properties, among them what was later called 'mass', that could not be reduced to geometry.

Descartes did not, like Galileo, try to discover empirically what laws were, in fact, exhibited by the natural world, but what laws it must follow on the abstract principles he adopted. He was a geometer *à l'outrance*, and his extreme rationalism was his undoing. It was related by Voltaire that when Newton tried to read Descartes' book he wrote 'error' repeatedly on the first seven or eight pages and then put it down.

The system of classical mechanics established in the 17th century, and still forming the basis of a large part of physics in the 20th, was developed by Huygens (1629–95), Newton (1642–1727) and others, from the principles, not of Descartes, but of Galileo. The dynamical inquiries of these mathematicians, though leading to the enunciation of a number of separate principles whose connection with each other was not at the time always clearly understood, such as the law of falling bodies, the concepts of inertia, force and mass, the parallelogram of forces and the equivalence of work and energy, really involved only one fundamental discovery. This was the principle, established experimentally, that the behaviour of bodies towards one another was one in which accelerations were determined, the ratio of the opposite accelerations they produced being constant and depending only on a characteristic of the bodies themselves, which was called mass. It was a fact which could be known only by observation that two geometrically equivalent bodies would move differently when placed in identical relations with the same other bodies. Where Galileo had halted before the real world and Descartes, geometrising from abstract principles, hid this physical property in vortices, Newton made an exact mathematical reduction of mass from the facts of experience. The relative masses of two such bodies were measured by the ratio of their opposite accelerations. Force might then be defined as that which disturbed a body from a state of rest or uniform rectilinear motion, and the force between two bodies, for example that of gravitation, was the product of either mass multiplied by its own acceleration. Inertial motion was an ideal limit, the state of motion of a body acted on by no other. The problem that had been so puzzling to those who first questioned the Aristotelian law of motion, why, excluding the resistance of the medium, bodies of different masses fell to the earth with the same acceleration, then found its solution in the distinction between mass, a property of the body providing internal resistance, and weight, caused by the external force of gravity acting on the body. Differences in weight might be considered as exactly counter-balanced by proportional differences in mass. And the same mass had a different weight according to its distance from the centre of the earth. When these conceptions were generalised by Newton, the old problems of the acceleration of freely falling bodies and of the continued motion of projectiles were finally solved; and when the same principles were carried once more into the sky in the theory of universal gravitation, Buridan's aspiration was realised, and the movements of the heavens, which Kepler had correctly described, were united with these homely phenomena in one mechanical system. This not only brought about the final destruction of the hierarchically ordered finite world of irreducibly different 'natures', which had formed the Aristotelian cosmos; it was a vast illumination of mind. The principles, first effectively established by Galileo, on which the new mechanics were constructed then seemed finally justified by their success.

(2) ASTRONOMY AND THE NEW MECHANICS

Though, after its arrival in Western Christendom in the 13th century, the Ptolemaic system had been commonly regarded as simply a geometrical calculating device, the need was felt for an astronomical system which would both 'save' the phenomena and also describe the 'actual' paths of the heavenly bodies through space. Since the 13th century, observation and the revision of tables had gone on in connection with the chronic desire to reform the calendar and with the practical demands of astrology and navigation. Regiomontanus had been summoned to Rome for consultation on the calendar in 1475, the year before he died, and his work was used by the Portuguese and Spanish ocean navigators. Some medieval writers, for instance Oresme and Nicholas of Cusa, had suggested alternatives to the geostatic system as a description of physical 'fact' and, in the early years of the 16th century, the Italian Celio Calcargini (1479–1541) put forward in a vague form a theory based on the earth's rotation. His countryman, Girolamo Fracastoro (1483–1553), attempted to revive the solid spheres of Ptolemy's *Hypotheses of the Planets*. It was left for Nicholas Copernicus (1473–1543) to elaborate a system which could replace Ptolemy's as a calculating device and yet represent physical 'fact', and also 'save' additional phenomena, such as the diameter of the moon, which according to Ptolemy's system should have undergone monthly variations of nearly a hundred per cent.

Copernicus was educated first at the University of Cracow and then at Bologna, where he studied law but also worked with the professor of astronomy, Domenico Maria Novara (1454–1504). Later he proceeded to Rome, to Padua where he studied medicine, and to Ferrara where he completed his law. The remainder of his life was spent as a canon of Frauenberg Cathedral in East Prussia, where he performed the functions of a cleric, doctor and diplomat and produced a scheme which was the basis of a reform of the currency. In the midst of this busy life he proceeded to reform astronomy. Here, though he made a few observations, his work was that of a mathematician. He is a supreme example of a man who revolutionised science by looking at the old facts in a new way. He took his data mainly from the *Epitome in Almagestum* (printed 1496) of Puerbach and Regiomontanus and from Gerard of Cremona's Latin translation of the *Almgest*, which was printed at Venice 1515. Novara, a leading Platonist, had taught him the desire to conceive of the constitution of the universe in terms of simple mathematical relationships, and, inspired by this, he set about producing his new system.

Martianus Capella had preserved for the succeeding centuries Heraclides' theory that Mercury and Venus, whose orbits are peculiar in their restricted angular ranges from the sun (the other planets move all round the zodiac), actually revolved round the sun, while the sun with the remaining heavenly bodies revolved round the earth. Copernicus made the whole planetary system, including the earth, revolve round a static sun in its centre. His reluctance to publish this theory, of which the manuscript was complete by 1532, seems to have depended largely on the fear that it would be considered absurd. He had been satirised on the stage near Frauenberg in 1531, and his anxiety would certainly have been confirmed had he lived to hear the comments of such diverse personalities as the Italian mathematician Francesco Maurolyco and the German revolutionary Martin Luther (1483–1546). 'The fool,' said Luther, 'would overturn the whole science of astronomy.' Copernicus eventually drew up a short summary (*Commentariolus*), which seems to have become known to the Pope, and in 1536 he was asked by Cardinal Nicolaus von Schönberg to make his theory known to the learned world. Georg Joachim (Rheticus), a professor at Wittenberg (who is notable for having introduced the improvement of making trigonometrical functions depend directly on the angle instead of on the arc), had journeyed to Frauenberg in 1539 to study Copernicus' manuscript, and in 1540 Rheticus published his *Narratio Prima de LibrisRevolutionum* concerning it. Copernicus' work was thus well advertised when, having been seen through the press by Rheticus, it appeared at Nuremberg in 1543, dedicated to Pope Paul III under the title *De Revolutionibus Orbium Cœlestium*. Its practical value was demonstrated when Erasmus Reinhold used it to calculate the *Prussian Tables* (1551), though these suffered from the inaccuracy of Copernicus' data, and when the figure for the length of the year given in the *De Revolutionibus* was made the basis of the reform of the calendar instituted by Pope Gregory XIII in 1582. In spite of the cautious preface by Osiander, stating the contrary, Copernicus seems to have considered the revolution of the earth as a physical fact and not a mere mathematical convenience. The *De Revolutionibus* thus posed the problems which occupied the greater part of physics down to Newton.

The Copernican revolution was no more than to assign the diurnal motion of the heavenly bodies to the rotation of the earth and their annual motion to the earth's revolution about the sun, and to work out, by the old devices of eccentrics and epicycles, the astronomical consequences of these postulates (Fig. 38). 'Therefore,' Copernicus said in *De Revolutionibus*, book 1, chapter 10,

FIG. 38. The Copernican system. From Copernicus' *De Revolutionibus Orbium Cælestium*, Nuremburg, 1543.

we are not ashamed to maintain that all that is beneath the moon, with the centre of the earth, describe among the other planets a great orbit round the sun which is the centre of the world; and that what appears to be a motion of the sun is in truth a motion of the earth; but that the size of the world is so great, that the distance of the earth from the sun, though appreciable in comparison to the orbits of the other planets, is as nothing when compared to the sphere of the fixed stars. And I hold it to be easier to concede this than to let the mind be distracted by an almost endless multitude of circles, which those are obliged to do who detain the earth in the centre of the world. The wisdom of nature is such that it produces nothing superfluous or useless but often produces many effects from one cause. If all this is difficult and almost incomprehensible or against the opinion of many people, we shall, please God, make it clearer than the sun, at least to those who know something of mathematics. The first principle therefore remains undisputed, that the size of the orbits is measured by the period of revolution, and the order of the spheres is then as follows, commencing with the uppermost. The first and highest sphere is that of the fixed stars, containing itself and everything and therefore immovable, being the place of the universe to which the motion and places of all other stars are referred. For while some think that it also changes somewhat [this refers to precession], we shall, when deducing the motion of the earth, assign another cause for this phenomenon. Next follows the first planet Saturn, which completes its circuit in thirty years, then Jupiter with a twelve years' period, then Mars, which moves round in two years. The fourth place in the order is that of the annual revolution, in which we have said that the earth is contained with the lunar orbit as an epicycle. In the fifth place Venus goes round in nine months, in the sixth Mercury with a period of eighty days. But in the midst of all stands the sun. For who could in this most beautiful temple place this lamp in another or better place than that from which it can at the same time illuminate the whole? Which some not unsuitably call the light of the world, others the soul or the ruler. Trismegistus calls it the visible God, the Electra of Sophocles the all-seeing. So indeed the sun, sitting on the royal throne, steers the revolving family of stars.

The consequences of Copernicus' postulates were of two kinds, physical and geometrical. The diurnal rotation of the earth encountered the Aristotelian and Ptolemaic physical objections about the arrow, based on the theory of natural motions, and the strong east wind (see above, p. 256). To these Copernicus replied in the same way as Oresme, making circular movement natural and saying that the air shared that of the earth. He held that falling and rising bodies had a double motion, a circular motion when in their natural place, and a rectilinear motion of displacement from, or return to, that place. The objection to this argument was that if bodies had a natural circular movement in one direction they should have a resistance, analogous to weight, to motion in the other. The answer to this, like that to the argument that the earth would be disrupted by what is now sometimes called 'centrifugal' force, which Copernicus merely said would be worse for the enormous celestial sphere if it rotated, had to await the mechanics of Galileo.

The annual motion of the earth in an eccentric circle round the sun Copernicus' critics objected to on three grounds. First, it conflicted with the Aristotelian theory of natural movements, which depended on the centre of the earth being at the centre of the universe. To this Copernicus replied with Nicholas of Cusa, though abandoning Cusa's theory of balancing heavy and light elements, that gravity was a local phenomenon representing the tendency of the matter of any astronomical body to form spherical masses. The second objection arose from the absence of observable annual stellar parallaxes, or differences in position of the stars. Copernicus attributed this to the enormous distance of the stellar sphere from the earth compared with the dimensions of the earth's orbit. The third objection continued to be a stumbling-block till Galileo changed the whole conception of motion, when it ceased to be relevant. The Aristotelians maintained that each elementary body had a single natural movement, but Copernicus gave the earth three motions: the two mentioned above which accounted, respectively, for the rising and setting of the heavenly bodies and for the passage of the sun along the ecliptic and the retrogradations and stations of the planets, and a third which was intended to account for the fact that the axis of the earth, notwithstanding the annual motion, always pointed to the same spot on the celestial sphere. This third motion was also made to account for the precession of the equinoxes and their illusory 'trepidations'.

With the sun and the celestial sphere, the boundary of the finite universe, at rest, Copernicus proceeded to provide the usual eccentrics, deferents and epicycles to account for the observed movements of the moon, sun and planets by means of perfect uniform circular motion. The geometrical advantages of his system were that he could account for the retrogradations of the planets as mere appearances due to a single movement of the earth, thus reducing the total number of circles from about 80 to 34. The 9th and 10th spheres were no longer necessary. He also had a criterion for assigning the relative distances to the planets, and could account simply for the various peculiarites of the planetary motions. But his belief in the imaginary trepidations of the equinoxes led to unnecessary complications and, by taking the centre of the earth's orbit as the centre of all the planets' motions, his treatment of Mars had considerable errors. Further, he relied on ancient and inaccurate data. This last defect was remedied by Tycho Brahe (1546–1601), who showed that the trepidations were due solely to errors in observation; and Johann Kepler (1571–1630), while considering Tycho's results, was to build his system from the orbit of Mars.

The Copernican system appealed first to three types of interest. The *Alfonsine Tables* had caused dissatisfaction both because they were out of date and no longer corresponded to the observed positions of stars and planets, and because they differed from Ptolemy on the precession of the equinoxes and added other spheres beyond his 9th, deviations offensive to humanists who believed that the perfection of knowledge was to be found in the classical writings. All practical astronomers, whatever their views on the hypothesis of the earth's rotation, thus turned to the 16th-century *Prussian Tables* calculated on Copernicus' system though, in fact, these were scarcely more accurate. And some humanists regarded Copernicus as the restorer of the classical purity of Ptolemy. Another group of writers, such as the physicist Benedetti, Bruno and Petrus Ramus (1515–72), saw in the Copernican system a stick with which to beat Aristotle. Finally, such men as Tycho Brahe, William Gilbert (1540–1603), Kepler and Galileo, faced the full meaning of *De Revolutionibus* and attempted to unify observations, geometrical descriptions and physical theory. It was because of the absence of such a unity that until the end of the 16th century, while everyone used the *Prussian Tables*, no one advanced astronomical theory. Tycho Brahe's contribution was to realise that such an advance demanded careful observation, and to make that observation.

Tycho's main work was done at Uraniborg, the observatory built for him in Denmark by the king. His first task was to improve the instruments then in use. He greatly increased their size, constructing a quadrant with a 19-foot radius and a celestial globe 5 feet in diameter, and he improved methods of sighting and graduation. He also determined the errors in his instruments, gave the limits of accuracy of his observations, and took account of the effect of atmospheric refraction on the apparent positions of heavenly bodies. It had been customary before Tycho to make observations in a somewhat haphazard manner, so that there had been no radical reform of the ancient data. Tycho made regular and systematic observations of known error, which revealed problems hitherto hidden in the previous inaccuracies.

Tycho's first problem arose when a new star appeared in the constellation Cassiopeia on 11th November, 1572, and remained until early in 1574. Scientific opinion received a marked shock from this object. Tycho attempted to determine its parallax and showed that this was so small that the star must be beyond the planets and adjacent to the Milky Way. Although he himself never fully accepted it, the mutability of celestial substance had thus been definitely demonstrated. Also, though comets had been regularly observed since the days of Regiomontanus, Tycho was able to show, with his superior instruments, that the comet of 1577 was beyond the sun and that its orbit must have passed through the solid celestial spheres, if these existed. He also departed from the Platonic ideal and suggested that the orbits of comets were not circular but oval. Further, Aristotelian theory held that comets were manifestations in the air. In 1557 Jean Pena, royal mathematician at Paris, had maintained on optical reasoning that some comets were beyond the moon and hence had rejected the spheres of fire and of the planets, and held that air extended to the fixed stars. Tycho went further and abandoned both the Aristotelian theory of comets and the solid spheres. At the same time, the discovery of land scattered all over the globe led other natural philosophers, such as Cardano, to abandon the theory of concentric spheres of earth and water based on the Aristotelian doctrine of natural place and motion. Land and sea they held to form one single sphere.

While Tycho provided the observations on which to base an accurate geometrical description of heavenly motions, he was led by physical as well as by Biblical difficulties to reject the rotation of the earth. He did not consider that Copernicus had answered the Aristotelian physical objections. Further, before the invention of the telescope had revealed the fact that the fixed stars, unlike the planets, appear as mere luminous points and not as discs, it was usually held that they shone by reflected light, and their brightness was taken as a measure of their magnitude. Tycho therefore deduced, from the absence of observable annual stellar parallax, that the Copernican system would involve the conclusion that the stars had diameters of incredible dimensions. He produced a system of his own (1588), in which the moon, sun and fixed stars revolved round a stationary earth while all the other 'planets' revolved round the sun. This was geometrically equivalent to the Copernican system, but escaped what he considered to be the latter's physical defects and included the benefits of his own observations. It remained an alternative to Copernicus (or Ptolemy) during the first half of the 17th century, and when Tycho bequeathed his observations to Kepler, who had come to work with him, he asked him to use it in the interpretation of his data.

Kepler did not do this. Michael Mästlin (1550–1631), under whom he had first studied, had, like Tycho, also calculated the orbit of the comet of 1577, and he declared the Copernican system alone capable of accounting for it. Kepler persisted in this opinion. He was also strongly influenced by Pythagoreanism. The vision of abstract harmony, according to which he believed the world to be constructed, sustained him through the drudgery of arithmetical computation to which he was consigned both by his astronomical researches and his work as a professional astrologer. Throughout his life he was inspired by the search for a simple mathematical law which would bind together the spatial distribution of the orbits and the motions of the members of the solar system. After numerous trials he arrived at the idea published in his *Mysterium Cosmographicum* (1596), that the spaces between the planetary orbits each corresponded, from Saturn to Mercury, to one of the five regular solids or 'Platonic bodies': cube, tetrahedron, dodecahedron, icosahedron and octahedron. He then went to Tycho Brahe, who had moved to Prague, from whom alone he could get the correct values of the mean distances and eccentricities that would confirm this theory. He was forced instead to abandon it, but his mathematical vision came to perceive in Tycho's data the foundations of celestial harmony. First, he saw that Copernicus had unnecessarily complicated matters by not allowing the planes of all the planetary orbits to pass through the sun. Even when this assumption was made there was still an error of 8 or 9 seconds in the arc of the orbit of Mars; and this could not be attributed to inaccuracy in the data. This forced him to abandon the assumptions that planetary orbits were circular and the movements of the planets uniform, and led him to formulate his first two laws: (1) Planets move in ellipses with the sun in one focus; (2) each planet moves, not uniformly, but so that a line joining its centre to that of the sun sweeps out equal areas in equal times (*De Motibus Stellæ Martis*, 1609) (Fig. 39). After ten years further labour he arrived at his third law, published in 1619 in the *De Harmonica Mundi*: (3) the squares of the periods of revolution of any two planets are proportional to the cubes of their mean distances from the sun.

These laws could scarcely have been formulated without the work of Greek geometers, especially Apollonius, on conic sections. This subject had been developed by Maurolyco and, in a commentary on Witelo (1604), by Kepler himself. In deducing his second law, Kepler made a contribution to mathematics, introducing the innovation, from which considerations of strict logic had restrained the Greeks, of considering an area as made up of an infinite number of lines generated by revolving a given curve about an axis (*cf.* above, p. 282). The work of the practical astronomer was also greatly assisted by improvements in methods of computation, first by the systematic use of decimal fractions

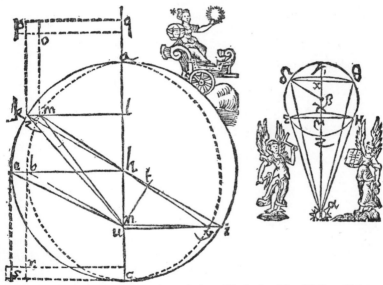

FIG. 39. Kepler's demonstration of the elliptical orbit of Mars. From *De Motibus Stellæ Martis*, Prague, 1609.

introduced by Stevin, but above all by the publication in 1614 of the discovery of logarithms by John Napier (1550–1617). Following this, other mathematicians calculated tables for trigonometrical functions and accommodated logarithms to the natural base *e*. The slide rule was invented by William Oughtred in 1622. Kepler made use of some of these innovations in reducing to order the practical results of his own and

Tycho's work for the *Rudolphine Tables*, published in 1627.

Kepler's three laws provided a final solution of the ancient problem of discovering an astronomical system which would both 'save' the phenomena and describe the 'actual' paths of the bodies through space. Copernicus' 'third motion' of the earth was abandoned since, there being no celestial spheres, the phenomena it was supposed to explain were attributed simply to the fact that the earth's axis remained parallel to itself in all positions. The independent invention of the telescope (with magnifications of up to about thirty) by Galileo added confirmation for the 'Copernican' theory. One of Tycho's objections to this theory was removed when Galileo was able to show, by finding the distance at which a stretched cord of known thickness would just eclipse them, that the fixed stars were not of the incredibly enormous dimensions Tycho had supposed they would have to be, on the assumption that brightness was proportional to magnitude, in order to be as bright as they were at a distance sufficient for them to show no parallax. Galileo also resolved parts of the Milky Way into individual stars. He also confirmed Copernicus' deduction that Venus, because of the position he held it to have inside the earth's orbit, would have phases like the moon; and in 1631 Pierre Gassendi observed the transit, which Kepler had predicted, of Venus across the sun's disc, and established that it described an orbit between the sun and the earth. The transit of Venus was observed also by the English astronomer Jeremiah Horrocks (1619–41). Galileo, in his *Siderius Nuntius* (1610), described the mountains on the moon, Saturn's rings (which he interpreted wrongly) and the four satellites of Jupiter, which he took as a model of Copernicus' solar system; and he was able to show that the variations in the apparent sizes of Mars, Jupiter and Saturn corresponded with the distances of these bodies from the earth according to the Copernican hypothesis. His observation of spots on the sun, by which he estimated its rate of rotation, also added evidence against the Aristotelian theory of immutability.

Sun-spots were also described by the Jesuit Father Scheiner (1611), who had constructed a telescope embodying improvements suggested by Kepler.

The astronomical theory of the early years of the 17th century was thus the achievement of the practical alternation of hypothesis and observation which had proceeded rapidly since Copernicus. Kepler himself had conceived astronomy to begin with observations, which were translated, by means of measuring instruments, into lengths and numbers for treatment by geometry, algebra and arithmetic. Next, hypotheses were formed which brought the observed relations together in geometrical systems which 'saved the appearances'. Finally, physics studied the causes of the phenomena related by an hypothesis, which must also be consistent with metaphysical principles. Kepler's research into mathematical relations had been to a considerable degree guided by the physical conceptions which he elaborated to account for the phenomena and to meet the objections to the earth's rotation. These physical conceptions may be described as an amalgam of the theories of *impetus* and Pythagorean gravity, which he derived from Nicholas of Cusa, with the theories by which William Gilbert (1540–1603) tried to explain his recent contributions to magnetism.

Gilbert was court physician to Queen Elizabeth, who gave him a pension to pursue his research. He took a considerable interest in astronomy, but his main achievement was to extend the work of Petrus Peregrinus on magnetism, which had been printed in 1558. Gilbert's *De Magnete* (1600), though containing some measurements, was entirely non-mathematical in treatment, and is the most striking illustration of the independence of the experimental and mathematical traditions in the 16th century. He derived his methods largely from Peregrinus and from practical compass-makers such as Robert Norman, a retired mariner whose book, *The Newe Attractive* (1581), contains the independent discovery of the magnetic dip, which had been observed first by Georg Hartmann in 1544. Gilbert extended Peregrinus' work to show that the strength and range of a uniform lodestone was proportional to size. He also showed that the angle of dip of a freely suspended needle varied with latitude. Peregrinus had likened the needle-lines traced on a spherical magnet to meridia, and called the points where they met poles. Gilbert inferred from the orientations in which magnets set with respect to the earth that the latter was itself a huge magnet with its poles near the geographical poles. This he confirmed by showing that iron ore was magnetised in the direction in which it lay in the earth. The properties of lodestones and of the compass were thus included in a general principle (Fig. 40).

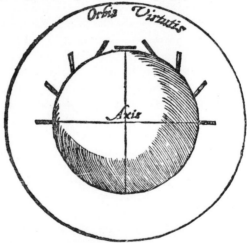

FIG. 40. The earth as a magnet, and magnetic dip. From Gilbert's *De Magnete*, London, 1600.

Gilbert also made a study of electrified bodies, which he called *electrica*. He showed that not only amber, but also other substances such as glass, sulphur and some precious stones, attracted small things when rubbed; he identified a body as being 'electric' by using a light metallic needle balanced on a point. He pointed out that while the lodestone attracted only magnetisable substances, which it arranged in definite orientations, and was unaffected by immersion in water or screens of paper or linen, electrified bodies attracted everything and heaped them into shapeless masses and were affected by screens and immersion. Niccolo Cabeo (1585–1650) later observed that bodies flew off again after being attracted; Sir Thomas Browne said they were *repelled*.

Gilbert's empiricism extended only as far as the facts he had established. He used a balance to disprove the old story, accepted by Cardano, that the magnet fed on iron, but his explanation of magnetism and electricity, though not inconsistent with the facts, did not arise out of them. His explanation was really an adaptation of Averroës' theory of 'magnetic species' in a setting of Neoplatonic animism. Beginning with the principle that a body could not act where it was not, he asserted that if there were action at a distance there must be an 'effluvium' carrying it. He assumed such an effluvium to surround the lodestone and to be released from electrified bodies by the warmth of friction. He then extended this theory to explain the earth's attraction for falling bodies, the effluvium here being the atmosphere. Without going into details, he attributed the diurnal rotation of the earth, which he accepted, to magnetic energy, and the orderly movements of the sun and planets to the interaction of their effluvia.

Kepler was himself interested in magnetism, and Gilbert's work stimulated him to use this phenomenon to explain the physics of the universe. Here he accepted the current Aristotelian conception of motion as a process requiring the continuous operation of a motive power. As a young man under Scaliger he had adopted the Averroïst doctrine of Intelligences moving the heavenly bodies, but he had afterwards abandoned it because he wanted to consider only mechanical causes. He explained the continued rotation of the earth by the *impetus* which God impressed on it at the creation. But, like Nicholas of Cusa, he identified this *impetus* with the earth's soul (*anima*), thus reinstating the equivalent of an Intelligence. This *impetus*, he held, did not corrupt, for, with the Pythagorean theory of gravity which he accepted, circular motion could, without contradiction, be considered the natural motion of earth. To answer the traditional objections to the earth's rotation he developed Gilbert's suggestions. He considered lines, or elastic chains of force, which he held to be magnetic, to emanate radially from the earth's *anima motrix* and carry round the moon, clouds and all bodies thrown above the surface of the earth. Similar lines from the *animæ motrices* of Jupiter and Saturn carried round their satellites, and lines from the sun carried round the whole planetary system. It was this theory of a magnetic force, which diminished as distance increased so that the velocity of a planet in its orbit varied inversely as the distance from the sun, which led him to his second law. The rotation of the sun swinging its magnetic lines in a vortex would move the planets in a circle. He therefore attributed their elliptical orbits to the attraction and repulsion of their poles. Further, just as the motive force of the sun was magnetic, so there was an analogy between magnetism and gravitation. Gravitation was the tendency of cognate bodies to unite and, if it were not for the motive power carrying the moon and earth round their orbits, they would rush together, meeting at an *intermediate* point. This last was an entirely new idea. The attraction of the moon was also the cause of tides.

Most of Kepler's contemporaries, whether Copernicans or not, were not satisfied with the replies offered in this ingenious and suggestive system to the ancient physical objections to the earth's rotation. For example, the magnetic chains would have made all movement of projectiles impossible. Like all his predecessors, Kepler was unable to escape from the Aristotelian conception of movement as a process requiring a continuously operating mover. The word *inertia*, which he used, meant for him an internal resistance like that postulated by Roger Bacon, implying such a mover; without this resistance motion would be instantaneous. The mechanical problems which puzzled him and his contemporaries were solved only when the concept of inertia had come to be considered as self-evident, and this became possible only after mechanics had returned once more to earth and, through the investigation of motion there, a profound philosophical revolution had been brought about in the interpretation of physics in terms of mathematics. This revolution was largely the work of Galileo (see above, pp. 289 *et seq.*).

With Galileo's conceptions of force and the composition of forces, the arguments against the rotation of the earth drawn by Aristotelians from projectiles and other bodies detached from the earth's surface lost their premises. In his *Two Principal Systems* which, curiously enough, were not the Tychonic and the Keplerian, which he ignored, but the Ptolemaic and the Copernican, Galileo pointed out that such bodies would retain the velocity received from the rotating earth unless forced to do otherwise. The remaining mechanical objection to the Copernican theory was from 'centrifugal force' which, though not clearly conceived of and mathematically formulated before Huygens, Galileo convincingly enough showed to depend not on the linear velocity of a point on the earth's surface, but on the angular velocity of rotation, and therefore to be no greater on the earth's surface than on the surface of a smaller body rotating once in 24 hours. This would be negligible compared with gravity. It was only with Newton that the old mechanical objections to the heliocentric theory were finally answered. Newton, in his *Principia Mathematica* (1686), explained Kepler's laws by means of his law of gravitation, and showed that according to this law it was impossible for the mighty ball of the sun to revolve round the diminutive earth. Another difficulty which Galileo had been unable to answer was the absence of stellar parallax and, in fact, this was observed for the first time in 1838 by F. W. Bessel in the star 61 Cygni, though James Bradley, when looking for parallax, had observed, in 1725, that the fixed stars described small ellipses within exactly the duration of the terrestial year and that stars from the poles of the ecliptic to the ecliptic described figures which were increasingly less circular and more approaching straight lines. This was convincing evidence for the movement of the earth in an ellipse round the sun, but Bradley recognised that what he had observed were not parallactic ellipses, but aberrational ellipses due to the earth's approach, on one side of its orbit, to the light coming from the stars, and recession from it on the other.

It was through his interest in the Copernican theory that Galileo got into trouble with the Inquisition, and his case is instructive in showing the contrast between what a man might believe he is doing in his own time and what he did for later times. To the 20th century, Galileo presents the ironic spectacle of a man who invited persecution for a view of science which he, more than any other individual scientist, helped to destroy. His troubles with the Inquisition came to a head at two periods, in 1616 and 1633. Those of 1616 were brought about by a pamphlet he wrote on the interpretation of the Bible, in which he said that while the Bible could not err its exponents might, and that no effect of nature of which the senses afforded evidence, or which was a necessary conclusion from that evidence, should be considered doubtful because the Scriptures seemed to state the contrary. The theologians found nothing objectionable in this, though they were not flattered to be taught their business by a layman; the same thing had, in fact, been asserted by St. Augustine. The trouble began with Galileo's rider that the Copernican system was a necessary conclusion from the evidence of the senses, for this would contradict the literal interpretation of certain Biblical texts, for instance Joshua's command: 'Sun, stand thou still upon Gibeon; and thou, Moon, in the valley of Ajalon. And the sun stood still, and the moon stayed . . .' (*Joshua*, X, 12, 13), which seemed to imply that normally the sun moved and the earth was still.

It was natural for an investigator of Galileo's time to take as his goal the discovery of reality and truth, in this respect agreeing with the medieval 'physicists' rather than the 'mathematicians', and not simply to stop at saving the appearances.

'The principal scope of Astronomers', Salviati said in the Third Day of the *Two Principal Systems*, 'is to render only reason for the appearances of the Celestial Bodies, and to them, and to the motions of the Stars, to accomodate such structures and compositions of Circles, that the motions following these calculations, answer to the said appearances. . . .' He went on to say of the Ptolemaic theory: 'although it satisfied an *Astronomer* meerly *Arithmetical*, yet it did not afford satisfaction or content to the *Astronomer Philosophical*.' And, he added, 'Copernicus very well understood, that if one might salve the Celestial appearances with false assumptions in nature, it might with much more ease be done by true suppositions.'

The difficulty of establishing necessary truths about the things of experience in any particular case had been a commonplace since the 13th century among those familiar with the later refinements of scholastic logic. Typical of the attitude of later scholastic logicians is the statement of the 16th-century Agostino Nifo in his *Expositio de Physico Auditu*, published in Venice in 1552, book 1, comm. text 4:

the science of nature is not a science *simpliciter*, like mathematics . . . That something is a cause can never be so certain as that an effect exists, for the existence of an effect is known to the senses. That it is the cause remains conjectural.

The attitude of several of the most prominent theologians to the Copernican theory was expressed by Cardinal Bellarmine in a letter written in 1615. He said:

If there were a real proof that the sun is in the centre of the universe, that the earth is in the third heaven [*i.e.*, sphere], and that the sun does not go round the earth but the earth round the sun, then we should have to proceed with great circumspection in explaining passages of Scripture which appear to teach the contrary, and rather admit that we did not understand them than declare an opinion to be false which is proved to be true. But as for myself, I shall not believe that there are such proofs until they are shown to me. Nor is a proof that, if the sun be supposed at the centre of the universe and the earth in the third heaven, the celestial appearances are thereby explained, equivalent to a proof that the sun actually is in the centre and the earth in the third heaven. The first kind of proof might, I believe, be found, but as for the second kind, I have the very gravest doubts, and in case of doubt we ought not to abandon the interpretation of the sacred text as given by the holy Fathers. (J. Brodrick, *The Life of Blessed Robert Francis, Cardinal Bellarmine, S.J., 1542–1621*, London, 1928, vol. 2, pp. 359–60.)

The theologians had no objection to the Copernican system as a hypothesis; it had been used as the basis of the Gregorian reform of the calendar in 1582 and, in fact, it had been presented as a hypothesis in Osiander's preface (then believed to be by Copernicus himself) to the *De Revolutionibus*. But owing to Galileo's persistence, in spite of the advice of his clerical friends to leave the Bible out of it, the matter was brought before the Holy Office in 1616. Whatever may have been the private views of such churchmen as Bellarmine, the theological consulters, who were predominantly Aristotelians, saw only the contrast between the naïvely realist meaning of the Copernican theory and the literal interpretation of the Biblical texts, though it would have been within the tradition of the Fathers to interpret the texts in question as simply using the language of common speech. They played for safety. They reported that the proposition that

'the sun is the centre of the world and altogether devoid of local motion' was 'foolish and absurd philosophically, and formally heretical, inasmuch as it expressly contradicts the doctrines of Holy Scripture in many places, both according to their literal meaning, and according to the common exposition and meaning of the holy Fathers and learned theologians'; and that the proposition that 'the earth is not the centre of the world nor immoveable, but moves as a whole, and also with a diurnal motion' was also likewise worthy of 'censure in philosophy' and 'at least erroneous in faith'.

Copernicus' book was placed on the Index, which meant that it should not be read by Catholics without making certain slight changes in it to make it quite clear that it was presenting only a hypothesis. Galileo's name was not mentioned in the decree, and nothing happened to him beyond being told that he must give up his opinion that the earth's motion was an established fact; he was at liberty to use it as a hypothesis.

Galileo could not very well give up an opinion he honestly held. He had disposed of all the arguments put forward against the earth's movements and, moreover, he thought that he could prove that only by assuming these movements was it possible to explain the tides. Though it is now possible to see the fallacy in his argument from the tides, it was then plausible, and it was natural for Galileo to take it as a necessary proof of his contention on the main point at issue in the controversy over the Copernican theory. This proof he eventually published in the *Two Principal Systems*, with an obviously insincere preface saying that he was putting forward the Copernican system only as a hypothesis. As a result he was brought before the Inquisition in 1633 for disobeying the decree of 1616. The Roman authorities were motivated, no doubt, by the desire to preserve the dogma of the inerrancy of the Holy Scriptures against private interpretations on the Protestant model, though many of them, including Vincenzo Maculano, the Commissary General who conducted the proceedings against Galileo, held the view that astronomical questions could not be decided from the Bible, which was concerned only with matters relating to salvation. Galileo himself, as Whitehead has put it, was 'given an honourable detention and a mild reproof, before dying peacefully in his bed'. Though an old man, he went on with his work on mechanics and published what is really his most important contribution to that subject, *Dialogues Concerning Two New Sciences*, in 1638. The case certainly damped the enthusiasm for astronomy in Catholic countries, though it did not prevent the new astronomy from becoming accepted, largely through Galileo's efforts.

Some three centuries after this, Einstein said that the state of motion or rest could be defined only by reference to a conventional standard; it was equally legitimate to take a

stationary earth or a stationary sun for the frame of reference.
Galileo suffered as a protest against so free a view of the
'Copernican' theory; but he was protesting against himself.
Einstein was able to advance the theory of relativity only
because he acted on the principle that the object of physical
science is to 'save the appearances' by mathematical abstractions postulated for no other purpose than to 'save the
appearances', and it was Galileo who, though himself
unaware of the full implications of what he was doing,
thrust this view upon his successors. It was not, in fact,
for more than a century afterwards, not till Kant, that
men began to realise clearly what physical scientists had
really been doing since Galileo (see below, pp. 396–402).

(3) PHYSIOLOGY AND THE METHOD OF
EXPERIMENT AND MEASUREMENT

Experimental physiology was another branch of science in
which the mathematical approach, which Galileo had used
with such success in mechanics and which was to achieve
such astonishing triumphs in astronomy, was used with great
effect in the 17th century.

Galileo himself had shown, while studying the strength and
cohesion of materials, that whereas weight increased as the
cube, the area of cross-section, on which strength depended,
increased only as the square of the linear dimensions. There
was thus a definite limit to the size of a land animal which
its limbs could bear and its muscles move, but animals living
in water, which supported the weight, might reach enormous
dimensions.

One of the first to apply Galileo's methods to physiological
problems was his colleague, the professor of medicine at
Padua, Santorio Santorii (1561–1636). He invented a
number of instruments such as a pulsilogium, or small
pendulum for measuring pulse-rate, and a clinical thermometer. He used the latter to estimate the heat of a patient's
heart by measuring the heat of the expired air, which was

supposed to come from the heart. He also made instruments to measure temperature in the mouth and others to be held in the hand. His method of measurement was to observe the distance which the liquid in the thermometer fell during 10 beats of a pulsilogium. As this depends not only on the patient's temperature but on the speed of his peripheral circulation, which increases with fever, Santorio's measurement of the rate of rise of temperature was probably an excellent indication of fever. In another work, *De Medicina Statica* (1614), he described an experiment which laid the foundation of the modern study of metabolism. He spent days on an enormous balance, weighing food and excrement, and estimated that the body lost weight through 'invisible perspiration'.

It was to William Harvey (1578–1657) that the revolution in physiology was chiefly due. Harvey, after graduating at Cambridge, spent five years at Padua under Hieronymo Fabrizio of Aquapendente (1537–1619), and there he learnt from his revered teacher to value the comparative method (see below, pp. 380–1). Most of his own researches into comparative anatomy were lost during the English Civil War, but in the two books which contain his extant contribution to science he emphasised the importance of comparative anatomy, both for its own sake and for elucidating the structure and physiology of man. He examined the hearts of a large number of vertebrates, including lizards, frogs and fish, and of invertebrates such as snails, a small transparent shrimp and insects. In insects he observed the pulsating dorsal vessel with a magnifying glass. Although his period at Padua coincided with Galileo's professorship there, there is no evidence that they ever met, nor did Harvey ever mention Galileo in his works. Nevertheless Harvey's method of restricting his research into biological processes to problems which could be solved by experiment and measurement might well have been learnt from the great mechanist. At any rate he breathed the same atmosphere and, although his references to logic were almost entirely to Aristotle, he also resembles Galileo in that his most important work was a perfect practical exhibition of the scholastic methods of 'resolution' and 'composition'.

Harvey's notes for lectures given at the Royal College of Physicians in London in 1615–16 show that he had then already arrived, through experiment and reflection, at the idea of the general circulation of the blood. Many of the constituents of this idea had, in fact, already been discovered by his predecessors. Leonardo da Vinci had maintained that the heart was a muscle, and made admirable drawings of it which included the discovery of the moderator band in the

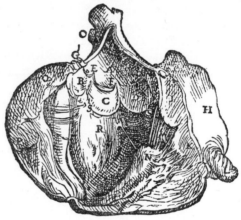

Fig. 41. The heart and its valves. From Vesalius' *De Humani Corporis Fabrica*, Basel, 1543.

sheep. He had also followed the movements of the heart in the pig by means of needles thrust through the chest wall into its substance, and constructed models to illustrate the action of the valves. His views on the movements of the blood were, however, almost entirely Galenic and, moreover, it is not known whether his anatomical manuscripts had an influence similar to those on mechanics (Plate 10). The French physician, Jean Fernel, seems to have been the first to have observed, in 1542, that, in contradiction to current teaching (see above, p. 134), when the ventricles contracted (systole) the arteries *increased* in size, and to have stated that this was because of the blood (and compressed spirits) forced into them. Then, in 1543, Vesalius published his observations showing that there were no pores through the interventricular septum (Fig. 41). This, together with the view that the heart was a muscle and had two and not three ventricles, had already been asserted by the 13th-century Egyptian (or Syrian) physician, Ibn An-Nafis. Ibn An-Nafis had maintained, as against Avicenna and Galen, that venous blood must pass from right to left ventricle via the artery-like vein (pulmonary artery), through the lungs, where it spread through their substance and mixed with the air in them, and then went back to left side of the heart in the vein-like artery (pulmonary vein). This work seems to have been unknown in the West; the first Western writer to put forward the theory of the pulmonary circulation (1553) was Miguel Serveto (1511–53), who mentioned in the course of a theological discussion that some blood passed from right to left ventricle via the lungs, where it changed colour. He supposed some also to pass through the interventricular septum. Serveto's interests were primarily theological and it seems likely that he derived these ideas from some other

'The heart drives out the blood in its restraining . . . This thing was ordained by Nature in order that, when the right ventricle begins to shut, the escape of the blood out of its big capacity should not suddenly cease, because some of that blood had to be given to the lung; and none of it would have been given, if the valves had prohibited the exit; (but this ventricle shut, when the lung had received its quantity of blood, and when the right ventricle could press through the pores of the medium wall into the left ventricle); and at this time the right auricle made itself the depository of the superabundance of the blood which it advances to the lung that suddenly renders it to the opening of this right ventricle, restoring itself through the blood which the liver gives it. How much blood is the liver able to give it through the opening of the heart? It gives as much of it as it consumes, *i.e.*, a minimum quantity, because in one hour about two thousand openings of the heart take place. There is great weight . . . 7 ounces an hour.' (*Quaderni d'Anatomia*, ed. O. C. L. Vangensten, A. Fonahn and H. Hopstock, Christiana, 1912, vol. 2, *f* . 17v.) [See Plate 10, facing p. 337.]

source. There is at present no evidence that either he or the Paduan anatomist Realdo Colombo (*c.* 1516–59) knew of Ibn An-Nafis, and it is usually suggested that it was Serveto who inspired Colombo. In view of the curious context in which Serveto announced the discovery, it has been suggested recently that the borrowing was more probably the other way round, if, indeed, both Colombo and Serveto did not derive the idea from oral teaching by Vesalius. Colombo himself, in his *De Re Anatomica* (1559), not only put forward the idea of the pulmonary circulation but also supported it with experiments. He noted, as Fernel had done, that cardiac systole (contraction) coincided with arterial *expansion* and cardiac diastole (expansion) with arterial contraction; and he showed, further, that the complete closure of the mitral valve prevented pulsation in the pulmonary vein. When he opened this vein he found not fumes, as the Galenists would have expected, but blood, and he concluded that blood passed from the lung (where a change in colour was observed) through the pulmonary vein back to the left side of the heart. Like Serveto, he believed that some blood passed also through the interventricular septum. Both writers held also to the Galenic view that blood was made in the liver and flowed through the heart to the veins. Thus neither had any idea of the true nature of blood and although Colombo had observed that the pulsation of the brain was synchronous with that of the arteries, he did not arrive at the idea of the general or systemic circulation.

The Dutch anatomist Volcher Coiter (1534–*c.* 1576) also made some experiments on the heart. He made a comparative study of the living hearts of kittens, chickens, vipers, lizards, frogs and eels and observed that in the excised organ the auricles contracted before the ventricles and that the heart was lengthened in systole and shortened in diastole. He also showed that a small detached piece of heart muscle would continue to beat.

Some observations on the movements of the blood were made also by the Italian physiologist and botanist, Andrea

Cesalpino (1519–1603). He said, in his *Quæstionum Peripateti-carum* (1571), that when the heart contracted it forced blood into the aorta and when it expanded it received blood from the vena cava. In his *Quæstionum Medicarum* (1593), book 2, question 17, he said:

The passages of the heart are so arranged by nature that from the vena cava a flow takes place into the right ventricle, whence the way is open into the lung. From the lung, moreover, there is another entrance into the left ventricle of the heart, from which there is a way open into the aorta artery, certain membranes being so placed at the mouths of the vessels that they prevent return. Thus there is a sort of perpetual movement from the vena cava through the heart and lungs into the aorta artery.

He showed also that when a vein was ligatured it swelled up on the side away from the heart, and he referred to *capilla-menta* into which both arteries and veins petered out, though he did not say that these vessels joined peripherally by means of capillaries and, in fact, spoke of arteries as ending in nerves. But in his last work in 1602–3 he formally stated that blood went *forth* from the heart through the veins as well as the arteries and, though he used the word *circulatio*, he under-stood it to mean a to-and-fro movement as in the rising and falling of fluid in chemical distillation. Thus he did not understand the general circulation any more than Colombo, or Carlo Ruini who, in 1598, also published a description of the pulmonary or lesser circulation in his treatise on the anatomy of the horse, or Fabrizio who, in 1603, gave the first clear and adequate figures of the valves in the veins but believed that their function was to counteract the effect of gravity and prevent the blood accumulating in the hands and feet. The theory of the general circulation of the blood was, in fact, advanced first by William Harvey.

Harvey published his great theory in 1628 in his *Exercitatio Anatomica de Motu Cordis et Sanguinis in Animalibus*. The work begins with a 'resolution' of the problem into its parts so that the cause might be discovered through its effects. Preliminary observations, many of which had already been made by

333

others, showed that the contraction of the heart was a muscular contraction beginning with the auricles and passing to the ventricles, whose contraction then caused the expansion of the arteries. This suggested that there was a flow of blood from the veins through the heart into the arteries, and the arrangement of the cardiac valves would prevent its return. He then showed that if either the pulmonary artery or the aorta alone were punctured, the contraction of the right ventricle was followed by a jet of blood from the former, and the contraction of the left ventricle by a jet of blood from the latter. In embryos, such as that of the chick, the blood entering the right auricle passed not to the lungs, which were not yet functioning, but through the *foramen ovale* into the left auricle and so via the left ventricle into the aorta. The two ventricles thus operated as one, and the condition in the embryo of animals with lungs corresponded to that in the adults of animals such as fish which had no lungs. In the adults of the animals with lungs the blood could not pass through the *foramen ovale*, which was closed, but had to go from the right to the left side of the heart via the tissue of the lungs themselves.

From the structure and continuous beat of the heart Harvey concluded that the flow of the blood through it was not only in one direction but also continuous. It would follow from this that unless there were some passage from the arteries back to the veins in the body at large, as well as in the lungs, the veins would soon be drained and the arteries would be ruptured from the quantity of blood flowing into them. There was, therefore, no escape from the following hypothesis which he enunciated in chapter 8 of *De Motu Cordis:*

I began to think whether there might not be *a motion, as it were, in a circle.* Now this I afterwards found to be true; and I finally saw that the blood, forced by the action of the left ventricle into the arteries, was distributed to the body at large, and its several parts, in the same manner as it is sent through the lungs, impelled by the right ventricle into the pulmonary artery, and that it then passed through the veins and along the vena cava, and so round to the left ventricle.

From the hypothesis of circulation Harvey then made a number of deductions which, if experimentally verified, would both confirm it and finally eliminate the rival hypothesis of Galen that the blood was continuously produced from the ingested food and ebbed and flowed in the heart and vessels. First, he demonstrated that the blood flowed continuously through the heart in the direction from veins to arteries only. In a serpent, whose vessels were conveniently arranged for experimental investigation, when the vena cava was pinched with forceps the heart drained and became pale, whereas when the aorta was similarly closed the heart became distended and purple. This was in keeping with the arrangement of the valves. He then showed that in the peripheræ of the body the blood flowed in the same continuous stream but, in those regions, from arteries to veins. In the limbs the arteries were deeply placed, while the veins were near the surface. A moderately tight ligature round the arm would constrict the latter but not the former, and he found that this produced a distension of the hand with blood. A very tight ligature stopped the pulse and flow of blood into the hand altogether and no distension was observed. Further, anatomical investigations showed that the valves were arranged in the veins so that the blood could flow only towards the heart, a fact which Fabrizio had not realised. Harvey then showed that when the arm was ligatured moderately tightly so that the veins swelled up, 'nodes' were formed at the position of the valves (Fig. 42). If the blood were pushed out of the vein below the valve by running the finger along it in the peripheral direction the emptied section remained flat, and he concluded that this was because the valve prevented the blood from running back into it. This explanation he confirmed by further experiments of the same kind. Finally, as the blood flowed continuously in one direction through the heart it could be calculated from the heart's capacity and rate of beat that it pumped through itself in an

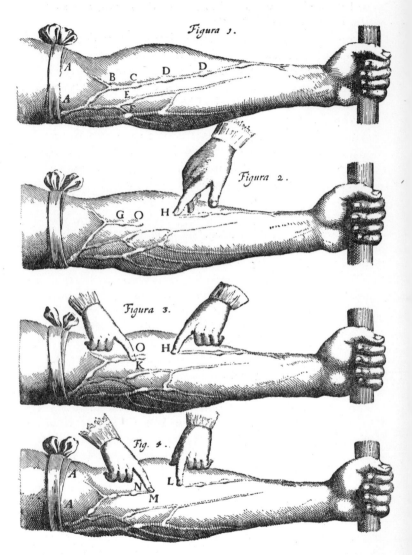

Fig. 42. Harvey's experiments showing swelling of nodes in veins at the valves. From *De Motu Cordis*, London, 1639 (1st edn. 1628).

PLATE 9   SURGERY

Using a *spongia soporifera*, trephining, operating for hernia and treating fractures, from Roland of Parma's *Livre de Chirurgie*. From British Museum MS. Sloane 1977 (XIII cent.)

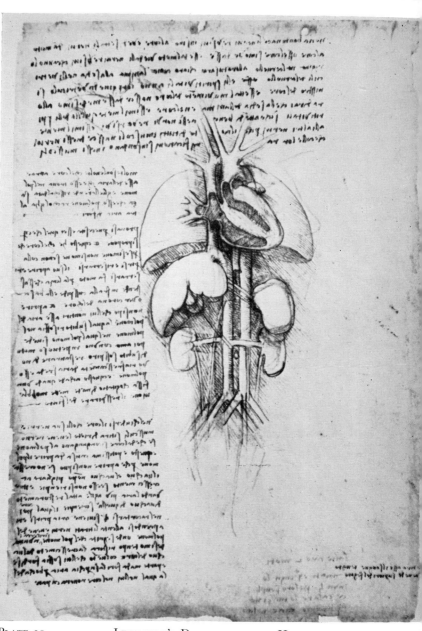

PLATE 10   LEONARDO'S DRAWING OF THE HEART
And associated blood vessels. From *Quaderni d'Anatomia 4*, Royal Library, Windsor
MS. By Gracious permission of H.M. the Queen—*see* note on p. 331.

hour about three times the weight of the body. Similar calculations were made for the quantity of blood passing through other parts of the body. Such a quantity could not possibly have been produced from the food. He therefore arrived at the following conclusion, in *De Motu Cordis*, chapter 14:

Since all things, both argument and ocular demonstration, show that the blood passes through the lungs and heart by the action of the [auricles and] ventricles, and is sent for distribution to all parts of the body, where it makes its way into the veins and pores of the flesh, and then flows by the veins from the circumference on every side to the centre, from the lesser to the greater veins, and is by them finally discharged into the vena cava and right auricle of the heart, and this in such a quantity or in such a flux and reflux thither by the arteries, hither by the veins, as cannot possibly be supplied by the ingesta, and is much greater than can be required for mere purposes of nutrition; it is absolutely necessary to conclude that the blood in the animal body is impelled in a circle, and is in a state of ceaseless motion; that this is the act or function which the heart performs by means of its pulse; and that it is the sole and only end of the motion and contraction of the heart.

Harvey's theory was an immense illumination to physiology, to which it directed the interest of biologists. His treatise also provided a model of method. After him, abstract discussion of such questions as the nature of life or of 'innate heat' gradually gave way to the empirical investigation of how the body worked. He himself had left somewhat vague the passage of the blood from arteries to veins, and the demonstration of his theory was finally completed when, in 1661, Malpighi observed, under the microscope, the flow of blood through the capillaries in the frog's lung. The study of the blood, the bearer of food and oxygen, was, in fact, well placed to lay the foundations of physiology, and Harvey's elucidation of its mechanics was followed later in the 17th century by the researches of Boyle and others into the chemical problem of respiration.

In his *Discours de la Méthode* (1637) Descartes had expressed the hope of arriving at rules which would reform medicine in the same way as he had attempted to reform the other sciences. He was one of the first to accept Harvey's discovery of the circulation of the blood, though he did not understand the pumping action of the heart which he still regarded as the centre of vital heat. In his *De Homine*, published posthumously in 1662, Descartes attempted to reconstruct the animate world on the principles of his physics. For a man who claimed to have divested himself of all former prejudices the result was strangely reminiscent of Galen, but it was Galen *more geometrico demonstrata*. 'I assume,' he said,

that the body is nothing else than a statue or machine of clay......I desire you to consider next that all the functions which I have attributed to this machine, such as the digestion of food, the beating of the heart and arteries, the nourishment and growth of the members, respiration, waking, and sleeping; the impressions of light, sounds, odours, tastes, heat and other such qualities on the organs of the external senses; the impression of their ideas on the common sense and the imagination; the retention of imprinting of these ideas upon the memory; the interior motions of the appetites and passions; and, finally, the external movements of all members, which follow so suitably as well the actions of objects which present themselves to sense, as the passions and impressions which are formed in the memory, that they imitate in the most perfect manner possible those of a real man; I desire, I say, that you consider that all these functions follow naturally in this machine simply from the arrangement of its parts, no more nor less than do the movements of a clock, or other *automata*, from that of its weights and its wheels; so that it is not at all necessary for their explanation to conceive in it of any other soul, vegetative or sensitive, nor of any other principle of motion and life, than its blood and its spirits, set in a motion by the heat of the fire which burns continually in its heart, and which is of a nature no different from all fires in inanimate bodies.

In Descartes' theory the body of human beings was haunted by a rational soul. Since the mind was an unextended thinking substance while the body was an unthinking extended substance, some of his critics and followers, such as

338

Gassendi and Malebranche, held that these two substances could have no point of contact. But Descartes himself held that they interacted at one point and one only, the pineal gland in the brain (Fig. 44; *cf.* Fig. 43). He regarded this as a sort of flat door which controlled the flow of animal spirits; these were distilled in the heart from the blood and flowed

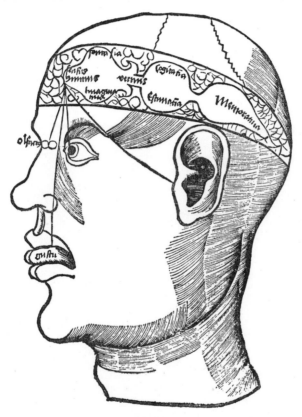

Fig. 43. The localised functions of the brain. From G. Reisch, *Margarita Philosophiae*, Heidelberg, 1504.

in the nerves, which he thought were fine hollow tubes. The mind acted on the body by turning this door in various directions and deflecting the animal spirits into one nerve or another. These spirits then flowed into the muscle at the end of the nerve concerned and made it swell up, thus moving the limb or part of the body to which it was attached. The movement of this door was the only action the mind had on the body. When, on the other hand, as a result of some event

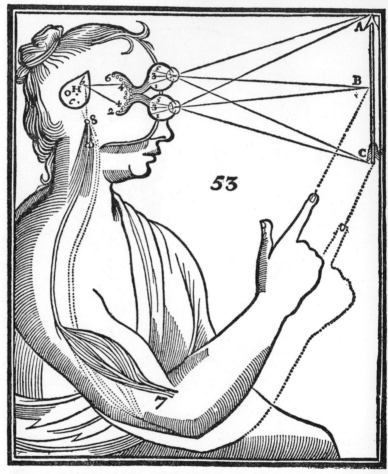

FIG. 44. Descartes' theory of perception showing the transmission of the nervous impulse from the eye to the pineal gland and thence to the muscles. From *De Homine*, Amsterdam, 1677 (1st edn. Lyons, 1662).

in the body, the animal spirits rushed up from the heart to the door with special violence and moved it themselves, the body acted on the mind and the latter had a sensation or emotion.

In contrast with man the brutes were simply *automata* and nothing more. Though animals were considerably more complicated, there was no difference in principle between them and the *automata* constructed by human ingenuity. 'There is,' wrote Descartes in a letter to the Marquis of Newcastle, on 23rd November, 1646,

no one of our external actions which can assure those who examine them that our body is anything more than a machine which moves itself, but which also has in it a mind which thinks— excepting words, or other signs . . .

The noises made by animals indicated no such controlling mind and we should not be deceived by their apparently purposive behaviour.

I know, indeed, that brutes do many things better than we do, but I am not surprised at it; for that, also, goes to prove that they act by force of nature and by springs, like a clock, which tells better what the hour is than our judgment can inform us. And, doubtless, when swallows come in the spring, they act in that like clocks. All that honey-bees do is of the same nature.

The mechanical principles that Harvey had adopted as a method were thus converted by Descartes into a metaphysics, and just as he had ignored the empiricism of Galileo so he did that of the English physiologist. All three men, however, inspired their successors to bring about the mechanisation of biology. The iatro-mechanical school adopted the principle that biological phenomena were to be investigated entirely by 'mathematical principles'. The stomach was a retort, the veins and arteries hydraulic tubes, the heart a spring, the viscera sieves and filters, the lung a bellows and the muscles and bones a system of cords, struts and pulleys. The adoption of such conceptions certainly exposed many problems for investigation by the now established mathematical and experimental methods, a particularly successful application being the study of the mechanics of the skeleton and muscular system by Giovanni Alfonso Borelli in his book, *On the Motion of Animals* (1680). But they were soon carried to naïve extremes which oversimplified the complexity and variety of physiological processes. Further, such principles entirely obliterated biological occurrences which could not be exhaustively reduced to the known principles of mechanics or expressed in terms of known mathematics. Recent research has corrected historical perspective by showing that such problems, the apparently purposive behaviour exhibited in the nest-building of birds and the adaptation of the parts of the body to each other and to the environment, continued to interest not only such naturalists as John Ray (1627–1704), who found in them proof of the wisdom of God in the works of creation, but also physical scientists such as Robert Boyle and Isaac Newton. Indeed, they still remain the hope, or the despair, of those who find it profitable to argue the question of vitalism and mechanism on metaphysical principles adopted, often unconsciously, from Descartes and his 17th-century critics.

(4) THE EXTENSION OF THE MATHEMATICAL METHOD
TO INSTRUMENTS AND MACHINES

As the 17th century progressed, experiment and the use of mathematics became so intimately linked that such a case as that of William Gilbert, who had carried on his experimental studies of magnetism almost without mathematics, would by the end of the century have been almost inconceivable. If causal relations such as those discovered by Gilbert remained incapable of expression in mathematical terms even by Galileo himself, it was generally believed that it was only a matter of time before the problem would be overcome and that this would depend largely on the development of more accurate instruments for measuring.

One of the instruments which Galileo did much to perfect was the clock. At the end of the 15th century the first clocks driven by a spring instead of by weights had been introduced in Nuremberg and this made possible the invention of the portable watch, as, for instance, the 'Nuremberg eggs'. The use of a spring introduced a new problem, for the force it exerted decreased as it became unwound. Various devices were designed to overcome this difficulty, the most successful being the so-called 'fusee' introduced in the middle of the 16th century by the Swiss, Jacob Zech. The main principle of this device was to make the driving barrel taper gradually, so that, as the spring became unwound, the loss of force was compensated by an increase in leverage provided by making the spring act on successively wider sections of the barrel. It was still not possible, however, to get a clock that would keep accurate time over a long period. This was becoming a necessity for several purposes, but particularly for the ocean-going navigation that had been expanding since the end of the 15th century. The only practical method of determining longitude depended on the accurate comparison of the time (by the sun) on the ship with that at some fixed point on the earth's surface, for instance Greenwich. Such a clock became possible when a pendulum was introduced as a regulating mechanism. In watches a balance-spring served the same purpose. In 1582 Galileo had discovered that a pendulum swung isochronously, and he suggested that this fact might be used in designing a clock. The first accurate clock was invented in 1657 by Huygens, when he put this suggestion into practice; but it was not until the 18th century that the navigational problem was finally overcome, when devices were introduced to compensate for the irregular motion of a ship and for changes in temperature.

Another form of measurement in which the demands of navigation and travel led to great improvements in the 16th and 17th centuries was the method of making maps. The sensational voyages of Bartholomew Diaz round the Cape of

343

Good Hope in 1486, of Christopher Columbus who reached America in 1492, of Vasco da Gama who reached India in 1497, and of many other sailors who searched for the North-West or the North-East passage, not only added a new world to European consciousness but also made accurate maps and methods of fixing position a fundamental necessity. The essential requirement for mapping the terrestrial globe was a linear measure of the arc of the meridian, for there were few astronomical estimations of latitude, and practically none for longitude, until the 18th century. Various improvements on medieval estimations of the degree were made during 16th and early 17th centuries, but the first accurate figure was given by the French mathematician, Jean Picard, in the second half of the 17th century. In spite of inaccurate figures for the degree, cartography improved greatly from the end of the 15th century, and this was in the first place due to a renewed interest in the maps of Ptolemy's *Geography* (see above, p. 182). Ptolemy had emphasised the need for the accurate fixing of position, and his maps were drawn on a complete network of parallels and meridians. In the 16th century charts were produced showing much more restricted areas than the medieval charts, and on these rhumb-lines were shown in a simplified form. The compass was used to establish the meridian line, the fact of magnetic variation with longitude being known and taken into consideration. Petrus Apianus, or Bienewitz, whose map, published in 1520, was one of the earliest to show America, in 1524 wrote a treatise on cartographical methods and in another work, *Cosmographicus Liber*, gave a list of latitudes and longitudes of many places in the known world illustrated with maps (Fig. 45). Another 16th-century cartographer, Gerard de Cremer or, as he was called, Mercator, of Louvain, in 1569 produced the well-known projection that is still in use showing the spherical earth on a two-dimensional paper. He also experimented with other kinds of projection and he took care to base his maps either on personal surveys, as in his map of Flanders, or on a critical comparison of the information collected by explorers. The same care was shown by other 16th-century cartographers such as Ortelius, who was geographer to the King of Spain, and Philip Cluvier, who published works on the historical geography of Germany and Italy.

Essential to accurate cartography on land were accurate

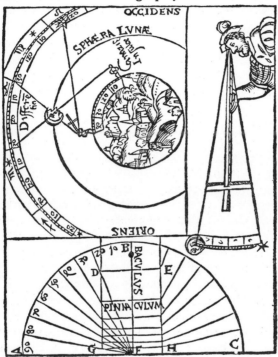

FIG. 45. A cross-staff in use for surveying. From *Petri Apiani Cosmographia*, Antwerp, 1539.

surveying methods, and these were improved in the 16th and 17th centuries. The use of the astrolabe, quadrant and cross-staff to measure height and distance was known in the Middle Ages, and in the 16th century Tartaglia and others showed how to fix position and survey land by compass-bearing and distance. In the late 15th and early 16th centuries very accurate maps were made of Alsace, Lorraine and the

Rhine Valley, notably by Waldseemüller of Strassburg (1511), in which roads were marked off in miles and a compass rose was shown. It is thought that these maps were made with a primitive theodolite known as the polimetrum. The method of triangulation, by which a whole country could be surveyed from an accurately measured base line but otherwise without direct measurement, was first published in print by the Flemish cartographer, Gemma Frisius, in 1533. In England, the first accurate maps were made by Saxton, at the end of the 16th century, and Norden, early in the 17th. An outstanding question which was not settled for some years was the adoption of a common prime meridian. English cartographers adopted Greenwich in the 17th century, but it was not generally accepted until 1925.

The first instrument for measuring temperature seems to have been invented by Galileo some time between 1592 and 1603, but three other investigators seem independently to have designed a thermometer, thermoscope, calendar-glass or weather-glass, as it was variously called, at about the same time. Galen had represented heat and cold by a numerical scale and, by the 16th century, though the senses were the only means of estimating temperature, the idea of degrees of these qualities had become a commonplace in medical and natural-philosophical literature (see above, pp. 263–4). The scales of degrees there described, such as that of eight degrees of each quality, were among those used in the earliest thermometers. These instruments were themselves also adaptations of ancient Greek inventions. Philo of Byzantium and Hero of Alexandria had both described experiments based on the expansion of air by heat (see above, p. 236, n. 1), and Latin versions of their works existed. That of Hero's *Pneumatica* was printed twice in the 16th century. The first thermometers, which were adaptations of some of their apparatus, consisted of a glass bulb with a stem dipping into water in a vessel. Air was driven out of the bulb by heat and, on cooling, water was drawn back into the stem. The stem was marked in degrees and, as the air in the bulb contracted and expanded, the movement of the water up and down it was used to measure temperature.

The attribution of the first invention of this instrument to Galileo rests solely on the testimony of his contemporaries, for it is described in none of his extant works. The first published account of it was given in 1611 in a commentary on Avicenna by the physiologist Santorio Santorii, who used it for clinical purposes. A similar instrument, which seems to have been a modification of Philo's apparatus, was used a few years later by Robert Fludd (1574–1651) to demonstrate the cosmic effects of light and darkness and heat and cold, to indicate or predict weather conditions, and to measure temperature changes. Another type of thermometer, consisting of a tube with a sealed bulb at each end, seems to have been invented by another contemporary, the Dutchman Cornelius Drebbell (1572–1634). This instrument depended for its operation on the difference in temperature between the air in each bulb, which moved coloured water up or down the stem.

These air thermometers were used for various purposes in the 17th century, though mostly for medical purposes. J. B. van Helmont (1577–1644), for example, used a modification of the open type to take body temperatu1e. They were very inaccurate and the open type was particularly sensitive to changes in atmospheric pressure. The French chemist Jean Rey adapted it in 1632 to form a water thermometer which measured temperature by the expansion and contraction of water instead of air; but technical difficulties prevented the construction of an accurate thermometer until the 18th century.

The desire to measure prompted the invention of an instrument which would give some idea of the weight of the atmosphere, an instrument for which Galileo was also initially responsible. Such observations as that water would not run out of a water clock while the hole at the top was closed were usually explained, after the 13th century, either by Roger Bacon's 'continuity of universal nature' or in terms of the void (see above, pp. 239–40). Galileo did not, like the Aristotelians, regard a void as an impossibility. He produced the earliest recorded artificial vacuum by drawing a piston from the bottom of an air-tight cylinder and, like Giles of Rome, he attributed the resistance encountered to the 'force of the vacuum'. When he learnt that a pump would not lift water above about 32 feet, he assumed that this was the limit of this force. In 1643 it was shown, at Torricelli's suggestion, that when a long tube with one end sealed was filled with mercury and inverted with its open end under mercury in a vessel, the length of the column of mercury standing in the tube was less than that of the water raised by a pump in proportion to the greater density of mercury. The empty space above the mercury became known as the 'Torricellian vacuum', and Torricelli attributed the effect to the weight of the atmosphere. Torricelli's apparatus was adapted to form the familiar J-tube barometer. His conclusions were confirmed when, under Pascal's direction, a barometer was carried to the top of the Puy de Dôme and it was found that the height of the mercury decreased with altitude, that is with the height of atmosphere above it.

The possibility of creating a vacuum led a number of scientists during the 16th and 17th centuries to try to devise a practical steam engine. The earliest of these were driven, in fact, not by the force of expansion of steam but by atmospheric pressure operating after steam in the cylinder had been condensed, though some writers, for instance de Caus in 1615 and Branca in 1629, suggested using the turbine device described by Hero of Alexandria, a jet of steam directed on to a wheel with blades. The most important practical problem for which steam engines were suggested was the pumping of water. The problem of keeping the ever-deepening mines free from water became increasingly serious throughout the 16th and 17th centuries. Agricola in his *De Re Metallica* described several types of device used for this purpose in the early 16th century: a chain of dippers worked by a crank turned by hand; a suction pump worked by a water wheel, with a cam to work the piston and with pipes made of hollow tree trunks clamped with iron bands (Fig. 46); a force pump worked by a crank; and a rag-and-chain device in which the buckets were replaced by balls of horse-hair and the motive power was provided by men walking a treadmill or a horse driving a whim. Pumps were needed also to provide water for fountains, and for town supplies. Augs-burg was supplied with water by a series of Archimedean screws turned by a driving shaft which raised the water to the tops of towers, from which it was distributed in pipes; London was supplied after 1582 by a force pump driven by a tide wheel set up near London Bridge by the German engineer, Peter Morice, and later by other horse-driven pumps; and pumps were used to supply Paris and other towns, and to work the fountains at Versailles and Toledo. As early as the mid-16th century Cardano had discussed methods of pro-ducing a vacuum by condensing steam, and in 1560 G. B. della Porta suggested using a device based on this principle for raising water. This suggestion was put forward again in 1663 by the Marquis of Worcester. A practical steam engine based on the same principle was patented in 1698 by Thomas Savery; it was used in at least one mine and to supply water to several country houses. A successful engine worked by atmospheric pressure was devised by Thomas Newcomen early in the 18th century, and even James Watts' engines were still primarily atmospheric. Towards the end of the century engines were invented which were driven by the expansive force of steam at high pressure.

The Torricellian vacuum was taken as a final refutation of Aristotle's arguments against the existence of void which, according to some of his followers, 'nature abhorred'. The arguments against the void, drawn from the Aristotelian law of motion, had already been disposed of by Galileo. But Aristotle himself had sometimes confused arguments against the existence of void, in the sense of 'non-being', with physical arguments against, for instance, the absence of a resisting medium. Many of his 17th-century critics did the same. The

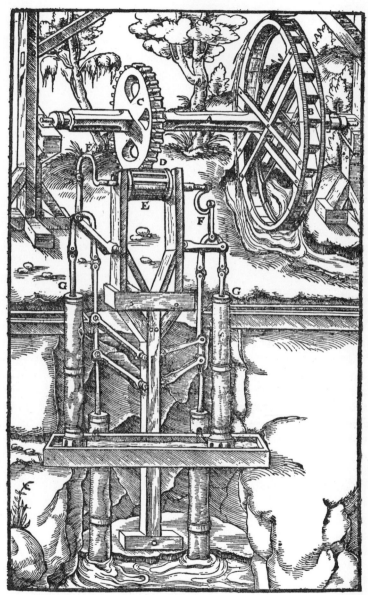

FIG. 46. A water-driven suction pump in use at a mine. From Agricola's
De Re Metallica, Basel, 1561 (1st edn. 1556).

Torricellian vacuum was not an ontological void such as Descartes, among others, could not accept. It was a space which, at least theoretically, contained no air or similar matter. Indeed, although later physicists were not so sensitive to metaphysical niceties as Descartes, they found it necessary to postulate a *plenum* of some sort, and this continued to play a variety of physical roles down to the 20th century. Torricelli showed that light was transmitted though a vacuum and, beginning with Gilbert's effluvia, 17th-century physicists filled up the void with a medium, the æther, capable of propagating all the known influences such as gravity, magnetism and light. Descartes himself attempted to explain magnetism by vortices which, like Averroës' *species magnetica*, entered by one pole of the magnet and left by the other. He held that these acted on iron because the resistance of its particles to the flow drew it to the magnet. Non-magnetisable substances did not offer such resistance.

Instruments designed for closer observation as well as for more accurate measurement were also constructed during the 17th century, the most important being the telescope and the compound microscope. The propagation of light was still explained by most 16th-century opticians in terms of the 'species' theory, which was in keeping with the geometrical discussions of the time. In the 16th century the first published attempt at a geometrical analysis of lenses and the eye was that by Maurolyco. He denied that the lens was the seat of vision, but could not understand the inverted image. Felix Plater (1536–1614) first recognised the true functions of the lens and retina; the anatomists Realdo Colombo and Hieronymo Fabrizio first drew the lens in the front part of the eye and not, as had been done previously, in the middle. A convenient method of isolating stars for observation had already been introduced by the Arabs and, with the spread of spectacles, the lens-grinding industry had developed in a number of centres. About 1600 Jan Lippershey and perhaps two other Dutchmen independently invented the telescope and the compound microscope by empirical combinations of lenses. Hearing of this, Galileo constructed the same instruments from his knowledge of refraction.[1] He did not fully understand this phenomenon and Kepler, in his commentary on Witelo (1611), gave a more intelligible theory. The true law of refraction, that the ratio of the sines of the angles of incidence and refraction is a constant depending on the media concerned, was only discovered a few years before 1626 by another Dutchman, Willibrord Snell (1591–1626). The law was formulated, probably in the first instance independently, by Descartes, who gave it its first publication in his *Dioptrique* in 1637.

Descartes attempted to conceive of the physical nature of light in a more strictly mathematical form than his predecessors. In accordance with his own mechanical principles he held that light consisted of particles of the *plenum* and that it was transmitted instantaneously by mechanical pressure from one particle to the next. Colour he held to depend on the different rotary velocities of the particles. When giving 'Snell's law' he presented it as a deduction from this conception of the nature of light, and in his *Météores* (1637) he then tried to use this law to explain the two phenomena exhibited by the rainbow, the bright circular bow and the colours. Theodoric of Freiberg, Themon Judæi and others had already reached a fairly good understanding of the bright bow (see above, p. 81), and their explanation was probably known, at least indirectly, to Antonio de Dominis (1611), who gave a somewhat inaccurate account of it, and to

(1) When the Frenchman, Jean Tarde, called on Galileo in 1614, he said 'Galileo told me that the tube of a telescope for observing the stars is no more than 2 feet in length; but to see objects well, which are very near, and which on account of their small size are hardly visible to the naked eye, the tube must be two or three times longer. He tells me that with this long tube he has seen flies which look as big as a lamb, are covered all over with hair, and have very pointed nails, by means of which they keep themselves up and walk on glass, although hanging feet upwards'. Galileo, *Opera*, Ed. Naz., Vol. 19, p. 589.

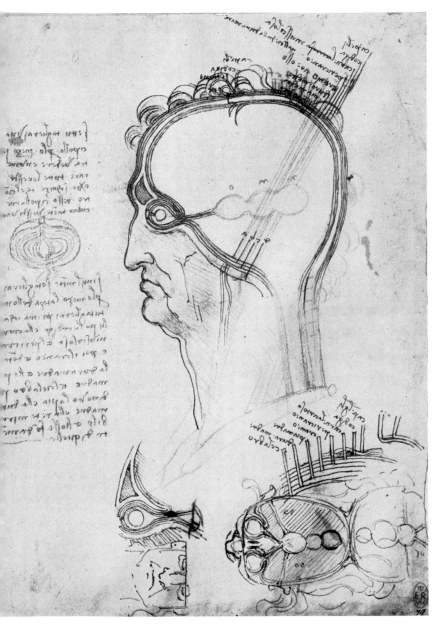

LEONARDO'S DRAWING OF THE HEAD AND EYE IN SECTION
From *Quaderni D'Anatomia 5*, Royal Library,
Windsor, MS. By Gracious permission of H.M. the Queen

PLATE 12   THE COMPARATIVE ANATOMY OF THE EAR OSSICLES
From Casserio's *De Vocis Auditisque Organis*, Ferrara, 1601

Descartes himself. Descartes, however, not only gave a complete account of the refraction and reflection of the rays in the water drops causing the rainbow, but also showed that those coming to the eye at an angle of about 41 degrees from their original direction from the sun were much more dense than those coming from other directions and so produced the primary bow. He definitely associated the colours with differential refrangibility, which he explained by his theory of rotating particles. Some time later Johann Marcus or Marci (1595–1667) showed that rays of a given colour were dispersed no further by a second prism. Neither Descartes nor Marcus was able to produce an adequate theory of colour, which had to wait until their experiments with prisms had been repeated and extended by Newton. This 17th-century work of Descartes, Newton, Hooke, Huygens and others on light made it possible for serviceable microscopes and telescopes to be constructed, but the usefulness of both these instruments was somewhat reduced by the failure to overcome the chromatic aberration, which became serious with powerful lenses. With telescopes the problem of getting a large magnification was overcome by using concave mirrors instead of lenses, but a really powerful microscope became possible only in the 19th century.

(5) CHEMISTRY

In chemistry, such progress as was achieved by the middle of the 17th century was the result rather of experiment and observation alone than of interpretation of facts in terms of mathematical generalisations. The expansion of alchemy and the pursuit of more strictly practical ends, such as painting and mining, had led, during the 14th and 15th centuries, to a fairly wide familiarity with ordinary chemical apparatus. Although this had included the balance, this instrument had not, as Cusa had suggested, been combined with *inventio*, or discovery, and the 'art of latitudes' for the development of a quantitative chemical theory. Mineral drugs had begun to come into pharmaceutical and medical practice, and through an extended study of them chemistry was given a marked impetus during the early decades of the 16th century by the bizarre Philippus Aureolus Theophrastus Bombastus von Hohenheim, or Paracelsus (1493–1541). Paracelsus was an accomplished experimenter and added a few facts to chemical knowledge, for instance the observation that while the vitriols were derived from a metal the alums were derived from an 'earth' (metallic oxide). He also contributed the *tria prima*, sulphur, mercury and salt, to chemical theory. The Arabs had held that sulphur and mercury were the chief constituents of metals, but Paracelsus made sulphur (fire, the inflammable principle), mercury (air, the fusible and volatile principle) and salt (earth, the incombustible and non-volatile principle) the immediate constituents of all material substances. The ultimate constituents of matter, of which these *tria prima* were themselves composed, were the four Aristotelian elements. He illustrated his theory by burning wood, which gave off flames and fumes and left ash.

The chief influence which Paracelsus had on chemistry was through his assertion that its main business was not with the transmutation of metals, though he held this to be possible, but with the preparation and purification of chemical substances for use as drugs. After him, chemistry became an essential part of medical training, and for nearly a century doctors were divided into paracelsists (or 'spagyrists') and herbalists, who kept to the old herbal drugs. The former were often very incautious in their remedies but, however disastrous for the patient, the contribution of iatrochemistry (medical chemistry) to chemistry itself is well illustrated by the clear and systematic account of techniques and substances given in the *Alchymia* (1597) of Andreas Libavius (1540–1616). Like the practical manuals of Vanoccio Biringuccio (1480–1539), Agricola and Bernard Palissy (1510–*c*. 1590) in other aspects of the subject,

Libavius' book shows the progress of the 16th century in the collection of fact.

The first serious improvements in method, aimed at the chemical analysis of the nature of matter, were made by Johann Baptista van Helmont. After graduating in medicine at Louvain, van Helmont made a wealthy marriage and settled down to the charitable practice of his profession and research in his laboratory. His writings, which he left unpublished, were collected after his death and published by his son under the title *Ortus Medicinæ*. An English translation, *Oriatrike or Physick Refined*, appeared in 1662. Van Helmont's empiricism showed the influence both of the practical chemists who had preceded him and, in spite of his attacks on the schools, of nominalism and Augustinian-Platonism. He held that the sources of human knowledge were both Divine illumination and sensory experience. 'The meanes of obtaining Sciences, are onely to pray, seek and knock', he said in the tract *Logica Inutilis* which forms chapter 6 of the *Oriatrike*. In the study of nature there was no true *inventio*, or discovery, but 'by bare observation' of concrete and measurable objects.

For when anyone sheweth me *lapis Calaminaris*, the preparing of *Cadmia* or *Brasse Oare*, the content of, or what is contained in Copper, the mixture and uses of *Aurichalcum*, or *Copper* and *Gold*, which things I knew not before, he teacheth, demonstrateth, and gives the knowledge of that, which before there was ignorance of.

But the logic of the school philosophers could not lead to such discoveries. By itself 'Logical invention is a meer re-taking of that which was known before'. After observation had been made, the investigator was led by *ratio*, that is formal logic and mathematics, to a knowledge of the active principles which in effect were analogous to the Aristotelian substantial forms, and were the source of the observed behaviour. But, van Helmont said, unless such reasoning was accompanied by intuition or illumination its conclusions were always uncertain.

Van Helmont made this theory of knowledge the basis of a

suggested reform of education. 'Certainly I could wish,' he said in the *Oriatrike*, chapter 7, referring to the schools' teaching of Aristotle and Galen,

that in so short a space of life, the Spring of young men, might not be hereafter seasoned with such trifles, and no longer with lying Sophistry. Indeed they should learn in that unprofitable three years space, and in the whole seven years, Arithmetick, the Science Mathematical, the Elements of Euclide, and then Geographie, with the circumstances of Seas, Rivers, Springs, Mountains, Provinces, and Minerals. And likewise, the properties, and Customs of Nations, Waters, Plants, living Creatures, Minerals, and places. Moreover, the use of the Ring, and of the Astrolabe. And then, let them come to the Study of Nature, let them learn to know and separate the first Beginnings of Bodies . . . And all those things, not indeed by a naked description of discourse, but by handicraft demonstration of the fire. For truly, nature measureth her works by distilling, moystening, drying, calcining, resolving, plainly by the same meanes, whereby glasses do accomplish those same operations. And so the Artificer by changing the operations of nature, obtains the properties and knowledge of the same.

Van Helmont held that there were two 'first beginnings' of bodies. He had performed Cusa's experiment with the willow (see above, p. 265), and this convinced him that the ultimate inert constituent of material substances was water. The active principle which disposed the water and constructed the specific concrete thing was a 'ferment or seminal beginning', which was generated in matter by the Divine light (or celestial influence). This last brought the 'archeus', the efficient cause enabling the ferment to construct the 'seed' which developed into a stone, metal, plant or animal. 'For,' as he said in the *Oriatrike*, chapter 4,

the seminal efficient cause containeth the Types or Patterns or things to be done by itself, the figure, motions, houre, respects, inclinations, fitnesses, equalizings, proportions, alienation, defect, and whatsoever falls in under the succession of dayes, as well in the business of generation, as of government.

Such bodies were constructed in accordance with the 'idea'

of the archeus. In the generation of animals the *archeus faber* of the male seed epigenetically constructed the embryo out of the materials provided by the female. Seeds of organic origin were not, however, indispensable for generation, and perfect animals might be produced when the archeus acted on a suitable ferment. Indeed, van Helmont held that the parent was only equivocally the efficient cause of the off-spring. It was the 'natural occasion' on which the seed was produced, but the effective efficient cause was God. This theory was similar to that of the 'occasionalists' (see below, pp. 394–5). He held that there were only two causes operating in natural events, the material and the efficient.

Van Helmont held that there were specific ferments and archei in the stomach, liver and other parts of the body; these controlled their functions, on which his views were in general Galenic. He held also that a disease was an alien entity imposing its way of life, or archeus, on that of the patient; and in developing this idea he became a pioneer in ætiology and morbid anatomy. By putting into practice the doctrine that knowledge of the ferments was to be derived from observation of their material effects, he was able also to assign specific functions to many of the Galenic and other principles. He demonstrated the acid digestion, or 'fermentation', in the stomach, and its neutralisation by the bile. These, he said, were the first two fermentations of the food passing through the body. The third took place in the mesentry; the fourth was in the heart, where the red blood became more yellow by the addition of vital spirits; the fifth was the conversion of arterial blood into vital spirit, mainly in the brain; the sixth was the elaboration of the nutritive principle in each part of the body from the blood. Van Helmont also anticipated something like the principle of the specific energy of nerves when he said that vital spirit conveyed to the tongue accounted for the perception of taste, but would not cause taste in the finger.

In pure chemistry, Van Helmont made systematic use of the balance and demonstrated the conservation of matter, which, he held, secondary causes could not destroy. He showed that if a certain weight of silica were converted into waterglass and the latter were then treated with acid, the precipitated silicic acid would on ignition yield the same weight of silica as that originally taken. He showed also that metals dissolved in the three main mineral acids could be recovered again, and realised that when one metal precipitated another from a solution of a salt this did not, as Paracelsus had thought, imply transmutation. Perhaps his most important work was on gases. He himself coined the name 'gas' from the Greek *chaos*. Several medieval and later writers had recognised the existence of aqueous and earthy 'exhalations' as well as air, but van Helmont was the first to make a scientific study of different kinds of gases. Here his research was made much more difficult by the lack of a convenient apparatus for collecting gases. The different kinds of gas he mentioned included a *gas carbonum* given off by burning charcoal (usually carbon dioxide but also carbon monoxide); a *gas sylvester* given off by fermenting must, by spa water, by treating a carbonate with acetic acid and also found in certain caves, which put out a flame (carbon dioxide); a red poisonous gas, which he also called *gas sylvester*, given off when aqua fortis acted on such metals as silver (nitric oxide); and an inflammable *gas pingue* formed by dry distillation of organic matter (a mixture of hydrogen, methane and carbon monoxide). Van Helmont also took an interest in respiration, of which he maintained the purpose to be not, as Galen had said, to cool but to maintain animal heat; this it did by a ferment in the left ventricle which changed the arterial blood into vital spirit.

Several other chemists made experiments with gases during the early decades of the 17th century in connection with the phenomena of combustion. According to the accepted theory, combustion involved the decomposition of compound substances with the loss of the inflammable 'oily' principle present in the 'sulphur'. Burning would thus result in a decrease in weight. Several observations were made, however, which led to the development of new ideas on this subject. The experiment of 'enclosed combustion', in which a candle was lighted in a glass upturned in a basin of water, had been described by Philo (see above, p. 236, n. 1), and Francis Bacon referred to it as a common experiment. It was repeated by Robert Fludd (1617), and when the water rose as the air was consumed he described the latter as 'nourishing' the flame. It had also been known by both Arab and 16th-century chemists that during calcination metals increased in weight, and in 1630 Jean Rey gave reasons for believing that the definite and limited 'augmentation' in weight, which he observed in the calx of lead and tin, could have come only from the air, which he said mixed with the calx and became attached to its most minute particles. He maintained, further, that all elements, including fire, had weight and that this weight was conserved throughout chemical changes. These facts and ideas were clearly incompatible with the theory of the 'oily' principle, and when this was developed as 'phlogiston' it had to be considered as having negative weight. But it was not until towards the end of the 18th century that combustion was firmly associated with oxidation, when it became the central question of the Chemical Revolution initiated by Lavoisier and his contemporaries.

The universal mechanism which accompanied the successes of mathematical physics entered chemistry through the development of the atomic theory. Such natural philosophers as Bruno, who had argued for the actual existence of natural or physical *minima*, continued the scholastic discussions of this problem; and it was given prominence by Francis Bacon who, though he changed his mind later, began with a favourable opinion of atoms and also said that heat was a condition produced by the vibration of corpuscles. Galileo said that change of substance 'may happen by a simple transposition of parts'. The first application of the atomic theory to chemistry was made by the Dutchman Daniel Sennert (1572–1637). Sennert maintained that substances subject to generation and corruption must be composed of simple bodies from which they arose and into which they were resolved. These simple bodies were physical and not merely mathematical *minima*, and were therefore atoms. He postulated four different kinds of atoms corresponding to each of the four Aristotelian elements, and elements of the second order (*prima mixta*) to which the Aristotelian elements gave rise when combined. He held that atoms, for example of gold in solution in acid and of mercury in sublimation, retained their individuality in combination, so that the original substances could be regained from compounds. Similar ideas were expressed by Joachim Jung (1587–1657), through whom they later became known to Robert Boyle (1627–91).

Contributions to the atomic theory were made also by Descartes, for although he did not believe in indivisible physical *minima* he tried to extend his mechanistic principles to chemistry by attributing the properties of various substances to the geometrical shapes of their constituent earthy particles. For instance, he supposed the particles of corrosive substances such as acids to be like sharp-pointed blades, while those of oils were branching and flexible. These ideas were used later by John Mayow (1643–79), and they became familiar to chemists through the *Cours de Chymie* (1675) by Nicolas Lémery (1645–1715). Another geometer, Gassendi, popularised the atoms of Epicurus (1649), maintaining, however, that they had not been in existence since eternity but had been created with their characteristic powers by God. He based his belief in the existence of void on Torricelli's experiments and, like Descartes, connected chemical properties with the shapes of the atoms. He also attributed combination into *molecula* or *corpuscula* to mechanisms such as hooks and eyes. Gassendi's system was the subject of an English work by Walter Charleton (1654), physician to Charles II and an early fellow of the Royal Society. The microscope had lent an interest to discovering the size of atoms and Charleton argued, from such phenomena as volatilisation and solution, that the smallest discernible microscopic particle contained ten hundred thousand million invisible particles. Through Charleton the atomic theory became well known in mid-17th century England. When it was adopted by Boyle, the empirical conceptions of van Helmont and the earlier practical chemists were transformed in accordance with mechanical principles, and chemistry, like physics, finally set out on its course of being reduced to a department of mathematics. After the discovery of 'combining weights' and Dalton's generalisation of the results in his atomic theory early in the 19th century, the fulfilment of that process became inevitable.

(6) BOTANY

Botanical studies up to the middle of the 17th century were confined principally to the business of collecting and classifying facts, and were left almost untouched by the mathematical revolution in scientific thought. In fact, even in the 20th century, botany, like many other branches of biology, remains singularly intractable to mathematical treatment. The theory in which the animate world eventually found a universal explanation, the theory of organic evolution, was based on logical rather than mathematical abstractions.

The dual interest of medical men in descriptive botany and anatomy, which continued into the 16th century, brought it about that these were the first aspects of biology to develop and that this was almost entirely the work of medical men. In was customary in some places, such as Montpellier, to take up botany in summer and anatomy in winter. The first books on scientific botany to be printed were nearly all herbals. The best of these, such as the *Latin Herbarius* (1484), which had probably already existed in manuscript, and the *German Herbarius* (1485), besides being compilations from classical, Arab and medieval authors, also included descriptions and illustrations of local, for instance German, plants. Rufinus, the best of the known medieval herbalists, seems, however, to have been forgotten.

Besides the medical interest in identifying plants for use as drugs, 16th-century doctors shared with lexicographers the humanist interest in identifying the plants mentioned in the recently printed Latin editions of Pliny (1469), Aristotle (1476), Dioscorides (1478) or Theophrastus (1483). More than one humanist naturalist, of whom the Swiss Conrad Gesner (1516–65) is a typical example, began by trying to find and identify in his own country, for purposes of textual criticism, the plants and animals mentioned by classical authors; and out of this developed an interest in local fauna and flora for their own sake. The extraordinary interest which animals, plants and rocks were arousing among such people by the middle of the 16th century is shown by the enormous correspondence on the subject, with descriptions of local expeditions and the transmission of specimens, drawings and descriptions, carried on by Gesner and other naturalists. It was soon realised, as indeed Albertus Magnus and Rufinus had known well, that there were other creatures in existence besides those known to the ancients. The classical limitations were finally destroyed by the new fauna, flora, foods and drugs coming to Europe from the New World and the East. Plants and animals were then described and drawn for their own sakes and called by their common vernacular names to a large extent without reference to the classics.

The first result of this 16th-century botanical activity, which was greatest in Germany, the Netherlands, southern France and Italy, was to increase the number of individual plants known. Lists of local flora and fauna were drawn up for various districts. Botanical gardens, which had long been kept by monasteries and, from the 14th century, had been planted by some medical schools, were established in various further university towns such as Padua (1545), Bologna (1567) and Leyden (1577). The last two were presided over respectively by Aldrovandi and Cesalpino, and by de l'Ecluse. Others were established later at Paris (1620), Oxford (1632) and other places. The practice of preserving dried plants, 'dry gardens', which began in Italy, also allowed botany to go on in the winter months. At the same time the Portuguese herbalist Garcia da Orta published a book on Indian plants at Goa (1663), and the Spaniard Nicolas Monardes published the first descriptions of 'el tabaco' and other American plants (1569–71).

In the northern school, whose interest was purely floristic, a continuous development of botanical ideas may be traced from the four 'fathers' of German botany to Gaspard Bauhin. For all the members of this school the primary intention was

Heinricus Füllmaurer.   Albertus Meyer.

FIG. 47. Botanists drawing plants. From Fuchs' *De Historia Stirpium*, Basel, 1542.

simply to make it possible to identify individual wild and cultivated plants and distinguish them from those resembling them. This led to concentration on accurate illustrations and descriptions. The illustrations, which in the herbal of Otto Brunfels (1530), the first of the German fathers, were made by Hans Weiditz, an artist of the school of Albrecht Dürer (1471–1528), were at first greatly superior to the pedantic traditional descriptions. With Jerome Bock (1539) and Valerius Cordus (1561) the latter began gradually to improve. The object of both illustrations and descriptions was simply to depict the most easily recognisable aspects of external appearance such as the form and disposition of roots and branches, the shape of the leaves and the colour and shape of the flowers (Fig. 47). There was no interest in the comparative morphology of the parts. For instance, the glossary of terms given by the third German father, Leonard Fuchs (1542), referred almost entirely to such general characters; and the earlier attempts at classification, for instance those made by Bock and the Netherlander Rembert Dodoens (1552), were based for the most part on artificial characteristics such as edibility, odour or medicinal properties.

Since the task of describing individual forms necessarily involved distinguishing them from near relations, some appreciation of 'natural' affinity was inevitable. Gesner, whose botanical work unfortunately was not published until long after his death and thus apparently had little or no influence on his contemporaries, distinguished different species of a given genus, for example Gentian, and also seems to have been the first to draw attention to the flower and fruit as diagnostic characters. Other writers, such as Dodoens and Charles de l'Ecluse (1576), though primarily interested simply in giving order to their work, placed together within each artificial division plants belonging to what are now recognised as natural groups. This practice had been carried even further by Mathias de Lobel (1571), like de l'Ecluse also a graduate of Montpellier, who had based his classification mainly on leaf structure. It reached its final stage in Gaspard Bauhin (1560–1624), professor of anatomy at Basel. Bauhin's descriptions are precise and diagnostic, as may be seen from that of the beet, which he called *Beta Cretica semine aculeato*, given in his *Prodomus Theatri Botanici* (1620).

From a short tapering root, by no means fibrous, spring several stalks about 18 inches long: they straggle over the ground, and are cylindrical in shape and furrowed, becoming gradually white near the root with a slight coating of down, and spreading out into little sprays. The plant has but few leaves, similar to those of *Beta nigra*, except that they are smaller, and supplied with long petioles. The flowers are small, and of a greenish yellow. The fruits one can see growing in large numbers close by the root, and from that point they spread along the stalk, at almost every leaf. They are rough and tubercled and separate into three reflexed points. In their cavity, one grain of the shape of an *Adonis* seed is contained; it is slightly rounded and ends in a point, and is covered with a double layer of reddish membrane, the inner one enclosing a white, farinaceous core.

The number of plants described by Bauhin had increased to about 6,000, as compared with the 500 or so given by Fuchs. He systematically used a binomial nomenclature, though he did not invent this system for it had occurred in a 15th-century manuscript of the *Circa Instans*. In his *Pinax Theatri Botanici* (1623), he gave an exhaustive account of the synonyms used by earlier botanists. In enumerating the plants described, he proceeded, as de Lobel had done, from supposedly less perfect forms, such as grasses and most of the Liliaceæ, through dicotyledonous herbs to shrubs and trees. Both he and de Lobel thus made a practical distinction between monocotyledons and dicotyledons and, as some of their predecessors had done also in varying degrees, put together plants belonging to such families as the Cruciferæ, Umbelliferæ, Papilionaceæ, Labiatcæ, Compositæ, etc. Such grouping was, however, based entirely on an instinctive appreciation of likeness in form and habit. There was no conscious recognition of comparative morphology, and no system was set out based on the understanding and analysis of morphological features. The main effort of the northern school was in fact towards the accumulation of more and more empirical descriptions, until by the end of the 17th century John Ray (1682) was able to cite 18,000 species.

The man who made it possible to reduce this mass of information to some sort of rational order was the Italian,

Andrea Cesalpino, professor of medicine first in Pisa and then in Rome (where he was also physician to Pope Clement VIII). Cesalpino brought to the study of botany not only the floristic knowledge of the herbalists, but also an interest in the detailed morphology of the separate parts of the plant and an Aristotelian mind capable of forming generalisations. He based his attempt, set out in the *De Plantis* (1583), to explain the 'real' or 'substantial' affinities between plants on the Aristotelian principle that the final cause of vegetative activity was nutrition, of which the reproduction of the species was simply an extension. In his day the role played by the leaves in nutrition was still unknown, and the nutritive materials were supposed to be absorbed by the roots from the soil and carried by the veins up the stem to produce the fruit. The centre of vital heat, corresponding to the heart in animals, was the pith, and Cesalpino held that it was also from the pith that the seeds were produced. The co-operation of the male and female parts of flowers in reproduction had also not yet been discovered, and he supposed that the flower was simply a system of protecting envelopes round the seed, comparable to the fœtal membranes of animals. On these principles he divided plants first, according to the nature of the stem conducting the nutritive materials, into woody and herbaceous plants and again, within these groups, according to the organs of fructification. Here he began with plants such as fungi, which he held had no seed but were spontaneously generated from decaying substances, and passed through others such as ferns, which propagated by a kind of 'wool', to plants with true seeds. He then classified these last according to the number, position and shape of the parts of the fruit, with sub-divisions based on root, stem and leaf. Characteristics such as colour, odour, taste or medicinal properties he considered to be mere accidents.

Cesalpino's attempt to deduce a 'natural' classification from the principles he had assumed was in result deplorable. The distinction between monocotyledons and dicotyledons was less clear than with the herbalists and, out of the 15 classes he made, only one, the Umbelliferæ, corresponds to what would now be recognised as a natural group. Nevertheless, his system was based on considerable knowledge and clear principles which, however wrong, were the first to be introduced by botanists of the time into the study of plants. His followers had something to work on. The first to criticise and develop Cesalpino's ideas was Joachim Jung (1587–1657), a German professor of medicine who probably came across his ideas while studying at Padua. Jung accepted the idea that nutrition was the fundamental vegetative function and, like Cesalpino, based his idea of species on reproduction. He made what was then a great advance by discussing morphology as far as possible in independence of physiological questions.

Theophrastus, whose *Historia Plantarum* had been translated into Latin by Theodore of Gaza (1483), had given morphological descriptions of the external parts of plants from root to fruit. He had also set forth the 'homology' of the perianth members of flowers, watched the development of seeds and to some extent distinguished between monocotyledons and dicotyledons. His interests had been by no means confined to morphology. He had made an attempt to understand the relation between structure and function, habits and geographical distribution, had described the fertilisation of the date palm and had tried to understand the caprification of the fig, though the flowers were distinguished only by Valerius Cordus. Theophrastus had also established the first rudiments of plant nomenclature, and there was practically no further development in the subject until similar morphological descriptions and distinctions were made by Jung.

Jung's precise definitions of the parts of plants, for which he made use of the logical refinements developed by the later scholastics and of his own mathematical gifts, were the foundation of subsequent comparative morphology. For instance, he defined the stem as that upper part of the plant above the root which stretched upwards in such a way that back, front and sides could not be distinguished, while in a leaf the bounding surfaces of the third dimension (apart from the length and breadth) in which it was extended from its point of origin were different from one another. The outer and inner surfaces of a leaf were thus differently organised and this, as well as the fact that they fell off in autumn, enabled compound leaves to be distinguished from branches. Botanists were not yet ready to follow this lead, and neither Jung nor Cesalpino had much effect on their contemporaries, who continued to devote their energies to empirical descriptions. It was only at the end of the 17th century that botanists once more recognised the need for a 'natural' system of classification and attempted to base it on comparative morphology. The culmination of their effort was the system of Linnæus (1707–78), who acknowledged his debt to both Cesalpino and Jung. When the 'natural' classification came itself to call for an explanation this was supplied by the theory of organic evolution.

(7) ANATOMY AND COMPARATIVE ANIMAL MORPHOLOGY AND EMBRYOLOGY

The great advances made in anatomy and zoology during the 16th and early 17th centuries were, like those in botany, due simply to a new precision of observation and remained largely untouched by mathematics. Just as 16th-century botany began with the object of identifying medicinally useful plants, so anatomy began with such aspects as would facilitate the work of surgeons and artists. What the practical needs of the surgeon chiefly required were good topographical descriptions; comparative morphology had little interest for him. The painters and sculptors, of whom several, such as Andrea Verrocchio (1435–88), Andrea Mantegna (d. 1516), Leonardo da Vinci, Dürer, Michelangelo (1475–1564) and Raphael (1483–1520), are known to have used the scalpel, required little more than surface anatomy and a knowledge of bones and muscles. As the century went on, however, a greater practical interest was taken both in functional questions and in the structure and habits of animals. In both developments by no means the least important factor was the brilliant revolution brought about by the artists themselves in anatomical illustration.

The artist who has left most evidence of his anatomical exercises is Leonardo da Vinci and, as in mechanics, his researches went far beyond the practical needs of his craft. He even planned a text-book of anatomy in collaboration with the Pavian professor Marcantonio della Torre (c. 1483–1512), who unfortunately died. Leonardo was guided by earlier text-books and repeated some of the old mistakes, such as drawing the lens in the centre of the eye. His claim always to have followed experience may be accepted in the same spirit as the same claim made by many of his predecessors. He made several original observations on both human and comparative anatomy, and carried out physiological experiments which were often fruitful and always ingenious. He was one of the first to make use of serial sections. The animals which he mentioned as the subjects of his researches included *Gordius*, moths, flies, fish, frog, crocodile, birds, horse, ox, sheep, bear, lion, dog, cat, bat, monkey. His best figures were of bones and muscles, those of the hand and shoulder being clear and substantially accurate. Others exhibited the action of muscles. He made models with bones and copper wire, and pointed out that the power of the biceps brachii depended on the position of its insertion with respect to the hand. He compared the limbs of man and horse, showing that the latter moved on the tips of its phalanges. He studied the wing and foot of the bird, the mechanics of flight and the operation of the diaphragm in breathing and defæcation. He studied the heart and blood vessels. He also made good drawings of the placenta of the cow, but was uncertain whether the maternal and fœtal blood streams were connected or not. One of his most ingenious feats was to make wax casts of the ventricles of the brain. He also carried out experiments on the spinal cord of the frog, and concluded that this organ was the 'centre of life'.

Leonardo made a further contribution to biology, as well as to geology, when he used inland shells to support Albert of Saxony's theory of the formation of mountains (above, p. 96). 'Why', he asked,

do we find the bones of great fishes and oysters and corals and various other shells and sea-snails on the high summits of mountains by the sea, just as we find them in low seas?[1]

There had been a continuous interest in local geology in Italy since the 13th century, and in his speculations on geology Leonardo made use of his own observations on the sea coast, the Alps and its streams and Tuscan rivers such as the Arno. He rejected the theories that fossils were not the remains of living things but were accidents or 'sports' of nature or had been spontaneously produced by astral influence, and that they were organic remains which had been transported from elsewhere by the Flood. He accepted instead Avicenna's theory of fossil formation which he had learnt from Albertus Magnus. He then maintained that the arrangement of shells in strata, with gregarious forms such as oysters and mussels in groups and solitary forms apart just as they were found living on the seashore, and with crabs' claws, shells with those of other species fastened to them, and bones and teeth of fish all mixed up together, suggested that fossils were the remains of animals which had formerly lived in the same place just as contemporary marine animals did. The mountains on which the shells were found had formerly formed the sea floor, which had been, and was still being, gradually raised by the deposit of river mud.

The shells, oysters and other similar animals which originate in sea-mud, bear witness to the changes of the earth round the centre of our elements. This is proved thus: Great rivers always run turbid, owing to the earth, which is stirred by the friction of

[1] J. P. Richter: *The Literary Works of Leonardo da Vinci*, 2nd ed., Oxford, 1939, vol. 2, p. 175

their waters at the bottom and on their shores; and this wearing disturbs the face of the strata made by the layers of shells, which lie on the surface of the marine mud, and which were produced there when the salt waters covered them; and these strata were covered again from time to time with mud of various thicknesses, or carried down to the sea by the rivers and floods of more or less extent; and thus these shells remained walled in and dead underneath these layers of mud raised to such a height that they came up from the bottom to the air. At the present time these bottoms are so high that they form hills or high mountains, and the rivers, which wear away the sides of these mountains, uncover the strata of these shells, and thus the softened side of the earth continually rises and the antipodes sink closer to the centre of the earth, and the ancient bottoms of the sea have become mountain ridges.[1]

The surgical developments of the 15th century, which received fresh impetus from the printing of the *De Medicina* of Celsus in 1478, first issued in anatomical discovery with Alexander Achillini's (1463–1512) description, in his commentary on Mondino, of 'Wharton's duct', of the entry of the bile duct into the duodenum and of the hammer and anvil bones of the middle ear. The clear influence of naturalistic art on anatomical illustration is first seen in the Italian work, *Fasciculo di Medicina* (1493), while Berengario da Carpi (d. 1550), professor of surgery in Bologna, was the first to print figures illustrating his text. In his commentary on Mondino (1521), Berengario also described a number of original observations. He demonstrated experimentally that the kidney was not a sieve, for when injected with hot water from a syringe it merely swelled up and no water passed through. He showed in a similar way that the bladder of a nine months' unborn child had no opening other than the urinary pores. He also denied the existence of the *rete mirabile* in man, gave the first clear accounts of the vermiform appendix, the thymus gland and other structures, had some idea of the action of the cardiac valves and coined the term *vas*

[1] Richter: vol. 2, pp. 146–7

deferens. Another surgeon of the same period who had a good practical knowledge of anatomy was Nicholas Massa, who published a work on the subject in 1536. The first to publish illustrations showing whole venous, arterial, nervous or other systems (1545) was Charles Estienne (1503–64), of the well-known family of French humanist printers. He also traced the blood vessels into the substance of the bone, noted the valves in the veins and studied the vascular system by injecting the vessels with air. Another work which illustrates the advances in anatomy made during the early decades of the 16th century is the tract published by Giambattista Canano (1515–79) in 1541, in which he showed each muscle separately in its relations with the bones.

Besides these improvements in knowledge of anatomy, a number of purely empirical advances were made in practical surgery in the 16th century. One of the greatest problems for an army surgeon was how to treat gunshot wounds. At first these were believed to be poisonous and were treated by scalding with oil of elders, with terrible results. One of the first doctors to abandon this practice was Ambrose Paré (1510–90), who described in his fascinating *Voyages en Divers Lieux* how he had so many men to treat after the attack on Turin, in 1537, when he was in the service of King Francis I of France, that he ran out of oil. Next morning he was amazed to find that the men who had been left untreated were much better than those whose wounds had been scalded with oil, and thereafter he gave up this practice. Paré also gave a good account of the treatment of fractures and dislocations, and of herniotomy and other operations. Surgery in northern Europe was still largely in the hands of comparatively uneducated barbers and cutters, though some of these showed considerable skill. The itinerant lithotomist Pierre Franco, for example, was the first to perform suprapubic lithotomy for removing stone in the bladder. In Italy, surgery was in the hands of anatomists with a university training, like Vesalius and Hieronymo Fabrizio, and so it could benefit from the improvement of academic knowledge. The work in plastic surgery which had begun in the 15th century was carried on in the 16th century by the Bolognese Gaspere Tagliacozzi, who restored a lost nose by transplanting a flap of skin from the arm, leaving one end still attached to the arm until the graft on the nose had established itself.

While these anatomists and surgeons were extending the practical achievements of their predecessors, medical men of another group were endeavouring, as in other sciences, to return to antiquity. The first humanist doctors, such as Thomas Linacre (c. 1460–1524), physician to Henry VIII, tutor to Princess Mary and founder and first president of the College of Physicians, or Johannes Günther (1487–1574), who at Paris numbered Vesalius, Serveto and Rondelet among his pupils, were literary men rather than anatomists. They encouraged, and co-operated in making, the new Latin translations of Galen and Hippocrates which, along with the old, were printed in numerous editions from the end of the 15th century. They devoted their energy to establishing the text of these authors rather than to observation, and Mondino was objectionable to them not so much because he disagreed with nature as because he disagreed with Galen. They also began a violent attack on the old Latinised Arabic terminology of Mondino, which they 'purified' by substituting classical Latin or Greek for Arabic words and transformed into the anatomical terminology still in use.

It was in this atmosphere of both practical observation and humanist prejudice and literary research that the so-called father of modern anatomy, the Netherlander Andreas Vesalius (1514–64), began his work. In it he exhibits both features. The *De Humani Corporis Fabrica* (1543) may be regarded as the outcome of an attempt to restore both the letter and the standards of Galen. In it Vesalius followed Galen, as well as other authors to whom he did not acknowledge his debt, in many of their mistakes as well as in their true observations. He placed the lens in the middle of the eye, repeated Mondino's misunderstanding of the

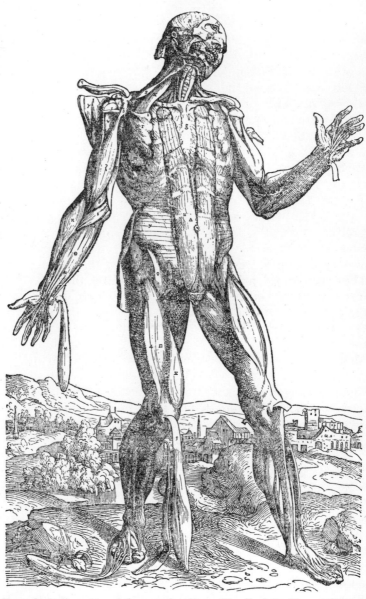

FIG. 48. A dissection of the muscles. From Vesalius' *De Humani Corporis Fabrica*.

generative organs, represented the kidney as a sieve and adduced some conclusions about human anatomy from the study of animals, a practice for which he criticised Galen. Further, he differed in no important respect from Galen in physiology. He shared his Greek master's eye for the exhibition of living function in anatomical structure, and he was fortunate in having this expressed for him in illustrations done by an excellent artist (Fig. 48). The function of an organ, according to Galen, was the final cause of its structure and mechanical action and thus the explanation of its presence. The inspiration of the anatomical research which he stimulated was strongly teleological, and Vesalius himself regarded the human body as the product of Divine crafts-manship. This must be accounted an important factor in the passion with which he pursued his dissections. His work contained by far the most detailed and extensive descriptions and illustrations yet published of all the systems and organs of the body. Though his account of the other organs usually does not compare with that of the bones and muscles, whose relations he illustrated very well, he nevertheless made a large number of new observations on veins, arteries and nerves, greatly extended the study of the brain though without entirely rejecting the *rete mirabile*, and showed that bristles could not be pushed through the supposed pores in the interventricular septum of the heart. He also repeated several of Galen's experiments on living animals and showed, for instance, that cutting the recurrent laryngeal nerve caused loss of voice. He showed that a nerve was not a hollow tube, though physiologists continued to believe the contrary until the 18th century. He showed also that an animal whose thoracic wall had been pierced could be kept alive by inflating the lungs with bellows.

A contemporary of Vesalius who, had his anatomical illustrations been published when they were completed in 1552, instead of in 1714, might have ranked with him as one of the founders of modern anatomy, was the Roman, Bartolomeo Eustachio (1520–74). He introduced the study of anatomical variations, particularly in the kidney, and gave excellent figures of the ear ossicles, the relations of the bronchi and blood vessels in the lung, the sympathetic nervous system, the larynx and the thoracic duct.

As events turned out, Vesalius, and not Eustachio, set his mark on anatomy. He made the centre of the subject Padua, where he was professor from 1537 until he became physician to the Emperor Charles V in 1544, and a large part of the subsequent history of anatomy down to Harvey was the story of Vesalius' pupils and successors. The first of these was his assistant Realdo Colombo (c. 1516–59), who experimentally demonstrated the pulmonary circulation of the blood (see above, p. 332). He was followed by Gabriel Fallopio (1523–62), who described the ovaries and the tubes called after him, the semi-circular canals of the ear and several other structures. Fallopio's own pupils extended the Vesalian tradition at Padua into the study of comparative anatomy, but in the meantime similar interests had begun to develop elsewhere.

Many of those who were attracted by the printed editions of Pliny or of the Latin translations of Aristotle's zoological works developed from being humanist lexicographers into naturalists. A good example of this is William Turner (c. 1508–68) whose book on birds (1544), while being largely a compilation and accepting some legends such as that of the barnacle goose, also contained some fresh observations. Sixteenth-century zoology thus began as a gloss on the classics written increasingly from nature. The system of classification recognised by Albertus Magnus in Aristotle's writings, which the Oxford scholar and doctor, Edward Wotton, attempted to restore (1552), was the framework of the subject.

Besides birds, the first animals to attract attention were fish. Accounts of several local fish fauna, those of the sea at Rome and Marseilles and of the river Moselle, were written during the first half of the 16th century, but the scientific study of marine animals really began with the *De Aquatilibus* (1553) of the French naturalist, Pierre Belon (1517–64). Belon had already become well known for his account of a voyage to the eastern Mediterranean, during which he made some interesting biological observations (1533). He took an ecological view of his group; his 'aquatiles' were the fish of 'cooks and lexicographers' and included cephalopods and cetacea as well as *pisces*. He made the first modern contributions to comparative anatomy. He dissected and compared three cetacean types, realised that they breathed air with lungs, and compared the heart and skeleton to those of man. He depicted the porpoise attached by the umbilical cord to the placenta, and the dolphin with its new-born young still surrounded by fœtal membranes. He also made a comparative study of fish anatomy and in another small book, *Histoire Naturelle des Oiseaux* (1555), in which he intuitively recognised certain natural groups of birds, he depicted the skeletons of a bird and a man side by side to show the morphological correspondences between them. Another Frenchman, Guillaume Rondelet (1507–66), who became professor of anatomy at Montpellier and may have been 'the Physitian our honest Master Rondibilis' of Rabelais (who had also studied medicine there), included a similar heterogeneous collection of aquatic animals in his *Histoire Naturelle des Poissons* (1554–5). This was also a valuable work. In it he pointed out the anatomical differences between the respiratory, alimentary, vascular and genital systems of gill- and lung-breathing aquatic vertebrates, and depicted the viviparous dolphin and the ovoviviparous shark. He endeavoured to discover the morphological correspondence between the parts of the mammalian and piscine hearts. He discussed the comparative anatomy of gills, which he considered to be cooling organs, but he also showed that fish kept in a vessel without access to air would suffocate. He considered the teleostean swim-bladder, which he discovered, to be a kind of lung. Another heterogeneous work on aquatic animals published

377

about the same time (1554), which is of interest in showing the influence of contemporary art on its excellent zoological illustrations, is that of H. Salviani (1514–72).

Another contemporary of these writers was the polyhistor and naturalist, Conrad Gesner. He attempted to draw up, on the lines of Albertus Magnus or Vincent of Beauvais, whom he quoted, an encyclopædia containing the observations of all his predecessors from Aristotle to Belon and Rondelet. In the course of this he also made observations of his own and, through his vast correspondence, was a stimulus to others. In the zoological part of this work, the *Historia Animalium* (1551–8), he seems to have been so uncertain about classification that he arranged the animals in alphabetical order. In other works, containing extracts from the *Historia*, he set them out according to the Aristotelian system, omitting only the insects. The material for the insects, which had been compiled by Gesner, Wotton and Thomas Penny (*c.* 1530–88), was eventually published as Thomas Mouffet's *Theatrum Insectorum* (1634). Mouffet's 'insects' were those of Aristotle, and included myriapods, arachnids and various sorts of worms as well as the modern group of insects. His book contained a number of fresh observations, most of them the work of Penny. Gesner's work as an encyclopædist and zoologist was continued by Ulysses Aldrovandi (1522–1605), professor of natural history at Bologna, who among other things wrote the first book on fishes which did not include other aquatic forms.

Both Gesner and Aldrovandi included in their encyclopædic labours catalogues of fossils, or 'figured stones', of which several collections had been made in the 16th century, including one by Pope Sixtus V at the Vatican. The fossils included in these collections were mainly echinoderms, mollusc shells and fish skeletons, and considerable interest attached to their origin. On this matter opinion in fact remained divided until the 18th century, and it was not easy to recognise the organic origin of some fossils. Those who held that fossils were not of organic origin explained them by such theories as astral influence or generation by subterranean vapours. Even among those who held that fossils were organic remains some believed them to have been transported to the mountains by the Flood. The theory that organisms had been fossilised where they had once lived and weie found had persisted in the writings of Albertus Magnus. Girolamo Fracastoro (1483–1553) accepted this view and so did Agricola, who held that the process of mineral-formation and fossilisation was due to a *succus lapidescens*, which may have meant precipitation from solution. Another writer, the French potter Bernard Palissy, who had learnt through Cardano of Leonardo's ideas on these questions, went further and arrived at some understanding of the significance of fossil forms for comparative morphology. He regretted that Belon and Rondelet had not described and drawn fossil fish as well as living forms; they would then have shown what kind of fish had lived in those regions at the time when the stones in which they were found had congealed. He himself made a collection of fossils, recognised the identity of a number of forms, such as sea-urchins and oysters, with their living relatives, and even distinguished marine, lake and river varieties. In contrast with these bold ideas, Gesner admitted some fossils as petrified animals but regarded others as products *sui generis* of the earth itself. He made an attempt to classify them, taking their shape, the things they resembled and so on, as his criteria. Aldrovandi regarded fossils not as the remains of normal living forms but as incomplete animals in which spontaneous generation had failed full accomplishment.

Another aspect of biology which received fresh attention during the 16th century was embryology, the study of which was revived by Aldrovandi, who was inspired by Aristotle and Albertus Magnus to follow the development of the chick by opening eggs at regular intervals. Into this he initiated his Dutch pupil, Volcher Coiter, who, before finally settling at Nuremberg, studied also under Fallopio, Eustachio and

Rondelet. He was thus an intellectual descendant of Vesalius, and the first of them to adopt the comparative method. In the chick, on which his observations were on Aristotelian lines, he discovered the blastoderm, but he left it for Aldrovandi to explain how the eggs passed from the ovary into the oviduct, and failed to recognise that the avian ovary was homologous with the mammalian 'female testis'. He made a systematic study of the growth of the human fœtal skeleton and pointed out that bones were preceded by cartilages. He also made a systematic study of the comparative anatomy of all vertebrate types except the fishes. His emphasis on points of difference, rather than homology, shows that he did not fully grasp the significance of the comparative method, but his comparisons, beautifully illustrated by himself, greatly extended the range of the subject. He was most successful in his treatment of skeletons, of which he compared those of many different types, from frog to man. He also made a comparative study of living hearts. He tried to interpret the structure of the mammalian lung in terms of the simpler organs of frogs and lizards, and understood the difference in their respiratory mechanisms. He also made a number of particular anatomical discoveries, of which that of the dorsal and ventral nerve roots was perhaps the most important, and he tried to classify mammals on an anatomical basis.

The comparative method was systematically extended to embryology by Fallopio's successor of Padua, Hieronymo Fabrizio, who was professor there at the same time as Galileo. Fabrizio made a number of contributions to anatomy. His embryological theory, like that of his pupil Harvey, was in principle entirely Aristotelian. But he held that the majority of animals were generated not spontaneously but from 'eggs', gave good figures of the later stages of development of the chick (Fig. 49 a; *cf.* 49 b) and made a careful study of the embryology of a large number of vertebrates. In the last he paid particular attention to the fœtal membranes and confirmed the assertion of Julius

Cæsar Arantius (1564) that although the fœtal and maternal vascular systems were brought into close contact with the placenta there was no free passage between them. He gave a clear account of other already known structures associated with the fœtal blood system, such as the *ductus arteriosus* and the *foramen ovale* (discovered by Botallus, 1564). The valves in the veins had been observed by a number of anatomists, but Fabrizio published the first clear and adequate pictures

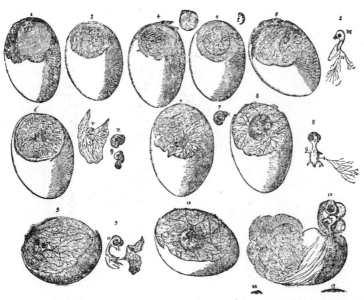

Fig. 49A. Embryology of the chick. From Fabrizio's *De Formatione Ovi et Pulli*, Padua, 1621.

of them (1603), which Harvey afterwards used to illustrate his book. In his comparative studies Fabrizio attempted to assess the points common to the various vertebrates and those defining specific differences. He held that each sense organ had its own special function and could perform no other, but although he drew the lens in its correct position in the eye he still believed that it was the seat of vision. He attempted to analyse the mechanics of locomotion, and

compared the actions of the internal skeleton of the vertebrate and the external skeleton of the arthropod. He
observed that the worm moved by the alternate contraction
of its longitudinal and circular muscles, and examined the
relation of the centre of gravity to posture in the bird. It
was not, however, until Borelli (1680) was able to make use
of Galileo's mechanics that these problems received an
adequate solution.

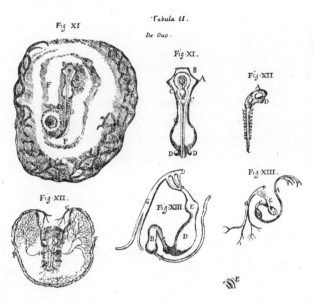

FIG. 49B. Embryology of the chick, showing the use of the microscope.
From Malpighi's *De Formatione Pulli in Ovo* (first published 1673), in
Opera Omnia, London, 1686.

Fabrizio's comparative method was carried still further by
his former servant and pupil, Giulio Casserio (1561–1616),
who succeeded him at Padua. Casserio has been described as
a great craftsman, who endeavoured to explain the fabric of
man by reference to that of the lower animals. He divided
his investigation, as Galen had done, into structure, action
and uses (function). His method was first to describe the

human condition in fœtus and adult and then to follow it through a long series of other animals. This is well illustrated in his study of the organs of the voice and hearing, during which he described the sound-producing organs of the cicada, the auditory ossicles of a large number of land vertebrates and discovered the internal ear of the pike (Plate 12).

Casserio's successor, Adriaan van der Spieghel (1578–1625), whose chief work was to improve anatomical terminology, was the last of the great Paduan line, and after his time animal biology itself developed in a different direction. His contemporary at Pavia, Gasparo Aselli (1581–1626), discovered the lacteal vessels while dissecting a dog which had just had a meal containing fat. These are lymphatic vessels which conduct into the blood stream at the jugular vein fatty substances absorbed in the intestine. Another contemporary, Marc Aurelio Severino (1580–1656), a pupil at Naples of the anti-Aristotelian philosopher Campanella, compiled on comparative anatomy a treatise entitled *Zootomia Democritæa* (1645) out of respect for his master's views. In this he recognised the unity of the vertebrates, including man, but he regarded man as the basic 'archetype', determined by Divine design, and divergences from this as due to differences in function. He discovered the heart of the higher crustacea, dissected but misunderstood that of cepholopods, recognised the respiratory function of fish gills, invented the method of studying blood vessels by injection with a solidifying medium and recommended the use of the microscope. Though he wrote after Harvey, he suffered from the same defects as his predecessors.

The effort of the 16th-century anatomists had been to explore, describe and compare the structure of the human and the animal body, to make some attempt to relate the results by a zoological classification and to understand the variety of animal forms. They laid the foundation of work which was to lead to the theory of organic evolution, but, not only were their conceptions of physiology vague, inaccurate and uncoordinated, but also their inferences did not arise out of a critical and comprehensive consideration of the facts. Their conceptions of biological function were, in fact, largely inherited from the past, and as yet remained unrelated to their discoveries of structure. These matters were being brought into relation by another son of Padua, William Harvey (see above, pp. 329 *et seq.*).

In embryology, Harvey made a number of advances. Although he has been criticised for his work on this subject, in fact he carried into this difficult field the same principles as he had used with such success in analysing the simpler problem of the movement of the blood. Among his positive contributions to comparative embryology were a number of particular observations on the placenta and other structures, the final recognition of the cicatricula on the yolk membrane as the point of origin of the chick embryo and a clear discussion of growth and differentiation. Another contribution was implied by his remark in his *Exercitationes de Generatione Animalium* (1651), exercitatio 62, that 'The egg is the common beginning for all animals'. Albertus Magnus, who had made a similar remark (see above, p. 123), certainly also accepted the spontaneous generation of the eggs or *ova* themselves; and since Harvey was not unequivocal on the point, opinions differ about whether he did too. Some passages do definitely suggest that he held all plants and animals to originate from 'seeds' arising from parents of the same species, though these 'seeds' might sometimes be too small to be seen. Francesco Redi, who first experimentally disproved spontaneous generation in insects (1668), read Harvey's views in this sense. Thus, although Harvey did not understand the nature of the *ovum*, which he still identified, in insects, with the larva or pupa and, in mammals, with small embryos surrounded by their membrane or chorion, his ideas, which crystallised into the *omne vivum ex ovo* that appeared on the frontispiece of his book, stimulated research into the subject by his followers.

Harvey's own observations led him to reject both the

Aristotelian and Galenic theories of fertilisation. According to Aristotle, the uterus of a fertilised female should have contained semen and blood, according to Galen a mixture of male and female semen. In the king's deer, which Harvey dissected at Hampton Court, he could find no such visible proof of conception for some months after mating. He was unfortunate, because in this respect deer are peculiar; but he could also see nothing for several days in more normal animals such as dogs and rabbits. He therefore concluded that the male contributed an immaterial influence like that of the stars or of a magnet, which set the female egg developing. Although the production of eggs in ovarian follicles was not discovered until after Harvey, he may thus be considered the originator of the 17th-century 'ovist' theory according to which the female contributed the whole of the embryo. After Leeuwenhoek, with his microscope, had discovered the spermatozoon (1677), the opposite school of animalculists made the same claim for the male, and the resulting controversy continued throughout most of the 18th century.

The other great embryological controversy over which Harvey's followers spent their energies was that of epigenesis and preformation. Harvey himself had clearly reaffirmed Aristotle's preference for the former, at least in sanguineous animals; he held development to be the production of structures *de novo* as the embryo approached the final adult form. After him ovists and animalculists alike held that the adult was formed by the 'evolution', or unfolding, of parts already completely present in the germ. This was more in keeping with the mechanism of the age, and the year after Harvey's death Gassendi published a theory of panspermatic preformationism based on his atomic theory. Some time earlier, an even completer mechanistic theory of biology had been worked out by Descartes (see above, pp. 337 *et seq.*).

This work on reproduction was to lead to the formulation of the germ theory of disease, though that was not fully understood until the time of Pasteur in the 19th century. In the early 16th century a theory that diseases were caused by the transference of *seminaria,* or seeds, was put forward by Fracastoro. He is famous for introducing the name syphilis and for describing that disease, which had first appeared in a virulent form in 1495 in Naples, then occupied by Spanish troops, during the siege by the soldiers of Charles VIII of France. He set forth his theory of disease in his *De Contagione,* published in 1546, in which he reiterated the already known facts that disease could be transmitted by direct contact, by clothing and utensils, and by infection at a distance as with smallpox or plague (see above, pp. 203–205). To explain such action at a distance, he made use of a modification of the old theory of the 'multiplication of species'; he said that during the putrefaction associated with disease minute particles of contagion were given off by exhalation and evaporation, and that these 'propagated their like' through the air or water or other media. When they entered another body, they spread through it and caused the putrefaction of that one of the four humours to which they had the closest analogy. To such *seminaria* Fracastoro attributed the spread of contagious phthisis, rabies and syphilis.

Fracastoro seems also to have been the first to recognise typhus, and the habit of carefully recording case-histories, which has been seen in the *consilia* and plague tracts made since the 13th century, produced a number of good accounts of diseases in the 16th century, for example the clear description of the sweating sickness published by John Caius in 1552. This practice increased in the 17th century and produced such excellent clinical records as Francis Glisson's account of infantile rickets in 1650, Sir Theodore Turquet of Mayerne's medical history of King James I, and the careful descriptions of measles, gout, malaria, syphilis and other diseases made by Thomas Sydenham (1624–89). This insistence on observation, and suspicion of the all-too-facile theories which had prevented new approaches to the facts, led to a great increase in empirical knowledge and in empirical methods of treatment; indeed even now, in the

20th century, medicine is still largely an empirical art. As early as the early 16th century, if not still earlier, mercury was used for syphilis, and from the early 17th century cinchona bark, the source of quinine, was used for malaria. A clear understanding of infectious diseases, as indeed the understanding of the causes of the functional and organic disorders of the body, had to await the gradual acquisition of the fundamental knowledge of biology and physiology during the 18th and 19th centuries.

(8) THE SCIENTIFIC REVOLUTION
AND THE NATURE OF SCIENCE

By the middle of the 17th century European science had gone a long way since Adelard of Bath had demanded explanations in terms of natural causation, and since the experimental and mathematical methods had begun to develop within the predominantly Aristotelian system of scientific thought of the 13th and 14th centuries. Certainly in experimental and mathematical technique revolutionary progress had been made by the 17th century, and this was to go on with breathtaking speed throughout that century. To take only one science as an example, astronomy in 1600 was Copernican, and not even completely so; in 1700 it was Newtonian, and supported by the impressive structure of Newtonian mechanics. And yet the statements on aims and methods expressed by the spokesmen of the new 17th-century science were remarkably similar to those expressed by their predecessors in the 13th and 14th centuries, who were, in fact, also spokesmen of modern science at an earlier stage in its history.

The utilitarian ideal, for example, was given expression by Francis Bacon in words remarkably similar to those of his 13th-century namesake, even down to the particular value he placed on the inductive method. 'I am labouring to lay the foundation', said Bacon in the preface to his *Great Instauration*, 'not of any sect or doctrine, but of human utility and power', and for him the purpose of science was power over nature. The object of the Great Instauration, or new method, was to show how to win back that dominion, which had been lost at the Fall. In the past, science had been static, while the mechanical arts had progressed, because in science observation had been neglected. It was only through observation that knowledge of nature could be gained; it was only knowledge that led to power; and the knowledge that the natural scientist was to look for was knowledge of the 'form', or causal essence, whose activity produced the effects observed. Knowledge of the form gave mastery over it and its properties, and so the positive task of Bacon's new method was to show how to obtain knowledge of the form.

Bacon's method was a combination of the inductive and deductive processes already seen in his medieval predecessors. His chief contribution to the theory of induction was to set out very clearly and in great detail both the method of reaching the definition of a 'common nature', or form, by collecting and comparing instances of its supposed effects, and the method of eliminating false forms (or what would now be called hypotheses) by what he called 'exclusion'. This was a development of Grosseteste's method of 'falsification'. Bacon said in the *Novum Organum*, book 1, aphorism 95, published in 1620:

Those who have handled sciences have been either men of experiment or men of dogmas. The men of experiment are like the ant; they only collect and use: the reasoners resemble spiders, who make cobwebs out of their own substance. But the bee takes a middle course, it gathers its material from the flowers of the garden and of the field, but transforms and digests it by a power of its own. Not unlike this is the true business of philosophy; for it neither relies solely or chiefly on the powers of the mind, nor does it take the matter which it gathers from natural history and mechanical experiments and lay it up in the memory whole, as it finds it; but lays it up in the understanding altered and digested. Therefore from a closer and purer league between these two faculties, the experimental and the rational (such as has never yet been made) much may be hoped. . . . Now [he went on in book 2, aphorism 10] my directions for the interpretation of nature embrace two generic divisions; the one how to educe and form axioms from experience; the other how to deduce and derive new experiments from axioms.

The first stage in the definition of a form, as, for instance, the form of heat, was to make three 'tables of instances' based on a purely empirical collection of observations. The first was a table of 'Essence and Presence' or agreement, which included all events where the form sought (*e.g.*, heat) was present; the second was a table of 'Deviation or of Absence in Proximity' which included all events where the effects of the form sought were not observed; the third was a table of 'Degrees or Comparison' which included instances of variations in the observed effects of the form sought either in the same or in different subjects. Induction then consisted simply of the inspection of these tables. 'The problem is' said Bacon in the *Novum Organum*, book 2, aphorisms 15 and 16,

upon a review of the instances, all and each, to find such a nature as is always present or absent with the given nature, and always increases and decreases with it . . . The first work therefore of true induction (as far as regards the discovery of Forms) is the rejection or exclusion of the several natures which are not found in some instance where the given nature is present, or are found in some instance where the given nature is absent, or are found to increase in some instance when the given nature decreases, or to decrease when the given nature increases. Then indeed after the rejection and exclusion had been duly made, there will remain at the bottom, all light opinions vanishing into smoke, a Form affirmative, solid and true and well defined.

Thus, after applying the tests of agreement, difference and concomitant variation, the form was found in the un-eliminated residue. The first stage in this process led only to the 'First Vintage' or a working hypothesis. From this, new consequences were deduced and tested by further observations and experiments until eventually, by repeated and varied observation followed by elimination, the true definition of the form was discovered, and this gave certain knowledge of the reality behind the observed effects. 'The Form of a thing', he said in *Novum Organum*, book 2, aphorism 13,

is the very thing itself, and the thing differs from the form no otherwise than as the apparent differs from the real, or the external from the internal, or the thing in reference to man from the thing in reference to the universe.

The form for Bacon was always some mechanical disposition; induction eliminated the qualitative and the sensible leaving geometrical fine structure and motion. The form of heat was thus motion of particles; the form of colours a geometrical disposition of lines. In fact, by Bacon's time the word 'nature' itself had come to mean mechanical properties, the *natura naturata* of the Renaissance. The spontaneous animating principle, *natura naturans*, of such writers as Leonardo da Vinci or Bernardino Telesio (1508–88) had disappeared.

The discovery of the form was the end of the 'experiments of Light' which occupied the essential first stage in science but, as Bacon put it in the *Great Instauration:*

those twin objects, human Knowledge and human Power, do really meet in one; and it is from ignorance of causes that operation fails.

The final purpose of science was power over nature. Moreover, he said in the *Novum Organum*, book 1, aphorisms 73 and 124:

fruits and works are as it were sponsors and sureties for the truth of philosophies . . . Truth therefore and utility are here the very same things: and works themselves are of greater value as pledges of truth than as contributing to the comforts of life.

Thus, when Bacon excluded final causes from science it was not because he did not believe in them, but because he could not imagine an applied teleology as there was an applied physics. By following his 'experimental philosophy' he held that future humanity would achieve an enormous increase in power and material progress. As he expressed it in the *Novum Organum*, book 1, aphorism 109:

There is therefore much ground for hoping that there are still laid up in the womb of nature many secrets of excellent use, having no affinity or parallelism with anything that is now known, but lying entirely out of the beat of the imagination, which have not yet been found out.

And he believed that the final achievement of the branch of science which he described in the *Advancement of Learning* (1605) as 'Natural Magic' would be the transmutation of the elements.

It was, in fact, through his utilitarianism rather than his inductive method that Bacon chiefly influenced his scientific followers, though his ideas on method seem to have had some effect in England. For example, Harvey said in his *De Generatione*, excercitatio 25: 'in the words of the learned Lord Verulam to "enter upon our second vintage" '; and Bacon's method was often mentioned with respect by members of the Royal Society during the second half of the 17th century. This was not always an unmixed benefit, for he sometimes led his followers into a blind empiricism which was a regression on the experimental method already practised by scientists for some time. His influence was shown chiefly in the formation of co-operative groups of scientists consciously directing their efforts towards improving the material conditions of life and towards commercial and governmental utilities. The scientific republic described in Bacon's allegory, *New Atlantis*, published in 1627, was an inspiration to some of the founders of the Royal Society and Bacon again became the hero of d'Alembert and the French encyclopædists of the 18th century.

This desire for certain knowledge of Nature, which inspired Francis Bacon's work on method, and which in fact since St. Augustine or indeed since Plato had inspired the whole rationalist tradition of European thought, with its belief that what is certain is true of reality, was the principal motive behind all 17th-century science; it is what made the 17th century so conscious of method. Until the end of the 17th century, when this Aristotelian form of predication of attributes as inhering in real persisting substances began to be criticised in the new empiricism of John Locke (1632–1704), all scientists were inspired by the faith that they were discovering through and behind the particular observed phenomena the intelligible structure of the real world. And so it was supremely important to have a method that would facilitate this discovery of real Nature behind the appearances and that would guarantee the certainty of the result. The same emphasis on method is seen in all science, whether in the numerous 'methods' put forward by botanists in search of a 'natural' as opposed to a merely artificial system of classification, or in the experimental method and the mathematical method of chemists and physicists.

The real physical world, or Nature, for all 17th-century science, except certain parts of biology, where the existence of organisms was still recognised, was something mathematical. It was this conception of Nature which raised some of the main philosophical problems of the 17th century. It made causation impossible, and it excluded from Nature two main classes of entities, qualities and minds, and so led to the distinction of primary and secondary qualities and to the dualism of mind and body. In some ways this represented a return to the position of Democritus.

The position was very clearly stated by Galileo in *Il Saggiatore*, question 48 (*cf.* above, pp. 295, 304). 'No sooner', he said,

do I form a conception of a material or corporeal substance, than I feel the need of conceiving that it has boundaries and shape; that relative to others it is great or small; that it is in this or that place and in this or that time; that it is moving or still; that it touches or does not touch another body; that it is one, few or many; nor can I, by any effort of imagination, dissociate it from these qualities (*condizioni*). On the other hand, I find no need to apprehend it as accompanied by such conditions as to be white or red, bitter or sweet, sounding or silent, pleasant or evil smelling. Perhaps, if the senses had not informed us of these qualities, the reason and imagination alone would never have arrived at them. Therefore I hold that these tastes, odours, colours, etc., on the part of the object in which they seem to reside, are nothing more than pure names, and exist only in the sensitive being; so that if the latter were removed these qualities would themselves vanish. But having given them special names different from those of the other primary and real qualities (*accidenti*), we would persuade ourselves that they also exist just as truly and really as the latter . . . But I hold that there exists nothing in external bodies for exciting in us tastes, odours and sounds but size, shape, quantity and slow or swift motion. And I conclude that if the ears, tongue and nose were removed, shape, quantity and motion would remain but there would be no odours, tastes or sounds, which apart from living creatures I believe to be mere words.

Essentially the same view of Nature was taken by Descartes and he set out to describe a method which would lead to certain knowledge of this reality. He held that in the analysis of experience the first act of the understanding was to intuit 'simple natures', *e.g.*, extension, figure, movement, existence, thought, which could not be reduced to anything simpler and therefore had no logical definitions. In his *Discours de la Méthode*, and again more fully in his *Regulæ ad Directionem Ingenii* published posthumously in 1701, he gave rules for choosing and arranging empirical knowledge for this act of intuition, including a form of induction involving the principle of elimination. The second act of the understanding was deduction of certain consequences from the intuited truths, and by this means essences were defined. The 'simple natures' that constituted the essences of the two ultimate substances into which the created world was divided he characterised in his *Principia Philosophiæ*, part 1, principle 53, as follows:

although any one attribute is sufficient to give us a knowledge of substance, there is always one principal property of substance

393

which constitutes its nature and essence, and on which all the others depend. Thus extension in length, breadth and depth, constitutes the nature of corporeal substance; and thought constitutes the nature of thinking substance. For all else that may be attributed of body presupposes extension, and is merely a mode of this extended thing; as everything that we find in mind is merely so many diverse forms of thinking. Thus, for example, we cannot conceive of figure except in an extended thing, nor of movement except in an extended space: so imagination, feeling, and will, only exist in a thinking thing.

Thus Descartes attempted to build a whole philosophy on the distinction between a mathematical objective world and a mental subjective world. By reducing matter to geometrical extension he denied the active principles in things and removed from matter all efficient and final causes; and by dividing created reality (*i.e.*, as distinct from God) into the two absolutely distinct categories, extension (*res extensa*) and thought (*res cogitans*), he made interaction between mind and body impossible (*cf.* above, pp. 338–341). Thus he completely removed the possibility of secondary causation, although this was recognised only by his followers. One way of providing for efficient causes in matter was to return, with Gassendi and Sir Kenelm Digby (1603–65), to a form of atomism and to lodge causality in the atoms themselves. Leibniz made a similar attempt to overcome this difficulty with his theory of monads. Events were explained by antecedent movements of particles, and when, in the 18th century, attempts were made on mechanical principles to explain biological adaptation and animal behaviour, which seemed to demand final causes, biologists such as Maupertuis (1698–1759) and Buffon (1707–88) did not hesitate to place even teleology in these atoms.

This explanation did not account for the interaction of mind and body. As Joseph Glanvill put it in *The Vanity of Dogmatizing* (1661) 'how the purer Spirit is united to this Clod, is a knot too hard for fallen Humanity to unty'. Cartesians such as Geulincx (1625–69), Louis de la Forge (in

1666), Géraud de Cordemoy (in 1666) and Nicolas Male-branche (1638–1715) attempted to get over the difficulty by the theory of 'occasionalism', in which all causal action was attributed to God. When an event A seemed to produce another event B, they held that what really happened was that A furnished the occasion for God voluntarily to produce B. And so although a physical event happening in the body might seem to produce a sensation in the mind, and an act of will might seem to produce a movement of the body, there was in fact no causal link between two such events except in God who produced them both. In His activities God usually followed fixed rules so that it was possible for natural philosophers to formulate scientific generalisations or laws.

'Occasionalism' did not give satisfaction for long and, in fact, the mind-body problem has remained one of the main problems of Western philosophy right down to the 20th century. During the 18th and 19th centuries philosophers of science simply rang the changes on the alternative possibilities. Cartesian dualism seeming to be a contradiction, they swung back and forth between the extremes of idealism and materialism, neither theory being able to establish itself finally because it denied some obvious facts asserted by the other. And so, because of Descartes, philosophers had to cut the world in two. On the one hand idealists, such as Hegel, had very little to do with natural science; on the other, scientists, left to themselves, drifted into strange fancies when they tried to give metaphysical interpretations of their results. Yet, to construct metaphysical systems was as natural to them as it is to all men. During the 18th century, popularisers of science like La Mettrie, D'Holbach, Condorcet and Cabanis were beginning to say that man was nothing but a machine, that consciousness was a secretion of the brain just as bile was a secretion of the liver. And so this materialism of the 18th century, this French materialism of the *Encyclopédie*, prepared the way for the naïve Anglo-German materialism that became associated with the theory of evolution in the 19th century.

These problems raised by Descartes served to bring out the contradictions implicit in 17th-century methods when linked with the conception of science as an attempt to discover Nature as an objective reality which could be certainly known. The attempt to avoid these contradictions gradually produced a new conception of science which has become fully clear only in the 20th century. Within the persistent search for certainty that can be seen in the various and changing metaphysical interpretations of natural science and in the recurrent dissatisfaction produced by the contradictions discovered in each successive system, there developed a tendency for science to reflex upon itself, for scientists to study their results rather as the products of a method than as discoveries about Nature. The first important stage in this process is to be found perhaps in Galileo's emphasis on the active role of the reason in constructing theories to correlate experience, though his 'mathematical realism' shows that he had lost some of the logical refinement found in scholastic thought. A good example is the conclusion which had led Grosseteste to put forward his method of falsification, that since, in the physical world, the same effect might follow from more than one cause, and since it was never possible to know all the possibilities, theories in natural science could never be certain. Only towards the end of the 17th century was some of this logical refinement recovered, largely because of the conception of scientific theories as the constructions of an active reason. This conception is to be found in the preface to Robert Hooke's *Micrographia* (1665), in which he said:

The Understanding is to order all the inferiour services of the lower Faculties; but yet it is to do this only as a lawful Master, and not as a Tyrant . . . It must watch the irregularities of the Senses, but it must not go before them, or prevent their information. It must examine, range, and dispose of the bank which is laid up in the Memory . . . So many are the links, upon which the true Philosophy depends, of which, if any one be loose, or weak, the whole chain is in danger of being dissolv'd; it is to begin with the Hands and Eyes, and to proceed on through the Memory, to be continued by the Reason; nor is it to stop there, but to come about to the Hands and Eyes again . . . If once this method were followed with diligence and attention, there is nothing that lyes within the power of human Wit (or which is far more effectual) of human Industry, which we might not compass; we might not only hope for Inventions to equalize those of Copernicus, Galileo, Gilbert, Harvy, and of others, whose names are almost lost, that were the Inventors of Gun-powder, the Seamans Compass, Printing, Etching, Graving, Microscopes, &c. but multitudes that may far exceed them.

Next after this conception of experimental science, which in fact summed up an older tradition of methodology, came Locke's theory that what we know is not objects in an external world but experience coming to us through our sense-organs. As early as Robert Boyle and, later, by George Berkeley (1685–1753), it was pointed out that the primary qualities or geometrical concepts, in terms of which mathematical-physics interpreted experience, were no less mental than secondary qualities, and that if either group of qualities had any claim to 'reality', then both had equal claims. Newton, carrying mathematics into physics to the farthest extent possible in his time, made his often-misinterpreted dictum, *'hypotheses non fingo'*. By this he did not mean that he never made hypotheses, for he made many; he drew a distinction between the generalisations of experimental data, as expressed in a mathematical formula, and physical hypotheses advanced to explain the *cause* of the observed phenomena. In much the same way astronomers for many centuries had drawn a distinction between mathematical theories, which simply 'saved the appearances', and physical theories, which explained the cause of the changes observed. Newton said in the General Scholium at the end of book 3 of the *Principia Mathematica:*

Hitherto we have explained the phenomena of the heavens and of our sea by the power of gravity, but have not yet assigned the cause of this power.

397

He went on:

I have not been able to discover the cause of those properties of gravity from phenomena, and I frame no hypotheses; for whatever is not deduced from phenomena is to be called an hypothesis; and hypotheses, whether metaphysical or physical, whether of occult qualities or mechanical, have no place in experimental philosophy. In this philosophy particular propositions are inferred from the phenomena, and afterwards rendered general by induction. Thus it was that the impenetrability, the mobility, and the impulsive force of bodies, and the laws of motion and of gravitation, were discovered.

Speaking of gravitational attraction, in *The System of the World*, section 2, he said:

our purpose is only to trace out the quantity and properties of this force from the phenomena, and to apply what we discover in some single cases as principles, by which, in a mathematical way, we may estimate the effects thereof in more involved cases; for it would be endless and impossible to bring every particular to direct and immediate observation. We said, *in a mathematical way*, to avoid all questions about the nature or quality of this force, which we would not be understood to determine by any hypothesis.

Newton himself certainly still believed that natural science was capable of discovering, in its theories, the real causes of phenomena; but his methods opened the way for others to assert that scientific theories were framed simply to 'save the appearances' and that further questions were pointless. Berkeley pointed out that there was no justification for Newton's conception of absolute space and that all motion was relative. David Hume (1711–76), the 18th-century Ockham, disposed of the old notion of cause in science. He showed that empirical data did not carry their own explanation and, of themselves, gave no grounds for belief in causality; yet he could see no other grounds for such a belief. He said that natural science merely described what was observed to happen and established empirical correlations, and that there was nothing objective in causal necessity beyond regular concomitance or sequence. He said, in section 4 of his *Inquiry Concerning Human Understanding:*

In a word, then, every effect is a distinct event from its cause. It could not, therefore, be discovered in the cause; and the first invention or conception of it, *a priori*, must be entirely arbitrary.

At the same time Buffon (1707–88) and other biologists were also, in their own way, reviving 14th-century nominalism. They maintained that there was nothing objective in biological species beyond a name shared by similar individuals. The first fully explicit statement of the actively constructive role of the scientist in asking the questions to which he wanted an answer, and in constructing theories from which to deduce the phenomena, was made by Immanuel Kant (1724–1804). Kant said in the preface to the second edition of his *Critique of Pure Reason:*

When Galilei let balls of a particular weight, which he had determined himself, roll down an inclined plane, or Torricelli made the air carry a weight, which he had previously determined to be equal to that of a definite volume of water; or when, in later times, Stahl changed metal into calx, and calx again into metal, by withdrawing and restoring something, a new light flashed on all students of nature. They comprehended that reason has insight into that only, which she herself produces on her own plan, and that she must move forward with the principles of her judgements, according to fixed law, and compel nature to answer her questions, but not let herself be led by nature, as it were in leading strings, because otherwise accidental observations, made on no previously fixed plan, will never converge towards a necessary law, which is the only thing that reason seeks and requires. Reason, holding in one hand its principles, according to which concordant phenomena alone can be admitted as laws of nature, and in the other hand the experiment, which it has devised according to those principles, must approach nature, in order to be taught by it: but not in the character of a pupil, who agrees to everything the master likes, but as an appointed judge, who compels the witnesses to answer the questions which he himself proposes. Therefore even the science of physics entirely owes the beneficial revolution in its character to the happy thought, that we ought to seek in nature (and not impart into it by means of fiction) whatever reason must learn from nature, and could not know by itself, and that we must do this in accordance with what reason itself has originally placed into nature. Thus only has the study of nature entered on the secure method of a science, after having for many centuries done nothing but grope in the dark.

With Kant natural science is seen to be a creative activity, not a mere dissection of Nature; scientific experiments and theories are seen to be the creations of an active reason attempting to make sense of the world, attempting to explain facts of observation by showing that they can be deduced from a theory. Science attempts to construct a whole interlocking system of theories from which more and more diverse forms of experience can be deduced.

More recent philosophies of science, and particularly some of those put forward in the 20th century, have emphasised even further this conception of Kant of the activity of the scientist and also his freedom from traditional metaphysical presuppositions; freedom, that is, in principle, for scientists have not always recognised it. Kant himself had believed that the scientist approached nature with certain necessary principles in his mind, of which Euclid's propositions were only explicit formulations, and that he necessarily presupposed these principles in all his knowledge and in all the theories with which he attempted to organise his experience.

Kant had regarded as the supreme example of his theory of science the Newtonian system of physics, but from the end of the 19th century physicists found that they could meet certain difficulties arising in physics only by abandoning some of the basic principles they had derived from Newton; they found that the 'appearances' could be 'saved' by using some of the non-Euclidean geometries developed earlier in the 19th century. So the internal developments of physics itself has disposed of the belief, that at least the particular set of principles found in Euclid's geometry must necessarily be assumed by the scientist. The conception has grown that any theoretical system can be used to correlate experience, provided it passes the tests of logical coherence and experimental verification. Apart from these, the choice of a system is simply a matter of convenience and convention.

Thus, in the unfolding of natural science since the 17th century, fundamental features have been exhibited which could be perceived only dimly, if at all, during the Scientific Revolution itself. Science is seen to be a conceptual system, a structure of hypotheses within which the more particular bear to the more general the relation of necessary consequence, the establishing of that relation constituting an explanation; and it is seen that there can never be any finality or certainty about a scientific theory, because it can never be shown that the particular facts or limited generalisations of facts which a given theory is constructed to explain could not equally well follow from some other theory.

It is, in fact, this conceptual character of the results of inductive science, with its perennial aim of 'saving the appearances' and saving them more and more completely, which allows to science one of its most essential characteristics, the possibility of growth. As long as it is believed, as it has been by 'naïve realists' from the Averroïsts of the Middle Ages to the mechanists and materialists of the 19th century and their followers in the 20th, that science is discovering in its theories real entities existing in the natural world, it is always possible to believe that a final discovery has been made and that no further questions need be asked. The Aristotelian system supported by the Averroïsts was seen, in the 17th century, to be as hypothetical as Newtonian mechanics appears in the 20th, because men ceased to regard the products of a previous attempt to explain observations as a final discovery of the nature of the physical world.

It has been the failure to appreciate this hypothetical and conceptual character of scientific theories that has been mainly responsible for the 'crisis of conscience' following the Scientific Revolution in Europe. In the 17th century, this crisis arose out of the contrast so vividly described by Sir Thomas Browne (1605–82), when he watched the new mathematical method stretch its dragon wings and separate created reality into the mechanical world of physics, indifferent to man, and the interior world of the human spirit, knowing beauty, conscience and the love of God. 'Thus is Man', he said in *Religio Medici* (1643), part 1, section 34,

that great and true Amphibium whose nature is disposed to live, not onely like other creatures in divers elements but in divided and distinguished worlds.

Confusion was added when biologists used organic adaptation as arguments to show the wisdom of God in the works of his creation, for it was pointed out that a lack of adaptation must then demonstrate a commensurate lack of wisdom. Further confusion came when Newton introduced God into his physical theories to restore the balance of the solar system, which he believed to be in slight disequilibrium, for he exposed himself to the retort, after Laplace showed that the solar system in fact maintained its own equilibrium, that the hypothesis of God was no longer necessary. And so the naïve realism with which men regarded the results of science led the religious minded to make play with a conceptual God introduced into, and eliminated from their theories according to the demands of the occasion. From the end of the 18th century things were made worse when the same naïve realism, now in the form of materialism, led some scientists and popularisers of science to speak as if 'matter' was the only 'reality' there was.

It can be seen clearly now in the 20th century, though it did not altogether escape notice in earlier times, that a scientific theory of itself never provides grounds for denying a belief held in a context outside the range of the scientific method; and further, that, although scientific theories are themselves conceptual and hypothetical, there is nothing in the scientific method that either denies or affirms the validity of other methods of making sense of experience, or the attainability of objective truth. Science can provide no capital for either theologians or atheists, moralists or libertines. It has nothing to say about æsthetics or ethics, about the existence of God or miracles. And whatever other philosophical disciplines may have to say about these subjects, they may speak independently of natural science, as it speaks, in its own language, independently of them. No construction of the mind can be used to set limits to the mind's activity, and the illumination that natural science has given in the modern world has depended precisely upon the practical recognition of this fact.

BIBLIOGRAPHY

Tᴵᴛʟᴇs ʜᴀᴠᴇ ʙᴇᴇɴ ʀᴇsᴛʀɪᴄᴛᴇᴅ to the most useful books on each topic. Reference has been made to recent articles of outstanding importance. The list has been limited to works in English and French except in cases where the only available work on an essential topic is in German or Italian.

Introduction

Some books on the philosophy of science may be recommended here:

P. W. Bʀɪᴅɢᴍᴀɴ, *The Logic of Modern Physics* (New York, 1928); W. I. B. Bᴇᴠᴇʀɪᴅɢᴇ, *The Art of Scientific Investigation* (London, 1950); W. K. Cʟɪꜰꜰᴏʀᴅ, *The Common Sense of the Exact Sciences*, 2nd ed. (New York, 1946); M. R. Cᴏʜᴇɴ and E. Nᴀɢᴇʟ, *An Introduction to Logic and Scientific Method* (London, 1934); H. Dɪɴɢʟᴇ, *Through Science to Philosophy* (Oxford, 1937); Sɪʀ Aʀᴛʜᴜʀ S. Eᴅᴅɪɴɢᴛᴏɴ, *The Philosophy of Physical Science* (Cambridge, 1939); F. Eɴʀɪǫᴜᴇs, *Problems of Science*, trans. K. Royce (Chicago, 1924); P. Fʀᴀɴᴋ, *Modern Science and its Philosophy* (Cambridge, Mass., 1950); J. S. Hᴀʟᴅᴀɴᴇ, *Mechanism, Life and Personality* (London, 1921); E. Mᴇʏᴇʀsᴏɴ, *De l'Explication dans les Sciences*, 2 vols. (Paris, 1921); K. Pᴇᴀʀsᴏɴ, *The Grammar of Science* (London, 1892); H. Pᴏɪɴᴄᴀʀᴇ́, *Science and Hypothesis* (London, 1905), *Science and Method* (London, 1914); Bᴇʀᴛʀᴀɴᴅ Rᴜssᴇʟʟ, *Introduction to Mathematical Philosophy* (London, 1919); Sɪʀ C. Sʜᴇʀʀɪɴɢᴛᴏɴ, *Man on His Nature* (Cambridge, 1942); A. N. Wʜɪᴛᴇʜᴇᴀᴅ, *An Introduction to Mathematics* (London, 1911); J. H. Wᴏᴏᴅɢᴇʀ, *Biological Principles* (London, 1929).

Chapter One

Basic books on the history of science in the Middle Ages are:—
P. Dᴜʜᴇᴍ, *Le Système du Monde*, 5 vols. (Paris, 1913–17), a classic work; C. H. Hᴀsᴋɪɴs, *Studies in the History of Mediaeval Science* (Cambridge, Mass., 1927); G. Sᴀʀᴛᴏɴ, *Introduction to the*

History of Science, 3 vols. (Baltimore, 1927–47); L. THORNDIKE, *A History of Magic and Experimental Science*, 6 vols. (New York, 1923–41).

Two admirable books on the history of the Middle Ages are:—

M. BLOCH, *La Société Féodale* (Paris, 1949); H. PIRENNE, *Economic and Social History of Medieval Europe* (London, 1936). For more detailed study there are *The Cambridge Economic History of Europe*, ed. J. H. Clapham and Eileen Power, vol. 1, *The Agrarian Life in the Middle Ages* (Cambridge, 1941), and *The Cambridge Medieval History*, ed. C. W. PREVITÉ-ORTOW and Z. N. BROOKE, 8 vols. (Cambridge, 1911–36).

Ancient Greek Philosophy and Science:

A. H. ARMSTRONG, *An Introduction to Ancient Philosophy* (London, 1949); C. BAILEY, *The Greek Atomists and Epicurus* (Oxford, 1928); L. BRUNSCHVICG, *Le Rôle du Pythagorisme dans l'Evolution des Idées* (Paris, 1937) (*Actualités Scientifiques et Industrielles 446*); J. BURNET, *Early Greek Philosophy* (London, 1930); P. BRUNET ET A. MIELI, *Histoire des Sciences: Antiquité* (Paris, 1935); F. M. CORNFORD, *The Laws of Motion in the Ancient Greek World* (Cambridge, 1931), *Before and After Socrates* (Cambridge, 1933), *Plato's Cosmology* (London, 1937), 'Greek philosophy and modern science' in *Background to Modern Science*, ed. J. NEEDHAM and W. PAGEL (Cambridge, 1938), *Plato and Parmenides* (London, 1939); R. G. COLLINGWOOD, *The Idea of Nature* (Oxford, 1945); B. FARRINGTON, *Science in Antiquity* (London, 1936), *Greek Science*, 2 vols. (London, 1944–49); K. FREEMAN, *Companion to the pre-Socratic Philosophers* (Oxford, 1946); *The Greek Herbal of Dioscorides*, ed. R. T. Gunther (Oxford, 1934); SIR THOMAS HEATH, *Mathematics in Aristotle* (Oxford, 1949); A. REYMOND, *History of the Sciences of Greco-Roman Antiquity* (London, 1937); A. REY, *La Science dans l'Antiquité*, 5 vols. (Paris, 1933–46); SIR W. D. ROSS, *Aristotle* (London, 1937).

Early Medieval Philosophy:

H. I. MARROU, *St. Augustin et le Fin de la Culture Antique* (Paris, 1938), *Histoire de l'Education dans l'Antiquité* (Paris, 1950); A CLERVAL, *Les Ecoles de Chartres* (Paris, 1895); C. DAWSON, 'St. Augustine and his Age', in *A Monument to St. Augustine* (London, 1930); E. GILSON, *La Philosophie au Moyen Age* (Paris, 1947)—an indispensable work; C. H. HASKINS, *The Renaissance of the Twelfth Century* (Cambridge, Mass., 1928); R. McKEON,

Selections from Medieval Philosophers, vol. 1 (New York, 1929) ;
E. C. MESSENGER, *Evolution and Theology* (London, 1931); G.
PARÉ, A. BRUNET et P. TREMBLAY, *La Renaissance du XIIe Siècle.
Les Ecoles et l'Enseignement* (Paris–Ottawa, 1933).

Geography:
G. H. T. KIMBLE, *Geography in the Middle Ages* (London, 1938).

Early Medieval Medicine:
G. W. CORNER, *Anatomical Texts of the Earlier Middle Ages*
(Washington, 1927); L. C. MACKINNEY, *Early Medieval Medicine*
(Baltimore, 1937); C. and D. SINGER, 'The origin of the medical
school of Salerno', in *Essays Presented to Karl Sudhoff*, ed. C. SINGER
and H. E. SIGERIST (Oxford and Zürich, 1924); J. F. PAYNE,
English Medicine in Anglo-Saxon Times (Oxford, 1904); J. J.
Walsh, *Medieval Medicine* (London, 1920).

Herbals:
R. T. GUNTHER, *The Herbal of Apuleius Barbaras* (Oxford, 1925) ;
C. SINGER, 'The herbal in antiquity', *Journal of Hellenic Studies*
(1927, vol. 47, pp. 1 *et seq.*).

Magic, and Macrocosm and Microcosm:
C. SINGER, 'The scientific views and visions of St. Hildegard',
in *Studies in the History and Method of Science*, vol. 1 (Oxford, 1917),
a collection of essays edited by C. SINGER, *From Magic to Science*
(London, 1928); L. THORNDIKE, *A History of Magic and Experimental Science*, 6 vols. (New York, 1923–41).

Chapter Two

Arab and Jewish Science and Philosophy:
Avicenna, Scientist and Philosopher, ed. G. M. WICKENS (London,
Luzac & Co., in press); E. G. BROWNE, *Arabian Medicine* (Cambridge, 1921); D. CAMPBELL, *Arabian Medicine and its Influence on
the Middle Ages* (London, 1926); L. GAUTHIER, *Ibn Rochd (Averroës)*
(Paris, 1948); I. HUSIK, *A History of Jewish Philosophy* (Philadelphia, 1916); E. C. KELLY, *A Treatise on the Smallpox and
Measles by Rhazes* (New York, 1939); M. MEYERHOF, 'A sketch
of Arab science', *Journal of the Egyptian Medical Association* (1936,
vol. 19. pp. 462 *et seq.*); A. MIELI, *La Science Arabe* (Leyden,
1938); G. QUADRI, *La Philosophie Arabe dans l'Europe Médiévale
des Origines à Averroës* (Paris, 1947); G. SARTON, *Introduction to the
History of Science* vols. 1 and 2; H. SUTER, *Die Mathematiker und*

Astronomen der Araber (*Abh. z. Geschichte der math. Wissenschaften*) (Leipzig, 1900, vol. 10; 1902, vol. 14); H. J. J. WINTER, articles in *Endeavour* (1950–1, vols. 9–10). See also *The Legacy of Israel*, ed. E. R. BEVAN and C. SINGER (Oxford, 1927) and *The Legacy of Islam*, ed. SIR T. ARNOLD and A. GUILLAUME (Oxford, 1931), and the bottom of this page.

Hindu Mathematics and Logic:

B. DATTA and A. N. SINGH, *History of Hindu Mathematics* (Lahore, 1935); A. B. KEITH, *Indian Logic and Atomism* (Oxford, 1921); R. SEAL, *The Positive Sciences of the Ancient Hindus* (London, 1915); D. E. SMITH and L. C. KARPINSKI, *The Hindu-Arabic System of Numerals* (Boston, 1911).

The Translations into Latin:

B. GEYER—Friedrich Ueberwegs, *Grundriss der Geschichte der Philosophie*, vol. 2 (Berlin, 1928); C. H. HASKINS, *Studies in the History of Mediaeval Science* (Cambridge, Mass., 1927); G. LACOMBE, *Aristoteles Latinus* (Rome, 1939)—an indispensible work of reference; G. SARTON, *An Introduction to the History of Science*, vols. 1–2; F. VAN STEENBERGHEN, *Aristote en Occident* (Louvain, 1946); A. VAN DER VYVER, 'Les plus anciens traductions latines médiévales (X-ᵉXIᵉ siècles) de traités d'astronomie et d'astrologie', *Osiris* (1936, vol. 1, pp. 658 *et seq.*), 'Les premières traductions latines (X-ᵉXIᵉ siècles) de traités Arabes sur l'astrolabe', *Iᵉʳ Congrès Internationale de Géographie Historique* (Bruxelles, 1931); S. D. WINGATE, *The Mediaeval Latin Versions of the Aristotelian Corpus* (London, 1931); M. DE WULF, *History of Medieval Philosophy*, vol. 1 (English translation, London, 1935).

Development of natural philosophy as a result of the translations:

A. BIRKENMAJER, 'Le rôle joué par les médicins et les naturalistes dans la réception d'Aristote au XIIᵉ et XIIIᵉ siècles', *La Pologne au VIᵉ Congrès Internationale des Sciences Historiques, Oslo, 1928* (Warsaw, 1930); A. G. LITTLE, *Franciscan Letters, Papers and Documents* (Manchester, 1943); *Roger Bacon Essays*, ed. A. G. LITTLE (Oxford, 1914); M. MEYERHOF, 'Von Alexandrien nach Bagdad', *Sitzungsberichte der Preussischen Akademie der Wissenschaften zu Berlin*, Philos.—hist. Klasse (1930, pp. 389 *et seq.*); S. PINES, 'Les précurseurs musulmans de la théorie de l'impetus', *Archeion* (1938, vol. 21, pp. 298 *et seq*); A. VAN DER VYVER, 'Les étapes du développement philosophique du haut moyen âge', *Revue Belge de Philologie et d'Histoire* (1929, vol. 8, pp. 425 *et seq.*), 'L'évolution scientifique du haut moyen âge', *Archeion* (1937, vol. 19, pp. 12 *et seq.*); E. WIEDEMANN, a series of important papers on Arabic science (see Sarton's *Introduction*).

Difficulties over the acceptance of Aristotle in Western Christendom:

D. A. CALLUS, 'Introduction of Aristotelian learning to Oxford', *Proceedings of the British Academy* (1943, vol. 29, pp. 229 *et seq.*); CHRISTOPHER DAWSON, *Mediæval Religion* (London, 1934); M. B. FOSTER, 'The Christian doctrine of the creation and the rise of modern natural science', *Mind* (1934, vol. 43, pp. 446 *et seq.*), 'Christian theology and modern science of nature', *Mind* (1935, vol. 44, pp. 439 *et seq.* and 1936, vol. 45, pp. 1 *et seq.*); M. D. KNOWLES, 'Some recent advance in the history of medieval thought', *Cambridge Historical Journal* (1947, vol. 9, pp. 22 *et seq.*), an excellent bibliographical study; H. RASHDALL, *The Universities of Europe in the Middle Ages*, 2nd edition prepared by F. M. POWICKE and A. B. EMDEN, 3 vols. (Oxford, 1936).

Chapter Three

13th-Century Philosophy in General:

L. BAUR, 'Die Philosophie des Robert Grosseteste', in *Beiträge zur Geschichte der Philosophie des Mittelalters* (1917, vol. 18, Heft 4–6); J. H. BRIDGES, *The Life and Work of Roger Bacon* (London, 1914); M. H. CARRÉ, *Realists and Nominalists* (Oxford, 1946); F. C. COPLESTON, *History of Philosophy, II, Augustine to Scotus* (London, 1950) ; T. CROWLEY, *Roger Bacon* (Louvain–Dublin, 1950); E. GILSON, *La Philosophie au Moyen Age* (Paris, 1947); G. VON HERTLING, 'Albertus Magnus', in *Beiträge zur Geschichte der Philosophie des Mittelalters* (1914, vol. 14, Heft 5–6); *Roger Bacon Essays*, ed. A. G. LITTLE (Oxford, 1914); A. G. LITTLE, 'Roger Bacon', *Proceedings of the British Academy* (1928, vol. 14, pp. 265 *et seq.*); C. K. MCKEON, *A Study of the Summa Philosophiæ of the Pseudo-Grosseteste* (New York, 1948); R. MCKEON, *Selections from Medieval Philosophers*, 2 vols. (New York, 1929–30); H. C. SCHEEBEN, 'Albert der Grosse, Zur Chronologie seines Lebens', in *Quellen und Forschungen zur Geschichte der Dominikanerordens in Deutschland* (1931, vol. 27); D. E. SHARP, *Franciscan Philosophy at Oxford in the 13th Century* (Oxford, 1930); P. A. WALZ (editor),

'Serta Albertina', in *Angelicum* (1944, vol. 21); M. DE WULF, *History of Medieval Philosophy*, vol. 2 (English trans., London, 1938).

Medieval Cosmology and Astronomy:

J. D. BOND, 'Richard of Wallingford', *Isis* (1922, vol. 4, pp. 458 *et seq.*); J. L. E. DREYER, *A History of Planetary Systems* (Cambridge, 1906); 'Medieval astronomy', in *Studies in the History and Method of Science*, ed. C. SINGER, vol. 2 (Oxford, 1921); P. DUHEM, *Le Système du Monde*, 5 vols. (Paris, 1913–17), 'Essai sur la notion de théorie physique de Platon à Galilée', *Annales de Philosophie Chrétienne* (1908, vol. 6, pp. 113 *et seq.*, 277 *et seq.*, 352 *et seq.*); R. T. GUNTHER, *Early Science in Oxford*, vol. 2 (Oxford, 1923), *The Astrolabes of the World* (Oxford, 1932); L. THORNDIKE, *The Sphere of Sacrobosco and its Commentators* (Chicago, 1949); J. K. WRIGHT, 'Notes on the knowledge of latitudes and longitudes in the Middle Ages', *Isis* (1923, vol. 5, pp. 75, *et seq.*).

Meteorology and Optics:

C. BAEUMKER, 'Witelo, ein Philosoph und Naturforscher des 13. Jahrhunderts', in *Beiträge zur Geschichte der Philosophie des Mittelalters* (1908, vol. 3, Heft 2); L. BAUR, 'Die Philosophie des Robert Grosseteste', *ibid.* (1917, vol. 18, Heft 4–6); G. HELLMANN *Neudrücke von Schriften und Karten über Meteorologie und Erdmagnetismus*, Nos. 12–15, (Berlin, 1899–1904), *Beiträge zur Geschichte der Meteorologie*, No. 8, 'Die Wettervorhersage im ausgehenden Mittelalter (XII. bis XV. Jahrhundert)' (Berlin, 1917); E. KREBS, 'Meister Dietrich (Theodoricus Teutonicus de Vriberg). Sein Leben, seine Werke, seine Wissenschaft', in *Beiträge Ges. Philos. Mittelalt.* (1906, vol. 5, Heft 5–6); C. SINGER, 'Steps leading to the invention of the first optical apparatus', in *Studies in the History and Method of Science*, vol. 2 (Oxford, 1921); THEODORICUS TEUTONICUS DE VRIBERG, *De Iride*, ed. J. WÜRSCHMIDT, in *Beiträge Ges. Philos. Mittelalt.* (1914, vol. 12, Heft 5–6).

Mechanics:

R. DUGAS, *Histoire de la Mécanique* (Neuchatel, 1950); P. DUHEM, *Les Origines de la Statique*, 2 vols. (Paris, 1905–6); B. GINSBERG, 'Duhem and Jordanus Nemorarius', *Isis* (1936, vol. 25, pp. 341 *et seq.*); P. TANNERY, *Mémoires Scientifiques*, vol. 5, *Sciences exactes au moyen âge*, published by J. L. Heiberg (Toulouse and Paris, 1922).

Magnetism:

E. O. VON LIPPMANN, 'Geschichte der Magnetnadel bis zur Erfindung des Kompasses (gegen 1300)', *Quellen und Studien zur Geschichte der Naturwissenschaften, etc.* (1932, vol. 3, pp. 1 *et seq.*); P. F. MOTTELAY, *Bibliographical History of Electricity and Magnetism* (London, 1922); PETRI PEREGRINI MARICURTENSIS *De Magnete*, ed. G. HELLMANN in *Neudrücke von Schriften und Karten über Meteorologie und Erdmagnetismus*, No. 10 (Berlin, 1898); E. SCHLUND, 'Peregrinus, sein Leben und seine Schriften', *Archivum Franciscanum Historicum* (1911, vol. 4, pp. 436 *et seq.*, 633 *et seq.*, vol. 5, pp. 22 *et seq.*); S. P. THOMPSON, 'Petrus Peregrinus de Maricourt and his Epistola de Magnete', *Proceedings of the British Academy* (1905–6, vol. 2, pp. 377 *et seq.*).

Geology:

F. D. ADAMS, *The Birth and Development of the Geological Sciences* (Baltimore, 1938); Avicenna, *De Congelatione et Conglutinatione Lapidum*, ed. E. J. HOLMYARD and D. C. MANDEVILLE (Paris, 1927); P. DUHEM, *Etudes sur Léonard de Vinci*, 2ᵉ série (Paris, 1909).

Chemistry:

P. E. M. BERTHELOT, *La Chimie au Moyen Age*, 3 vols. (Paris, 1893); R. J. FORBES, *A Short History of the Art of Distillation* (Leyden, 1948); E. J. HOLMYARD, *Makers of Chemistry* (Oxford, 1931); P. KRAUS, *Jābir Ibn Hayyan*, 2 vols. (Cairo, 1942–3); J. A. STILLMAN, *The Story of Early Chemistry* (New York, 1924); F. STRUNZ, *Geschichte der Naturwissenschaften im Mittelalter* (Stuttgart, 1910); F. SHERWOOD TAYLOR, 'A survey of Greek alchemy,' *Journal of Hellenic Studies* (1930, vol. 1, pp. 109 *et seq.*), 'The Origins of Greek alchemy', *Ambix* (1937, vol. 1, pp. 30 *et seq.*), *The Alchemists: Founders of Modern Chemistry* (New York, 1949).

Biology:

P. AIKEN, 'The animal history of Albertus Magnus and Thomas of Cantimpré', *Speculum* (1947, vol. 22, pp. 205 *et seq.*); ALBERTUS MAGNUS, *De Vegetabilibus*, ed. C. JESSEN (Berlin, 1867), *De Animalibus*, ed. H. STADLER in *Beiträge Ges. Philos. Mittelalt.* (1916–20, vols. 15–16); A. ARBER, *Herbals* (Cambridge, 1938), *The Natural Philosophy of Plant Form* (Cambridge, 1950); H. BALSS, *Albertus Magnus als Zoologe* (München, 1928); H. S. BENNETT,

'Science and information in English writings of the 15th century', *Modern Language Review* (1944, vol. 39, pp. 1 *et seq.*); A. BIESE, *The Development of the Feeling for Nature in the Middle Ages and Modern Times* (London, 1905); M. DE BOUARD, 'Encyclopédies mediévales', *Revue des Questions Historiques* (1930, vol. 112, pp. 258 *et seq.*); J. V. CARUS, *Geschichte der Zoologie* (München, 1872); A. C. CROMBIE, 'Cybo d'Hyères: a 14th-century zoologist', *Endeavour* (1952, in press); A. FELLNER, *Albertus Magnus als, Botaniker* (Wien, 1881); H. W. K. FISCHER, *Mittelalterliche Pflanzenkunde* (München, 1929); S. KILLERMANN, *Die Vogelkunde des Albertus Magnus, 1207–80* (Regensburg, 1910), 'Das Tierbuch des Petrus Candidus 1460', in *Zoologische Annalen* (1914, vol. 6, pp. 113 *et seq.*); G. LOISEL, *Histoire des Ménagéries de l'Antiquité a nos Jours*, vol. 1 (Paris, 1913); T. E. LONES, *Aristotle's Researches into Natural Science* (London, 1912); E. MÂLE, *Religious Art in France in the 13th Century* (3rd edition, trans. by D. Nussy, London, 1913); N. PEVSNER, *The Leaves of Southwell* (London, 1945); A. PLATT, 'Aristotle on the heart', in *Studies in the History and Method of Science*, ed. C. SINGER, vol. 2 (Oxford, 1921); E. H. F. MEYER, *Geschichte der Botanik*, vol. 4 (Königsberg, 1857); E. S. RUSSELL, *Form and Function* (London, 1916); G. SENN, *Die Entwicklung der biologischen Forschungsmethode in der Antike* (Aarau, 1933); C. SINGER, 'Greek biology and its relation to the rise of modern biology', in *Studies in the History and Method of Science*, vol. 2 (Oxford, 1921), *The Evolution of Anatomy* (London, 1925), *Greek Biology and Greek Medicine* (Oxford, 1922); F. STRUNZ, *Albertus Magnus* (Wien und Leipzig, 1926); H. O. TAYLOR, *Greek Biology and Medicine* (London, 1923); D'ARCY W. THOMPSON, *On Aristotle as a Biologist* (Oxford, 1913); L. THORNDIKE and F. S. BENJAMIN, *The Herbal of Rufinus* (Chicago, 1945); J. WIMMER, *Deutsches Pflanzenleben nach Albertus Magnus* (Halle-a-S., 1908); C. A. WOOD and M. F. FYFE, *The Art of Falconry . . . of Frederick II* (Stanford, 1943).

Chapter Four

General:

P. BOISSONADE, *Life and Work in Medieval Europe*, trans. Eileen Power (London, 1927); F. M. FELDHAUS, *Die Technik der Vorzeit, der geschichtlichen Zeit und der Naturvölker* (Leipzig und Berlin, 1914), *Die Technik der Antike und des Mittelalters* (Potsdam, 1931); R. J. FORBES, *Man the Maker* (London, 1950); LEFEBVRE DES NOËTTES, 'La "nuit" du moyen âge et son inventaire', *Mercure de France* (1932, vol. 235, pp. 572 *et seq.*); L. MUMFORD, *Technics and Civilization* (London, 1934); A. NEUBURGER, *The Technical Arts and Sciences of the Ancients* (London, 1930); J. R. PARTINGTON, *Origins and Development of Applied Chemistry* (London, 1935); A. UCCELLI *et alii*, 'La Storia della Tecnica' in *Enciclopedia Storica delle Scienze e delle loro Applicazione* (vol. 2, Milan, 1944); A. P. USHER, *A History of Mechanical Inventions* (New York, 1929); LYNN WHITE, Jr., 'Technology and invention in the Middle Ages', *Speculum* (1940, vol. 15, pp. 141 *et seq.*), with an excellent bibliography.

Music:

G. REESE, *Music in the Middle Ages* (London, 1941).

Agriculture and Stock Breeding:

SIR F. CRISP, *Medieval Gardens* (London, 1924); H. C. DARBY, *The Medieval Fenland* (Cambridge, 1940); LORD ERNLE, *English Farming, Past and Present*, 5th edition, edited by Sir A. D. Hall (London, 1936); M. L. GOTHEIN, *A History of Garden Art*, trans. Mrs. Archer–Hind (London, 1928); N. B. S. GRAS, *A History of Agriculture in Europe and America* (New York, 1925); LEFEBVRE DES NOËTTES, *L'Attelage, le Cheval de Selle à Travers les Âges*, 2 vols. (Paris, 1931); L. MOULÉ, *Histoire de la Médecine Vétérinaire*, 4 parts (Paris, 1891–1911); SIR F. SMITH, *The Early History of Veterinary Literature*, vol. 1 (London, 1919).

Building and Machines:

T. F. CARTER, *The Invention of Printing in China and its Spread Westwards*, 2nd ed. (New York, 1931); E. M. CARUS-WILSON, 'An industrial revolution in the 13th century', *Economic History Review* (1941, vol. 12, pp. 39 *et seq.*); C. L. SAGUI, 'La meunier de Barbegal (France) et les roues hydrauliques chez les anciens et au moyen âge', *Isis* (1948, vol. 38, pp. 225, *et seq.*); E. E. VIOLLET-LE-DUC, *Dictionnaire Raisonné de l'Architecture Française*

BIBLIOGRAPHY

du XIe au XVIe Siècle, 10 vols. (Paris, 1854–68); G. H. WEST, *Gothic Architecture in England and France* (London, 1927).

Maps:
C. R. BEAZLEY, *The Dawn of Modern Geography*, 3 vols. (London, 1897–1906); D. B. DURAND, 'The earliest modern maps of Germany and Central Europe', *Isis* (1933, vol. 19, pp. 486 *et seq.*); *Four Maps of Great Britain by Matthew Paris* (London, 1928); R. V. TOOLEY, *Maps and Map-Makers* (London, 1949).

Industrial Chemistry:
L. C. GOODRICH and FENG CHIA-SHENG, 'The early development of firearms in China', *Isis* (1946, vol. 36, pp. 114 *et seq.*); E. B. HAYNES, *Glass* (London, 1948); H. W. L. HIME, *The Origin of Artillery* (London, 1915); J. B. HURRY, *The Woad Plant and its Dye* (London, 1930); R. P. JOHNSON, 'Compositiones variæ', in *Illinois Studies in Language and Literature* (1939, vol. 23, pp. 3 *et seq.*); B. RATHGEN, *Das Geschütz im Mittelalter* (Berlin, 1928); L. F. SALZMANN, *English Industries in the Middle Ages* (Oxford, 1923); C. SINGER, *The Earliest Chemical Industry* (London, 1949); *Bergwerk-und Probierbüchlein*, trans. A. G. Sisco and C. S. Smith (New York, 1949); J. M. STILLMAN, *The Story of Early Chemistry* (New York, 1924); D. V. THOMPSON, JR., *The Materials of Medieval Painting* (London, 1936); WANG LING, 'On the invention and use of gunpowder and firearms in China', *Isis* (1947, vol. 37, pp. 160 *et seq.*).

Medicine:
SIR T. C. ALLBUTT, *The Historical Relations of Medicine and Surgery to the End of the Sixteenth Century* (London, 1905); A. M. CAMPBELL, *The Black Death and Men of Learning* (New York, 1931); P. DIEPGEN, 'Die Bedeutung des Mittelalters für den Fortschritt in der Medizin', in *Essays Presented to Karl Sudhoff*, ed. C. Singer and H. E. Sigerist (Oxford and Zurich, 1924); J. GRIER, *A History of Pharmacy* (London, 1937); D. GUTHRIE, *A History of Medicine* (Edinburgh, 1945); J. F. K. HECKER, *The Epidemics of the Middle Ages* (trans. Babington, London, 1859); C. A. MERCIER, *Leper Houses and Mediæval Hospitals* (London, 1915); G. H. OLIVER, *History of the Invention and Discovery of Spectacles* (London, 1913); E. RIESEMAN, *The Story of Medicine in the Middle Ages* (New York, 1935); C. SINGER, *A Short History of Medicine* (Oxford, 1928); R. VERRIER, *Etudes sur Arnald de Villeneuve*

413

(Leyden, 1947); C. H. LA WALL, *Four Thousand Years of Pharmacy* (Philadelphia, 1927); J. J. WALSH, *Medieval Medicine* (London, 1920).

Chapter Five

Mathematics:

W. W. ROUSE BALL, *A Short Account of the History of Mathematics* (London, 1901); C. B. BOYER, *The Concepts of the Calculus* (New York, 1939); F. CAJORI, *A History of Mathematical Notations* (London, 1929); M. CANTOR, *Vorlesungen über Geschichte der Mathematik*, vol. 2 (Leipzig, 1900); G. F. HILL, *The Development of Arabic Numerals in Europe* (Oxford, 1915); G. LIBRI, *Histoire des Sciences mathématiques en Italie*, 4 vols. (Paris, 1838–41).

Philosophy and Scientific Method:

N. ABBAGNANO, *Guglielmo di Ockham* (Lanciano, 1931); P. BOEHNER, G. E. MOHAN, E. A. MOODY and A. C. PEGIS, several articles on William of Ockham in *Franciscan Studies* (1941–50, N.S. vols. 1–10), *Traditio* (1943–6, vols. 1–4), and *Speculum* (1948, vol. 23); R. CARTON, *L'Expérience Physique chez Roger Bacon* (*Etudes de Philosophie Médiévale* II, Paris, 1924); M. PATRONNIER DE GANDILLAC, *La Philosophie de Nicholas de Cuès* (Aubier, 1941); G. DE LAGARDE, *La Naissance de l'Esprit Laïque au Déclin du Moyen Age*, vols. 3–5 (Paris, 1942–6); M. DE WULF, *Histoire de la Philosophie Médiévale*, vol. 3 (Louvain et Paris, 1947); E. GILSON, *The Unity of Philosophic Experience* (London, 1938); M. GRABMANN, *Geschichte der Scholastischen Methode*, 2 vols. (Freiburg-i.-B., 1909–11); C. R. S. HARRIS, *Duns Scotus* (Oxford, 1927); E. LONGPRÉ, *La Philosophie du B. Duns Scotus* (Paris, 1926); R. McKEON, *Selections from Medieval Philosophers*, vol. 2 (New York, 1930), 'Artistotle's conception of the development and the nature of scientific method', *Journal of the History of Ideas* (1947, vol. 8, pp. 3 et seq.); A. MANSION, 'L'induction chez Albert le Grand', *Revue Néo-Scolastique* (1906, vol. 13, pp. 115 et seq., 246 et seq.); C. MICHALSKI, 'Le criticisme et le scepticisme dans la philosophie du 14ème, siecle', in *Bulletin de l'Académie Polonaise des Sciences et des Lettres*, Classe d'histoire et de philosophie (1925), 'Les courants critiques et sceptiques dans la philosophie du 14ème siècle, *ibid.*; E. A. MOODY, *The Logic of William of Ockham* (New York, 1935); C. V. PRANTL, *Geschichte der Logik im Abendlande*, 4 vols. (Leipzig, 1855–70); J. H. RANDALL, 'The development of scientific method

BIBLIOGRAPHY

in the school of Padua', *Journal of the History of Ideas* (1940, vol. 1, pp. 177 *et seq.*); H. RASHDALL, 'Nicholas de Ultricuria, a medieval Hume', *Proceedings of the Aristotelian Society* (1907, N.S., vol. 7, pp. 1 *et seq.*); D. E. SHARP, *Franciscan Philosophy at Oxford in the 13th Century* (Oxford, 1930); L. THORNDIKE, *Science and Thought in the 15th Century* (New York, 1929); J. R. WEINBERG, *Nicolaus of Autrecourt* (Princeton, 1948).

Late Medieval Physics:
M. CLAGETT, 'Some general aspects of physics in the middle ages', *Isis* (1948, vol. 39, pp. 29 *et seq.*); P. DUHEM, *La Théorie Physique* (Paris, 1906), 'Roger Bacon et l'horreur du vide', in *Roger Bacon Essays*, ed. A. G. Little (Oxford, 1914), *Le Système du Monde*, 5 vols. (Paris, 1913–17), *Les Origines de la Statique*, vol. 2 (Paris, 1906), *Etudes sur Léonard de Vinci*, 2ᵉ série (Paris, 1909), 'Physics—History of' in *Catholic Encyclopædia* (New York, 1911); J. LAPPE, 'Nicolaus von Autrecourt', in *Beiträge zur Geschichte der Philosophie des Mittelalters* (1908, vol. 6, Heft 2); A. MAIER, *An der Grenze von Scholastik und Naturwissenschaft* (Essen, 1943), *Die Vorläufer Galileis in 14. Jahrhundert* (Rome, 1949); J. R. O'DONNELL 'The Philosophy of Nicholas of Autrecourt', in *Mediæval Studies* (1942, vol. 4, pp. 97 *et seq.*); S. PINES, *Beiträge zur Islamischen Atomenlehre* (Berlin, 1936).

Dynamics:
P. BOEHNER, *The Tractatus de Successivis attrib. to William of Ockham* (*Franciscan Inst. Publ.* 1, New York, 1944); E. BORCHERT, 'Die Lehre von der Bewegung bei Nicolaus Oresme', in *Beiträge zur Geschichte der Philosophie des Mittelalters* (1934, vol. 31, Heft 3); M. D. CHENU, 'Aux origines de la science moderne', *Revue des Sciences Philosophiques et Théologiques* (1940, vol. 29, pp. 206 *et seq.*); M. CLAGETT, 'Giovanni Marliani and the late Medieval Physics', in *Columbia University Studies in History, Economics and Public Law* (1941, No. 483); P. DUHEM, *Le Mouvement Absolu et le Mouvement Relatif* (reprinted from the *Revue de Philosophie*, vols. 11–14, 1907–9), 'Essai sur la notion de théorie physique de Platon à Galilée', *Annales de Philosophie Chrétienne* (1908, vol. 6, pp. 352 *et seq.*), *Etudes sur Léonard de Vinci*, 3ᵉ série (Paris, 1913); D. B. DURAND, 'Nicole Oresme and the mediaeval origins of modern science', *Speculum* (1941, vol. 16, pp. 167 *et seq.*); A. KOYRÉ, 'Le vide et l'espace infini au XIVᵉ siècle', *Archives*

d'*Histoire Doctrinale et Littéraire du Moyen Age* (1949, vol. 24, pp. 45 et seq.); A. MAIER, *Zwei Grundprobleme der Scholastischen Natur-Philosophie* (Rome, 1951); C. MICHALSKI, 'La physique nouvelle et les différents courants philosophiques au 14ème siècle, *Bull. de L'Acad. Polonaise des Sciences et des Lettres*, Classe d'hist. et de philos. (1927, part 1, pp. 93–164); E. A. MOODY, 'Galileo and Avempace', *J. History of Ideas* (1951, vol. 12, pp. 163–93, 375–422); NICOLE ORESME, *Le Livre du Ciel et du Monde*, ed. A. D. MENUT and A. J. DENOMY, in *Mediaeval Studies* (1941–3, vols. 3–5).

Mathematical Physics:

T. B. BIRCH, 'The theory of continuity of William of Ockham', *Philosophy of Science* (1936, vol. 3, pp. 494 et seq.); R. CAVERNI, *Storia del Methodo Sperimentale in Italia*, 5 vols. (Firenze, 1891–8); J. L. E. DREYER, *A History of Planetary Systems* (Cambridge, 1906); P. DUHEM, *Etudes sur Léonard de Vinci*, 3e sèrie (Paris, 1913); A. MAIER, *An der Grenze . . ., Vorlauffer Galileis . . ., Zwei Grundprobleme . . .* (see pp. 415–16); H. WIELEITNER, 'Der "tractatus de latitudinibus formarum" des Oresme', *Bibliotheca Mathematica* (1913, vol. 13, pp. 115 et seq.), 'Ueber den Functionsbegriff und die graphische Darstellung bei Oresme', *ibid.* (1914, vol. 14, pp. 193 et seq.).

The Literary Renaissance of the 15th Century:

H. BARON, 'Towards a more positive evaluation of the 15th-century Renaissance', *Journal of the History of Ideas* (1943, vol. 4, pp. 21 et seq.); J. BURCHARDT, *The Civilization of the Renaissance in Italy* (London, 1937); E. CASSIRER, P. O. KRISTELLER & J. H. RANDALL, JR., *The Renaissance Philosophy of Man* (Chicago, 1948); D. V. DURAND, 'Tradition and innovation in 15th-century Italy', *Journal of the History of Ideas* (1943, vol. 4, pp. 1 et seq.); M. FUCHS, *Histoire de la Langue Française*, ed. F. Brunot, vol. 6, part 1 (Paris, 1930); W. K. FERGUSON, *The Renaissance in Historical Thought* (Cambridge, Mass., 1948); F. A. JOHNSON and S. V. LARKEY, 'Science', *Modern Language Quarterly* (1941, vol. 2, pp. 363 et seq.); A. C. KLEBS, 'Incunabula scientifica et medica', *Osiris* (1937, vol. 4, pp. 1 et seq.); H. WEISINGER, 'The idea of the Renaissance and the rise of modern science', *Lychnos* (1946–7, pp. 11 et seq.); SIR J. E. SANDYS, *A History of Classical Scholarship*, vol. 1 (Cambridge, 1921).

BIBLIOGRAPHY

Chapter Six

General

H. BUTTERFIELD, *The Origins of Modern Science* (London, 1949); SIR W. C. DAMPIER, *A History of Science* (Cambridge, 1949); SIR W. C. DAMPIER-WHETHAM and M. D. WHETHAM, *Cambridge Readings in the Literature of Science* (Cambridge, 1928); R. T. GUNTHER, *Early Science in Oxford*, 14 vols. (Oxford, 1923–45), *Early Science in Cambridge* (Oxford, 1937); S. LILLEY, *Men, Machines and History* (London, 1948); T. A. RICKARD, *Man and Metals*, 2 vols. (New York, 1932); C. SINGER, *A Short History of Science* (Oxford, 1941); L. THORNDIKE, *A History of Magic and Experimental Science*, vols. 5–6 (New York, 1941); W. WHEWELL, *History of the Inductive Sciences*, 3 vols. (London, 1857), *Philosophy of the Inductive Sciences*, 2 vols. (London, 1847); W. P. D. WIGHTMAN, *The Growth of Scientific Ideas* (Edinburgh, 1950); A. WOLF, *A History of Science, Technology and Philosophy in the 16th and 17th Centuries*. Revised by D. McKIE (London, 1951).

Scientific Thought in a New Social Setting:

H. BROWN, 'The utilitarian motive in the age of Descartes', *Annals of Science* (1936, vol. 1, pp. 182 *et seq.*); G. N. CLARK, *Science and Social Welfare in the Age of Newton* (Oxford, 1937), *The Seventeenth Century* (Oxford, 1947); L. P. V. FEBVRE, *Le Problème de l'Incroyance au XVIᵉ Siècle* (Paris, 1947); W. E. HOUGHTON, 'The history of trades', *Journal of the History of Ideas* (1941, vol. 2, pp. 33 *et seq.*); R. F. JONES, *Ancients and Moderns* (*Washington Univ. Studies*, N. S. Lang & Lit. VI, St. Louis, 1936); R. K. MERTON, 'Science, technology and society in 17th-century England', *Osiris* (1938, vol. 4, pp. 360 *et seq*); M. ORNSTEIN [Bronfenbrenner] *The Role of Scientific Societies in the Seventeenth Century* (Chicago, 1938); L. PASTOR, *The History of the Popes*, vols. 25 and 29, trans. E. Graf (London, 1937 and 1938); P. SMITH, *A History of Modern Culture*, 2 vols. (London, 1930–4); T. SPRATT, *A History of the Royal Society of London* (London, 1667); E. ZILSEL, 'The sociological roots of science', *American Journal of Sociology* (1942, vol. 47, pp. 544 *et seq.*).

Mathematics and Mechanics:

L. BRUNSCHVICG, *Les Etapes de la Philosophie Mathématique* (Paris, 1947); E. A. BURTT, *The Metaphysical Foundations of Modern*

417

Physical Science (London, 1932); F. CAJORI, *A History of Mathematics* (New York, 1924), *A History of Mathematical Notations*, 2 vols. (London, 1929); M. CANTOR, *Vorlesungen über Geschichte der Mathematik*, vol. 2 (Leipzig, 1900); E. CASSIRER, 'Mathematische Mystik und Mathematische Naturwissenschaft', *Lychnos* (1940, pp. 248 *et seq*), 'Galileo's Platonism', in *Studies and Essays . . . offered . . . to George Sarton*, ed. M. F. Ashley-Montagu (New York, 1947); R. DUGAS, *Histoire de la Mécanique* (Neuchatel, 1950); LANE COOPER, *Aristotle, Galileo and the Tower of Pisa* (New York, 1935); A. C. CROMBIE, 'Galileo's "Dialogues Concerning the Two Principal Systems of the World",' *Dominican Studies* (1950, vol. 3, pp. 105 *et seq*.); F. ENRIQUES, *Le Matematiche nella Storia e nella Cultura* (Bologna, 1938); J. J. FAHIE, *Galileo, His Life and Works* (London, 1903), 'The Scientific Works of Galileo 1564–1642', in *Studies in The History and Method of Science*, ed. C. Singer, vol. 2 (Oxford, 1921); A. GEWIRTZ, 'Experience and the non-mathematical in the Cartesian method', *Journal of the History of Ideas* (1941, vol. 2, pp. 183 *et seq*.); L. R. HEATH, *The Concept of Time* (Chicago, 1936); A. KOYRÉ, *Etudes Galiléennes*, Paris, 1939, (*Actualités Scientifiques et Industrielles*, nos. 852–4), 'Galileo and Plato', *Journal of the History of Ideas* (1943, vol. 4, pp. 400 *et seq*.); R. LENOBLE, *Mersenne ou la Naissance du Mécanisme* (Paris, 1943); E. MACH, *The Science of Mechanics*, trans. by T. J. McCormack (La Salle, 1942); G. MCCOLLEY, 'The 17th-century doctrine of a plurality of worlds', *Annals of Science* (1936, vol. 1, pp. 385 *et seq*.); D. E. SMITH, *A History of Mathematics*, 2 vols. (Boston, 1923–5); A. J. SNOW, *Matter and Gravity in Newton's Physical Philosophy* (London, 1926); E. W. STRONG, *Procedures and Metaphysics* (Berkeley, 1936); F. SHERWOOD TAYLOR, *Galileo and the Freedom of Thought* (London, 1938); P. P. WIENER, 'The tradition behind Galileo's methodology', *Osiris* (1936, vol. 1, pp. 733 *et seq*.).

Astronomy:

A. ARMITAGE, *Copernicus* (London, 1938), *A Century of Astronomy* (London, 1950); J. BRODRICK, *The Life and Work of Blessed Robert, Cardinal Bellarmine* (London, 1928); H. DINGLE, 'Copernicus's work', *Polish Science and Learning* (1943, June), 'Tycho Brahe', *Endeavour* (1946, vol. 5, pp. 137 *et seq*.); J. L. E. DREYER, *Tycho Brahe* (Edinburgh, 1890), *A History of Planetary Systems* (Cambridge, 1906); P. DUHEM, *Le Mouvement Absolu et le Mouvement*

BIBLIOGRAPHY

Relatif (reprinted from *Rev. Philos.* 1907–9), 'Essai sur la notion de théorie en Physique de Platon à Galilée', *Annales de Philosophie Chrétienne* (1908, vol. 6, pp. 352 *et seq.*, 482 *et seq.*, 561 *et seq.*); A. FAVARO, *Galileo Galilei e l'Inquisizione. Documenti del processo Galileiano* . . . (Florence, 1907); J. A. GADE, *The Life and Times of Tycho Brahe* (Princeton, 1947); K. VON GEBLER, *Galileo Galilei and the Roman Curia*, trans. Mrs. G. Sturge (London, 1879); F. R. JOHNSON, *Astronomical Thought in Renaissance England* (Baltimore, 1937); A. MERCATI, *Il Sommario del Processo di Giordano Bruno* (Studi e Testi, Rome, 1942); L. PASTOR, *The History of the Popes*, vols. 25 and 29, trans. E. Graf (London, 1937 and 1938); E. ROSEN, *Three Copernican Treatises* (New York, 1939); D. W. SINGER, *Giordano Bruno. His Life and Thought* (New York–London, 1950); L. THORNDIKE, *A History of Magic and Experimental Science*, vols. 5–6 (New York, 1941); E. WOHLWILL, *Galilei und sein Kampf für die Kopernickanische Lehre* (Hamburg and Leipzig, 1909); R. WOLF, *Geschichte der Astronomie* (München, 1877).

Magnetism and Light:

CAJORI, *A History of Physics* (New York, 1929); N. H. DE V. HEATHCOTE, 'Guericke's sulphur globe', *Annals of Science* (1950, vol. 6, pp. 293–305); A. C. MITCHELL, 'Chapters in the history of terrestrial magnetism', *Terrestrial Magnetism and Atmospheric Electricity* (1932, vol. 37, pp. 105 *et seq.*, 1937, vol. 42, pp. 241 *et seq.*, 1939, vol. 44, pp. 77, *et seq.*); R. E. OCKENDEN, 'Marco Antonio de Dominis and his explanation of the rainbow', *Isis* (1936, vol. 26, pp. 40 *et seq.*); M. ROBERTS and E. R. THOMAS, *Newton and the Origin of Colours* (London, 1934); L. ROSENFELD, 'La théorie des couleurs de Newton et ses adversaires, *Isis* (1927, vol. 9, pp. 44 *et seq.*), 'Marcus Marcis Untersuchungen über des Prisma und ihr Verhältnis zu Newtons Farbentheorie', *Isis* (1932, vol. 17, pp. 325 *et seq.*); J. F. SCOTT, 'Descartes' contributions to optics', *Bulletin of the British Society for the History of Science* (1951, vol. 1, pp. 109–10); E. T. WHITTAKER, *A History of Theories of Ether and Electricity* (Edinburgh, 1951); E. ZILSEL, 'The origins of William Gilbert's scientific method', *Journal of the History of Ideas* (1941, vol. 2, pp. 1 *et seq.*).

Scientific Instruments:

L. C. BOLTON, *Time Measurement* (London, 1924); A. N. DISNEY, C. F. HILL and W. E. W. BAKER, *Origin and Development of the Microscope* (London, 1928); R. S. CLAY and T. S. COURT, *The History of the Microscope* (London, 1932); H. T. PLEDGE, *Science since 1500* (London, 1939); C. SINGER, 'Steps leading to the invention of the first optical apparatus', in *Studies in the History and Method of Science*, vol. 2 (Oxford, 1921); F. SHERWOOD TAYLOR, 'The origin of the thermometer', *Annals of Science* (1942, vol. 5, pp. 129 *et seq.*); R. W. SYMONDS, *A History of English Clocks* (London, 1947).

Exploration:

N. H. DE V. HEATHCOTE, 'Christopher Columbus and the discovery of magnetic variation', *Science Progress* (1932, July, pp. 82 *et seq.*), 'Early nautical charts', *Annals of Science* (1936, vol. 1, pp. 13 *et seq.*); G. H. T. KIMBLE, *Geography in the Middle Ages* (London, 1938); A. P. NEWTON, *Travel and Travellers of the Middle Ages* (London, 1926); E. G. R. TAYLOR, *Tudor Geography, 1485–1583* (London, 1930); E. G. R. TAYLOR, *Late Tudor and Early Stuart Geography, 1583–1650* (London, 1934).

Experimental Physiology:

J. P. ARCIERI, *The Circulation of the Blood and Andrea Cesalpino of Brezzia* (New York, 1945); H. P. BAYON, 'William Harvey, physician and biologist, his precursors, opponents and successors', *Annals of Science* (1938, vol. 3, pp. 59 *et seq.*, 435 *et seq.*; 1939, vol. 4, pp. 65 *et seq.*, 329 *et seq.*); A. G. BERTHIER, 'Le méchanisme cartésien et la physiologie au 17ᵉᵐᵉ siècle', *Isis* (1914, vol. 2, pp. 37 *et seq*, 1920, vol. 3, pp. 21 *et seq.*); A. CASTIGLIONI, *The Renaissance of Medicine in Italy* (Baltimore, 1934), 'Galileo Galilei and his influence on the evolution of medical thought', *Bulletin of the History of Medicine* (1942, vol. 12, pp. 226 *et seq.*); L. D. COHEN, 'Descartes and Henry More on the beast-machine', *Annals of Science* (1936, vol. 1, pp. 48 *et seq*); D'ARCY POWER, *William Harvey* (London, 1897); SIR M. FOSTER, *Lectures on the History of Physiology during the Sixteenth, Seventeenth and Eighteenth Centuries* (Cambridge, 1901); K. J. FRANKLIN, *A Short History of Physiology* (London, 1933), 'A survey of the growth of knowledge about certain parts of the fœtal cardiovascular apparatus, and about the fœtal circulation, in man and some other animals, Part I: Galen to Harvey', *Annals of Science* (1941, vol. 5, pp. 57 *et seq.*); J. F. FULTON, *Selected Readings*

BIBLIOGRAPHY

in the History of Physiology (London, 1930); E. GILSON, *Etudes sur le Rôle de la Pensée Médiévale dans la Formation du Système Cartésien* (*Etudes de la Philosophie Médiévale* XIII, Paris, 1930); M. MEYERHOFF, 'Ibn An-Nafis (13th century) and his theory of the lesser circulation', *Isis* (1935, vol. 23, pp. 100 *et seq.*); SIR W. OSLER, *The Growth of Truth as Illustrated in the Discovery of the Circulation of the Blood* (Harveyan Oration, London, 1906); P. A. ROBIN, *The Old Physiology in English Literature* (London, 1911); SIR H. ROLLESTON, 'The reception of Harvey's doctrine of the circulation of the blood in England', in *Essays . . . presented to Karl Sudhoff*, ed. C. Singer and H. E. Sigerist (Oxford and Zürich, 1924); C. SINGER, *The Discovery of the Circulation of the Blood* (London, 1922); W. STERLING, *Some Apostles of Physiology* (London, 1902); R. B. HERVEY WYATT, *William Harvey* (London, 1924).

Chemistry:

T. L. DAVIS, 'Boyle's conception of the elements compared with that of Lavoisier', *Isis* (1931, vol. 16, pp. 82 *et seq.*); E. J. HOLMYARD, *Makers of Chemistry* (Oxford, 1931); K. LASSWITZ, *Geschichte der Atomistik vom Mittelalter bis Newton*, 2 vols. (Leipzig, 1926); W. PAGEL, 'The religious and philosophical aspects of van Helmont's science and medicine', *Bulletin of the History of Medicine* (1944, Supplement 2); J. R. PARTINGTON, *A Short History of Chemistry* (London, 1937), 'Jean Baptista van Helmont', *Annals of Science* (1936, vol. 1, pp. 359 *et seq.*), 'The origins of the atomic theory', *Annals of Science* (1939, vol. 4, pp. 245 *et seq.*); J. M. STILLMAN, *The Story of Early Chemistry* (New York, 1924).

Botany:

A. ARBER, *Herbals* (Cambridge, 1938); W. BLUNT, *The Art of Botanical Illustration* (London, 1950); F. G. D. DREWITT, *The Romance of the Apothecaries' Garden at Chelsea* (London, 1928); E. GUYÉNOT, *Les Sciences de la Vie au 17ᵉ et 18ᵉ Siècles* (Paris, 1941); C. E. RAVEN, *English Naturalists from Neckam to Ray* (Cambridge, 1947); J. SACHS, *History of Botany, 1530–1860* (Oxford, 1890); C. SINGER, 'Greek biology and its relation to the rise of modern biology', in *Studies in the History and Method of Science*, vol. 2 (Oxford 1921); L. THORNDIKE, *A History of Magic and Experimental Science*, vol. 6 (New York, 1941).

Anatomy and Zoology:

L. Choulant, *History and Bibliography of Anatomic Illustrations*, trans. and annotated by M. Frank (New York, 1945); F. J. Cole, *A History of Comparative Anatomy* (London, 1944); A. Fonahn, *Arabic and Latin Anatomical Terminology* (Norwegian Acad., hist. class., 1921, No. 7); E. W. Gudger, 'The five great naturalists of the 16th century, Belon, Rondelet, Salviani, Gesner, and Aldrovandi: a chapter in the history of ichthyology', *Isis* (1934, vol. 22, pp. 21 *et seq.*); E. Guyénot, *Les Sciences de la Vie aux 17ᵉ et 18ᵉ Siècles* (Paris, 1941); H. Hopstock, 'Leonardo as anatomist', in *Studies in the History and Method of Science*, ed. C. Singer, vol. 2 (Oxford, 1921); W. H. Locy, *The Growth of Biology* (London, 1925); J. P. McMurrich, *Leonardo da Vinci, the Anatomist* (Baltimore, 1930); E. Nordenskiöld, *The History of Biology* (London, 1929); E. Radl, *Geschichte der Biologischen Theorien*, Part 1 (Leipzig, 1905); C. Singer, *The Evolution of Anatomy* (London, 1925), *A Short History of Biology* (Oxford, 1950); C. Singer and C. Rabin, *A Prelude to Modern Science* (Cambridge, 1946); L. Thorndike, *A History of Magic and Experimental Science*, vols. 5 and 6 (New York, 1941).

Embryology:

H. P. Bayon, 'William Harvey (1578–1657): his application of biological experiment, clinical observation and comparative anatomy to the problems of generation', *Journal of the History of Medicine* (1947, vol. 2, pp. 51 *et seq.*); F. J. Cole, *Early Theories of Sexual Generation* (Oxford, 1930); *The Embryological Treatises of Hieronymus Fabricius*, ed. H. B. Adelmann (New York, 1942); A. W. Meyer, *The Rise of Embryology* (Stanford, 1939); J. Needham, *A History of Embryology* (Cambridge, 1934).

Medicine:

A. Castiglioni, *A History of Medicine*, trans. E. B. Krumbhaar (New York, 1947); P. Delaunay, *La Vie Médicale aux 16ᵉᵐᵉ, 17ᵉᵐᵉ et 18ᵉᵐᵉ Siècles* (Paris, 1935); F. H. Garrison, *An Introduction to the History of Medicine* (Philadelphia, 1929); D. Guthrie, *A History of Medicine* (Edinburgh, 1945); R. A. Leonardo, *A History of Surgery* (New York, 1942); H. E. Sigerist, *Paracelsus in the Light of Four Hundred Years* (New York, 1941); C. Singer, *A Short History of Medicine* (Oxford, 1928), C. J. S. Thompson, *The History and Evolution of Surgical Instruments* (New York, 1942).

BIBLIOGRAPHY

Geology:

F. D. ADAMS, *The Birth and Development of the Geological Sciences* (Baltimore, 1938); K. A. VON ZITTEL, *History of Geology and Palæontology* (London, 1901).

Science in the Modern World:

E. BRÉHIER, *Histoire de la Philosophie*, vol. 2, Part 1 (Paris, 1942); C. D. BROAD, *The Philosophy of Francis Bacon* (Cambridge, 1926), 'The new philosophy: Bruno to Descartes', *Cambridge Historical Journal* (1944, vol. 8, pp. 36 *et seq.*); E. A. BURTT, *The Metaphysical Foundations of Modern Physical Science* (London, 1932); E. CASSIRER, *Das Erkenntnisproblem in der Philosophie und Wissenschaft der neueren Zeit*, 3 vols. (Berlin, 1906–20); F. A. LANGE, *Geschichte des Materialismus*, vol. 1 (Leipzig, 1873); R. I. MARKUS, 'Method and metaphysics: the origins of some Cartesian presuppositions of the Renaissance', *Dominican Studies* (1949, vol. 2, pp. 356 *et seq.*); A. N. WHITEHEAD, *Science and the Modern World* (London, 1926); B. WILLEY, *The Seventeenth Century Background* (London, 1934).

NOTE

For further writings on the history of science there are the bibliographies in Brunet et Mieli's *Histoire des Sciences: Antiquité*, in Sarton's *Introduction*, and those published regularly in *Isis*. See also *The Early History of Science: A Short Handlist* (Historical Association, London, 1950). For recent specialised studies on medieval science there is the bibliography of my *Robert Grosseteste and the Origins of Experimental Science* (Oxford, at the Clarendon Press, in press).

INDEX

Guy de Chauliac, 107, 137, 139, 202, 204, *206–8*.

HALY ABBAS, 20, 25, 32, 199, 204
Harriot, T., 281
Hartmann, G., 319
Harvey, W., 9, 224, *329–38*, 341, 380–1, *383–5*, 391, 397, 420–2
Hausbuch Mittelalterliches, 145
Hegel, G. W. F., 395
Helperic, 11
Henricus Aristippus, 27
Henry of Hesse, 119, 268
Henry the Navigator, 183
Heraclides of Pontus, 62, 243, 308
Hereford *Mappa Mundi*, 151
Hermann of Carinthia, 20
Hermann the Lame, 64
Hero of Alexandria, 22, 29, 32, 143, *156–7*, 215, 236–40, 245, 280, 346, 348
Herophilus, 134
Heytesbury, William of, 261, 296
Hildegarde of Bingen, *9–10, 108*, 198
Hindus and Hindu science, 27, *32–5*, 69, 145, 188, 199, 201, *215–7*, 269, 407
Hipparchus, 58, 69, 254
Hippocrates, 10, 20, 22, 27, 32, 42, 120, 122, 131, 143, 198–9, 203, 373
Hood, T., 276
Hooke, R., 173, 353, 394–5
Horrocks, J., 318
Horse, *163–5*, 189, 191, 193, 272, 349, 412
Hospitals, 209–11
Hrabanus Maurus, 4
Hucbald, 153
Hugh of St. Victor, 51, 146–9, 214
Humanism and science, xi, 242, *268–70*, 276, 281, 313, *361–2*, 367, *372–3, 376–8*, 416
Hume, D., 233, *398*
Hunain ibn Ishaq, 199
Huygens, Christian, 263, 277, 306, 323, 343, 353

IBN AL-KHATIB, 204
Ibn An-Nafis, 331–2
Ibn Khatima, 204
Impetus, 250–8, 267, 271–2, 279–80, 285, 287, 290, 299, 301, 303, 319, 321, 407, 415
Induction, theory of, *46–8, 76–7*, 197, 212–3, *217–34*, 269–70, 275, 290–2, 329–30, 353, 387–91, 393, 397, 401, 414, 427
Inertia, *249*, 271, 289, *299–307*, 322–3
Infinity, 14–15, *50*, 84, 125, *236–44, 248–50*, 271, 284, 292, 298, *300–5*, 317
Instruments, scientific, ix, xiv, 11, *63–9*, 73–7, *88*, 98, 100–5, 144–5, 147, 150–1, 153–5, 156–70, 168, *180–1, 183–97*, 190, 195–7, 207–8, 225, *263–8*, 272, 275–7, 280, 285–6, 298, 314–5, *318–20*, 323–4, *328–9, 342–53*, 356, *358*, 382, 383, 387, 407, 409–10, 421
Isaac Israëli, 198, 199, 228
Isidore of Seville, *3–5*, 8, 24, 198, 214, 238

JABIR IBN HAYYAN, 24, 100–1, 410
Jacob ben Makir, 68
Jacopo da Forli, 229, 268
James of Venice, 20
Jean de Jandun, 130, 242
Jean de Linières, 68, 150
Jean de Murs, 67, 155
Jehan de Brie, 129
John of Burgundy, 203
John of Milano, 126–8
John of St. Amand, 89–90, 228
John of Salisbury, 31
John the Saracen, 25
John of Seville, 20, 26
Jordanus Nemorarius, *83–7*, 176, 216, 246, 266, 269, 278–9, 288, 409
Josquin des Près, 154
Jung, J., 116, *360*, 367–8

KANT, IMMANUEL, xv, 328, *399–400*
Kepler, J., 62, 225, 282, 295–6, 303, 305, 307, 313–23, 352